Engineering Science Series

EDITED BY EARLE RAYMOND HEDRICK

FUNDAMENTAL ELECTRONICS
AND VACUUM TUBES

ENGINEERING SCIENCE SERIES

FUNDAMENTAL ELECTRONICS AND VACUUM TUBES

BY

ARTHUR LEMUEL ALBERT, M.S.

PROFESSOR OF COMMUNICATION ENGINEERING
OREGON STATE COLLEGE

NEW YORK
THE MACMILLAN COMPANY
1938

SET UP AND ELECTROTYPED BY
THE LANCASTER PRESS, INC., LANCASTER, PA.

PRINTED IN THE UNITED STATES OF AMERICA

PREFACE

It is now recognized that all students of electrical engineering should receive instruction in electronics and vacuum tubes.

This book is designed for use in college and university courses covering the fundamentals of electronics and vacuum tubes. It is written for the students and instructors in such courses; all other uses have been subjugated to this end. It should, however, be of much assistance to practicing engineers and to electrical workers who desire to review, or to study, the basic principles of the subject.

As an examination of the table of contents will indicate, the division of the material briefly is as follows: The fundamental principles of electronics and related phenomena; the electronic principles of vacuum (including gas) tubes; the use of vacuum tubes as circuit elements; and photoelectric devices, cathode-ray tubes, and measurements.

Care has been taken to keep the material well balanced. No attempt has been made to cover completely both the communication and the power (industrial) applications. Instead, vacuum tubes and their companion electronic devices have been treated as fundamental to both fields. This adapts the text for use by students majoring either in communication or power.

It is believed that the students should thoroughly understand the underlying principles before attempting mathematical analyses. Such material can best be presented by lectures and by outside assignments as the students become qualified. The references made throughout the text expedite this procedure. It should not be inferred, however, that the book is merely descriptive. Every attempt has been made to keep the treatment in accordance with the high standards of the engineering profession.

In preparing the manuscript, the latest obtainable standards of the American Institute of Electrical Engineers and of the Institute of Radio Engineers have been followed closely. It is suggested that the instructor, and if possible the students as well, have available the latest copies of these standards. Electrical terms, accepted by the profession as a whole, instead of the unfamiliar terminology of the specialist, have been used.

It is hoped that the many carefully selected references will encourage the students to do outside reading. Knowing where and how to gather information is often more important than factual knowledge.

A few suggested assignments have been included. To avoid mere slide-rule manipulations, to develop judgment, and to insure the consultation of other writers, many of these assignments have been made somewhat general in nature. In some instances, the answer will not be found within this book. Simple problems based on the various equations can easily be supplied by the instructor. Attention is called to the excellent problems existing in *Physics of Electron Tubes* by Koller, in *Principles of Radio Engineering* by Glasgow, in *Radio Engineering* by Terman and in *Fundamentals of Vacuum Tubes* by Eastman.

Since data regarding vacuum tubes are readily available in tube manuals, very few tables have been included. It is suggested that all who study this book have available the latest *RCA Receiving Tube Manual*, and if possible catalogs and material from other manufacturers as well.

The method of presentation used in much of this book was suggested by the splendid writings of Dr. H. A. Pidgeon of Bell Telephone Laboratories. In the preparation of the manuscript, the works of many authorities were consulted; this privilege has been invaluable and is gratefully acknowledged. The cooperation of the American Institute of Electrical Engineers, the Institute of Radio Engineers, John Wiley & Sons, McGraw-Hill Book Company, the management of Electronics, Bell Telephone Laboratories, and others, in releasing material for publication is greatly appreciated.

Among the manufacturing companies, grateful acknowledgment is due RCA Manufacturing Company, Western Electric Company, Westinghouse Electric and Manufacturing Company, General Electric Company, Weston Electrical Instrument Corporation, Thordarson Electric Manufacturing Company, and others.

It is with deep gratitude that acknowledgment is made of the assistance given by Professor Knox McIlwain of the Moore School of Electrical Engineering, University of Pennsylvania. Throughout the preparation of the manuscript, and during its revision and publication, his services were available as a consultant. His suggestions and assistance have been invaluable.

It is a pleasure to thank members of the faculty and students of the Department of Electrial Engineering at Oregon State College for their assistance. The suggestions of Mr. F. Alton Everest of this department have been especially useful. The interest of Dean R. H. Dearborn of the School of Engineering has made this work possible. This opportunity is also taken to thank my wife for her assistance with the preparation of the manuscript and with the details of publishing.

ARTHUR L. ALBERT

October, 1938

CONTENTS

FUNDAMENTAL ELECTRONICS AND VACUUM TUBES

CHAPTER 1

BASIC ELECTRONIC THEORY

This book is devoted to a study of the fundamentals of electronics, to the application of these principles to vacuum tubes and associated devices, and to the uses of these tubes and devices in electric circuits.

In order fully to understand the theories of such phenomena as thermionic emission and photoelectric emission, it is necessary first to study the electronic nature of matter. To explain the phenomena occurring in high-vacuum and gas tubes requires a knowledge of the theories of conduction through gases. Explanations of other phenomena, such as the photovoltaic effect, are developed from theories of electric conductivity in solids.

It is desirable, therefore, that the opening chapter should include certain theories of modern physics upon which the science and application of electronics, for engineering purposes, is based. In presenting this material, the historical development will be traced. Elementary concepts and simple illustrations, justifiable in a book of this nature, will be used throughout.

1. The Structure of Matter.—Prior to 1931, it was generally assumed that the smallest indivisible particles † of matter were the negative **electron** and the positive **proton**. All matter was thought of as being composed of these electrically-charged particles.

Scientific progress since this date has, however, reopened for consideration the question of the ultimate nature of matter. It is now believed by some scientists that there are *at least eight* elementary particles. This does not mean, however, that each of these elementary particles is "indivisible" or "ultimate" in nature. It is thought probable that *some* of these particles, such as the negative electron, are truly ultimate and indivisible, although as K. K. Darrow, an authority

---

† From the beginning, man has assigned to the elementary particles of matter the properties and characteristics of the physical bodies about him. Whether or not such assumptions are correct is a debatable question. It is, however, proper to describe them in the clearest possible manner even if such descriptions are somewhat overdrawn and useful only in forming mental pictures. Statements regarding the size of electrons and protons, atom models, and similar descriptions should be regarded in this light.

1

in this field, writes,[1] "such a statement as this can never be perfectly proved."

Certain of these eight elementary particles should be considered [1] as being composite in nature. They are the simplest possible structures which can be built out of the ultimate particles such as the negative electrons. For instance, investigations with the cyclotron,[2] and by other means, show quite conclusively that the *proton is divisible*, and that it is composed of a **positron** having a charge equal to that of the electron, and a **neutron,** having no charge, but having the mass of the proton.

However, the electronic effects of greatest importance to electrical engineers can be explained in terms of the *negative* electron and the *positive* proton. The following discussions will accordingly be limited to these particles. The terms **electron** and **proton** will be used instead of negative electron and positive proton, except in instances where it seems advisable to emphasize the nature of their charge.

2. The Electron.—The first use of the word electron is usually attributed [4] to Stoney in the year 1891. It has been pointed out, however, that this word was used [6] (but not precisely in the modern sense) not only by the ancient Greeks, but also by writers at least as early as 1864. The **electron** is defined [3] as " the natural, elementary quantity of negative electricity." The charge or quantity of negative electricity of the electron is given as 1.592×10^{-19} coulomb, or 4.774×10^{-10} statcoulomb, and the mass *at rest* as 9.00×10^{-28} gram.

Various other interesting properties have been computed for the electron. Among these is its apparent radius, given [4] as 1.9×10^{-13} centimeter, and qualified as being uncertain. (This value has also been computed to be 1.85×10^{-13} centimeter.) There is some question as to the advisability of attempting to give any physical dimensions to an electron.

The ratio e/m (the charge to the mass) was first measured by J. J. Thompson as the result of experiments beginning about 1895. From the values given above for the electron this ratio is now believed to be about 5.3×10^{17} statcoulombs per gram. Much later Millikan, between 1908 and 1917, determined [4, 5] accurately the charge on the electron.

It can be shown [5] that an electron possesses inertia and mass by virtue of its charge. An electron in motion constitutes a current of electricity, the magnitude of the current being determined by the *number* of electrons passing a given point *per second*. Thus, when an electron is accelerated, the surrounding magnetic field caused by the motion is increased. An expenditure of energy is required to increase a magnetic field and hence a *force* is required to accelerate an electron. This means that a force is required to accelerate an electron *because of its electrical charge alone.* These relations substantiate the theory that matter is electrical in nature.

It has been shown both theoretically and experimentally by Lorentz and others that the apparent mass of an electron increases with an increase of velocity. Below 1/10 the velocity of light, there is little change in the mass. Above this value it increases [5] more rapidly, so that at 0.98 the velocity of light, the mass of an electron is 5 times its mass when at rest. At the velocity of light, the mass is theoretically infinite. The Lorentz formula is given [4, 5] as

$$m = m_0 \left(1 - \frac{v_p^2}{v_l^2} \right)^{-1/2} \tag{1-1}$$

where m is the apparent mass of the electron at any velocity v_p, m_0 is the mass at rest, and v_l is the velocity of light.

Electrons in Electric Fields.—The electron behaves like a negatively charged particle, and is therefore influenced by an electric [3] (also called electrostatic or dielectric) field. Thus, suppose that an electron is between the two parallel plates of Fig. 1–1, and that these plates are in an *evacuated* tube. If a difference of potential or voltage is applied between the two plates as indicated, the electron will be acted on by the electric field existing between the two plates.

If the distance d between the plates is small compared with the dimensions of the plates, the field between the plates will be uniform. The applied voltage will then be uniformly distributed across the space between the plates. The voltage gradient, or *electrostatic volts* per unit distance, is equal to the applied voltage in *volts* divided by $300 \times d$. If d is in centimeters, this is also equal to the field intensity F or to the electric lines of force per square centimeter in vacuum.

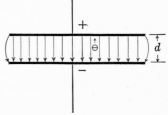

Fig. 1–1. An electron in an electric field produced by a potential difference between two electrodes will be drawn toward the positive electrode.

The force in dynes acting on the electron of Fig. 1–1 will be

$$f = Fe, \tag{1-2}$$

where F is the field intensity as previously defined, and e is the charge on the electron in statcoulombs (page 2). (This equation and those which follow are derived for an electron, but apply also to gas ions, page 10.)

Since force equals mass times acceleration, the electron of Fig. 1–1 will experience an acceleration in centimeters per second per second equal to

$$a = \frac{Fe}{m}, \tag{1-3}$$

where m is the mass of the electron in grams (m is assumed to be constant for all velocities below 1/10 that of light).

Work is equal to force times distance, and thus as an electron moves a distance d centimeters in a uniform electric field the work in ergs done is

$$W = Fed, \quad \text{or} \quad W = Ve, \tag{1-4}$$

because the voltage V in such a field is equal to Fd (that is, to the product of field intensity and distance). Since in equation (1–4) the value e is a constant for electrons, the work is often expressed in **electron volts,** defined [3] as "the amount of energy gained by an electron in passing from one point to another when the potential of the second point is one volt higher than the first."

If an electron is caused to move against the force of the field, e.g., if it were shot toward the *negative* plate, the electron will do work, will lose kinetic energy, and will slow down. If, on the other hand, an electron is free to move in the field toward the *positive* plate, it has work done upon it, gathers speed, and hence its kinetic energy is increased. The work done Ve when an electron moves between two points is equal to $1/2\ mv^2$, where v is the change in velocity. Therefore,

$$Ve = \frac{mv^2}{2}, \quad \text{and} \quad v = \left(\frac{2Ve}{m}\right)^{1/2}. \tag{1-5}$$

Thus, if an electron falls unimpeded through a difference of potential of one volt, its final velocity would be $v = (2 \times 1/300 \times 4.774 \times 10^{-10} \times 1/9 \times 10^{-28})^{1/2} = 0.00595 \times 10^{10}$ centimeters per second. Although this is less than 1/10 the velocity of light (3×10^{10} cm. per sec.), a simple conversion shows it is the enormous velocity of about *370 miles per second.*

Electrons in Magnetic Fields.—An electron or an ion in motion constitutes a current of electricity and establishes a magnetic field. This magnetic field will react with other magnetic fields and will produce a force which acts on the electron. This is similar to the force acting on a wire which carries a current in a magnetic field.

Since the charge e on an electron is 4.774 × 10⁻¹⁰ statcoulomb, and since one statcoulomb equals 0.333 × 10⁻⁹ coulomb, the charge on an electron is approximately 1.591 × 10⁻¹⁹ coulomb. The reciprocal of this, 6.29 × 10¹⁸, is the number of electrons in one coulomb of electricity. If electricity flows at the rate of one coulomb per second, the current is one ampere.

The force F *in dynes* exerted on a wire l centimeters long carrying a current of I amperes and situated at right angles to the magnetic lines of force in a field having an intensity of H lines per square centimeter is

$$F = \frac{IlH}{10}.$$ (1–6)

Similarly, the force in dynes acting on an electron traveling in a magnetic field at a velocity of v centimeters per second will be (since $I = Q/t$, and l or distance $= vt$)

$$F = \frac{Hve}{10} = Hv\,1.591 \times 10^{-20}.$$ (1–7)

Equation (1–7) is illustrated by Fig. 1–2. The stream of electrons is shot into the magnetic field in a vacuum. The magnetic lines of force are assumed perpendicular to the page, and to be *directed up*. Since a beam of electrons is opposite in direction to conventional current flow, the individual electrons will be deflected and will follow the circular path shown, although a wire would be merely pushed out of the field. This difference is because an electron behaves like a charged particle; the force *at each instant* is at right angles to the direction of travel *at that instant*.

Increasing the velocity of the electrons will *increase* the radius of the

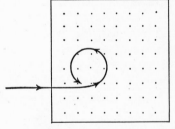

Fig. 1–2. A high-velocity electron shot into a magnetic field will follow the path shown. The dots represent lines of magnetic force directed out.

path; increasing the strength of the field will *decrease* the radius. If an electron is in a combined electric and magnetic field, it will experience two forces, the resultant being the vector sum of the two forces.

3. The Proton.—The **proton** is defined [3] for engineering purposes as "the natural, elementary quantity of positive electricity." The mass of the proton *at rest* is given as 1847 times the mass of the electron, or 1.662 × 10⁻²⁴ gram. The *positive* charge on the proton is equal to the *negative* charge on the electron. It is more difficult to study the proton

than the electron, and hence the characteristics of the proton are less definitely known. As previously mentioned, recent studies indicate that it is divisible into a positron and a neutron.

Calculations [4] give the proton an apparent radius of *about* 10^{-16} centimeter but this value is, of course, uncertain. This is often assumed to be 1/1847 the apparent radius of an electron on the basis of the ratio of the masses as given in the preceding paragraph. Assuming that these calculations and the other data are correct, the proton may be pictured as a particle very much smaller than the electron, but with a mass 1847 times as great. The mass of the proton also depends on its velocity.

4. The Atom.—The **atom** may be regarded as the smallest particle of an *element* which can exist either alone, in combination with other atoms of the *same* element, or in combination with atoms of *other* elements.

Rutherford is credited [4] with first suggesting that the atom of matter might consist of a central positive nucleus surrounded by rotating electrons. The electrostatic forces between the positive nucleus and the negative electrons would be equal and opposite to the centrifugal force of the electrons. One serious objection to this model is that such an atom would disintegrate because the revolving electrons would radiate electromagnetic energy of very short wavelength. To meet this objection, the quantum theory was evolved.

The Quantum Theory.—This theory was developed by Planck, Einstein, Bohr, and others at the beginning of the century. It explains, as will be shown later, why the atom does not continuously radiate electromagnetic energy and thus disintegrate. It is also of great importance in explaining photoelectric effects.

According to this viewpoint, energy is not transferred continuously, but in small amounts or **quanta.** This is best explained on the basis of light (or heat) waves. The amount of electromagnetic energy contained in a quantum is given by the product $h\nu$, where h is Planck's universal constant equal [5] to 6.55×10^{-27} erg-second, and ν is the frequency of the light wave. Since the frequencies of the various types of light are different, the *quanta are also different* for each type of radiation.

On this basis electromagnetic radiations (such as light and heat waves) can be thought of as consisting of waves such as shown in Fig. 1–3. These waves flow out from the source in "spurts" as indicated. Each spurt contains a certain quantum of energy equal to $h\nu$.

Since ultra-violet light is of shorter wavelength (and higher frequency) than red light, the quantum is greater for ultraviolet. Similarly, x-rays are of still shorter wavelength, and hence contain more energy. A more intense beam of light consists of more quanta arriving during a given time.

The exact nature of light waves is a debatable question. For years it had been assumed that light was merely an electromagnetic wave motion. But, it has been shown by Compton that light also exhibits the properties of particles. To explain this, Compton states,[7] "We continue to think of light as propagated as electromagnetic waves; yet the energy of

FIG. 1–3. According to the quantum theory, a light wave consists of a series of "spurts," each containing a definite amount of energy $h\nu$.

the light is concentrated in particles associated with the waves, and whenever the light does something, it does it as particles."

The Bohr Atom.—An atom model was developed by Bohr about 1913. He pictured the atom to be somewhat like a miniature solar system with a positive nucleus surrounded by orbital electrons. He avoided the disintegration difficulties of the Rutherford model by assuming that the electrons rotated only in certain orbits, and that they did not radiate electromagnetic energy *while in these orbits*. The radiation of energy (or the absorption of energy) occurred only when they *changed* orbits. This is in accordance with the quantum theory; an orbital electron can absorb or radiate energy only in definite amounts or quanta. The orbital electron in an atom cannot accept or eject energy *continuously*, but only as it changes from one orbit (or energy level) to another.

According to Bohr, the simplest of all elements is the **hydrogen atom.** The normal unexcited hydrogen atom consists of a single negative electron revolving about a single positive proton. The distance from the proton to the revolving electron is many thousand times the radius of the electron. The next of the Bohr atoms is **helium.** It is pictured in Fig. 1–4, and consists of a nucleus of four protons and two electrons which are bound together, and has two revolving electrons. It will be noted that the charges are balanced, giving a neutral atom. **Lithium** is the next element of the series, and it has *two kinds of atoms*, called the **isotopes** of lithium. One of these has a nucleus of six protons and three electrons, and the other has a nucleus of seven protons and

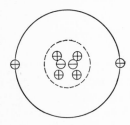

FIG. 1–4. Bohr model of a helium atom. The central nucleus consists of four protons and two electrons. Two electrons are in orbits. Recent studies indicate that the proton is composed of a positron and a neutron.

four electrons. In each atom the resultant nuclear charge is + 3, and *each* atom has, accordingly, three orbital electrons. Although these two lithium atoms are constructed differently, they have the same number of orbital electrons and hence exhibit similar *chemical* properties.

The *atomic weights* of these three elements are: hydrogen, 1.008; helium, 4.00; and lithium, 6.940. Remembering that hydrogen has one revolving electron, helium two, and lithium three, it is seen that there exists a relation between atomic weight and orbital electrons. For the Bohr atom model this relation is as follows: If the elements are arranged according to their ascending atomic weights and numbered in order, then hydrogen is 1, helium is 2, lithium is 3, etc. These numbers are called the **atomic numbers;** they also indicate the number of orbital electrons in each atom.

It was shown in a preceding section that the protons were much more massive than the electrons. This mass is due to the neutrons which they contain. Thus the *mass* of an atom is largely concentrated in the nucleus. As previously mentioned, the chemical activity seems to be determined by the orbital electrons.

It is apparent that the heavier elements have structures becoming increasingly complex, and naturally these structures are less definitely understood. In general, the following statement applies to *most* of the atoms: The number of orbital electrons is equal to the *atomic number;* the number of protons is equal to the *atomic weight* (considering isotopes); and the number of electrons in the nucleus equals the number of protons minus the number of orbital electrons.

It is not the purpose of this discussion to penetrate far into the structure of the atom; such information is contained in textbooks on modern physics. There is, however, such a close *apparent* relation between certain phenomena such as thermionic emission and atom structure, and photoelectric emission and atom structure, that additional atom study is advisable. Although the electrons appear to move in definite orbits, there are one or more possible orbits at each quantum level. Although the innermost orbit is circu-

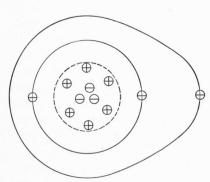

Fig. 1–5. In the Bohr model of the lithium atom, the central nucleus consists of three electrons and six protons. There are two electrons in a circular orbit and one in an elliptical orbit.

lar, according [4] to Sommerfeld the other orbits are elliptical. Thus, the lithium atom would be somewhat as shown in Fig. 1–5.

The apparent arrangements of the orbital electrons in certain of the elements, including several very important in electrical work, are given by Table I. It is seen that there is a very definite similarity existing

TABLE I

POSSIBLE ARRANGEMENT OF ELECTRONS FOR CERTAIN ELEMENTS

ELEMENT	ATOMIC NUMBER	NUMBER OF ELECTRONS AT EACH QUANTUM LEVEL					
		1	2	3	4	5	6
Helium	2	2					
Neon	10	2	8				
Argon	18	2	8	8			
Krypton	36	2	8	18	8		
Xenon	54	2	8	18	18	8	
* Radon	86	2	8	18	32	18	8
Lithium	3	2	1				
Sodium	11	2	8	1			
Potassium	19	2	8	8	1		
Rubidium	37	2	8	18	8	1	
Caesium	55	2	8	18	18	8	1

* Also called Niton.

among the elements of the first half of this table, and a different similarity existing among those of the last half. This means that the first half should have similar characteristics and that the second group should also be similar to each other. Such similarity is found experimentally. The first group (excepting Helium) has 8 electrons in the outer orbit producing a stable atom. These elements are the inert gases which form no chemical compounds with atoms of other gases. Certain of these inert gases are used in gas-filled tubes. The second group includes the rare earth metals some of which are used as the active material in phototubes. Each of these has only one electron in the outer orbit, resulting in an unstable structure. It has also been found that the best conductors, copper and silver, are characterized by having but one electron in the outer orbit. Additional information on conduction in solids will be found later in this chapter.

This atom model has many short-comings, and is not accepted at present as being the final explanation of atomic theory. The objections are based on the work of many investigators, some of which will be briefly summarized.

Largely as a result of the works of de Broglie, Schrödinger, and Heisenberg, electrons were shown mathematically to exhibit the properties, not only of particles, but also of waves.[5] Davisson and Germer in 1927 showed experimentally that electrons had the characteristics of waves; this was also demonstrated by others. Thus, it appears that an electron behaves both as a particle and as a wave, *and that it is both*.[5]

Although the Bohr atom model is not entirely satisfactory, it provides an extremely useful *picture* and as such is widely used today in scientific and engineering work. It will accordingly be employed throughout this book.

5. The Ion.—An ion is defined [3] as " an electrified portion of matter of subatomic, atomic, or molecular dimensions." The term ion includes many types of charged particles. The simplest ion is an electron which has been torn away from an otherwise neutral atom. This **negative ion** (electron) has but little mass, and is rapidly accelerated and hence obtains a high velocity in an electric field. When an atom loses an electron, it leaves a massive *positively* charged particle or **positive ion**. These massive positive ions are not so easily accelerated, and hence do not reach the same velocity as electrons when subjected to the same electric field. Furthermore, a stray electron may become attached to an otherwise neutral atom, producing a massive negative ion. Other more complicated ions [8] consisting of charged clusters of atoms or molecules can also exist. For the purpose of this book, the only ions of importance are: *first*, the electrons, and *second*, positive ions resulting when a neutral atom loses an electron.

Ions are created from neutral matter by detaching one or more electrons from a neutral atom. To do this energy must be supplied to the atom. This energy can come from several sources, the most important being from an impact with another particle, from electromagnetic waves (light beams, x-rays, gamma rays, cosmic rays, etc.), from a chemical reaction, or from heat. Ionization by energy derived from heat (thermionic emission) is of great importance in vacuum tube design. It will be considered in detail in Chapter 3. Ionization by chemical reaction is of importance in electrochemistry but of little import in electronic tubes, and will therefore not be discussed herein. Ionization by energy derived from electromagnetic waves (photoemission) is of practical importance chiefly in photoelectric phenomena and will be discussed in Chapter 2. Ionization by collision is important in high-vacuum tubes in that electrons are knocked out of the electrodes by electrons landing thereon. It is of additional importance in gas-filled tubes since certain of the gas molecules may become ionized (see § 6). A description of ionization by collision will give an idea of the mechanism of ionization by any means.

Ionization by Collision.—As Hull points out,[9] when an electron collides with an atom one of *four* things may happen: (1) nothing at all, (2) deflection of the electron, (3) excitation of the atom, or (4) ionization of the atom. At electron energies of less than about one volt (page 4) nothing at all happens when an electron collides with an atom of an inert gas. The electron passes through the atom with no loss of energy and with only a slight chance of deflection.[9] This is in accordance with expectations based on the Bohr atom model (page 7) which assumes that the relative distances between the nucleus and the revolving electrons are very great.

If the velocity of the colliding electron is increased, but is still below a critical value, collisions are more frequent and these collisions deflect the electron with (almost) no loss of energy. This is in accordance with the quantum viewpoint; an atom can take energy from a colliding electron only in definite amounts. This amount of energy must be sufficient to raise the atom which is struck to an **excited state,** or to the **ionization state.**[9]

When a rapidly-moving electron having sufficient energy collides with an atom it will ionize the atom by knocking one or more electrons out of it. If it does not transfer sufficient energy, it may merely *excite* the atom. To excite an atom, the transferred energy must be just sufficient to displace an outer electron from its normal orbit to one at a higher energy level; it must not be sufficient to ionize the atom. Hull, in Reference 9, includes a table of data from the work of P. T. Smith. This table, part of which is included in Table II, shows that for the three gases listed this minimum critical value is more than 10 electron volts. An atom may have several excitation levels.

TABLE II

GAS	FIRST CRITICAL EXCITATION POTENTIAL VOLTS	IONIZING POTENTIAL VOLTS	MEAN FREE PATH OF ELECTRON, 1 MM. MERCURY 0° CENTIGRADE
Helium	19.73	24.48	0.1203 cm.
Neon	16.60	21.47	0.0753 cm.
Argon	11.57	15.69	0.0431 cm.

The normal life of an excited atom is about 10^{-7} or 10^{-8} second.[10] In most excited atoms the electrons return to the normal orbits during this period, and the excess energy is *radiated*, often as visible light. Some excited atoms may persist in a **metastable condition** [9] for a considerable period, however, and such abnormal atoms will accordingly increase the probability of ionization.

An excited atom may be ionized by being struck by another electron with sufficient energy to complete the process; or, it may obtain the additional energy by absorbing a quantum of radiation of the proper wavelength. These quanta are called **photons** of light and may be of visible wavelength. Since these photons cause ionization they act in the role of electrons.[9] A third possibility is that the excited atom might obtain the required energy by collision with another excited atom. Ionization in this manner by successive stages is called **cumulative ionization.**

If the velocity is sufficient to cause ionization, a massive positive ion (the atom minus an electron) and negative ions (the original electron and the removed electron) result. These electrons may then be accelerated by the voltage applied between electrodes and may cause additional ionization.

The process of ionization is a very interesting one. For additional information Reference 11 should be consulted. These two articles are very authoritative and complete.

6. Electronic Phenomena in Gases.—In a preceding article it was shown that all matter was composed of atoms, and that they, in turn, consisted of a nucleus of electrons and protons, surrounded by revolving electrons. The structures of several of the gas atoms were discussed in some detail.

In a gas under ordinary conditions of temperature and pressure, the atoms may exist singly, or two or more may cluster together. Thus, the gas **molecules,** which may be thought of as the smallest particles of the gas having independent existence, *may be* atoms, *or may be* clusters of atoms. In the **monatomic gases** such as neon, argon, mercury vapor, etc., the individual gas atoms exist separately. In hydrogen and in other gases, however, two or more atoms combine to form a gas molecule. In most gases the molecules are clusters of atoms. The general term molecule may, therefore, imply either *a single atom* or *a group of associated atoms.*

In one cubic centimeter of *any* gas at 0° C. and at atmospheric pressure there are 2.71×10^{19} gas molecules.[4] The molecules of a gas are in violent motion, and if the gas is enclosed in a container, they continually bombard the walls, thus exerting forces producing gas pressure.

The molecules of a gas, according to the kinetic theory, occupy only a small part of the total space. The average velocity of the molecules in a gas is

$$v = \left(\frac{3p}{d} \right)^{1/2}, \tag{1-8}$$

where v is in centimeters per second, when p is the pressure of the gas in dynes per square centimeter, and d is the density in grams per cubic centimeter.[4]   Gas pressure can be increased either by heating the gas so that the molecules are in more violent motion, or by pumping more gas molecules into the container.

Not only do the gas molecules continually strike the walls of the container, but also, they strike each other; this is a random effect.   The *average* distance a molecule moves without a collision with another molecule is called the **mean free path.**   This term is also applied to atoms and electrons, and it is important, therefore, to state the type of particle when discussing the mean free path.

Thus the probability of a free electron striking a molecule depends on the number of molecules present and their size; that is, upon the pressure and the nature of the gas.

An electron may move only a short distance before a collision occurs, or, it may move a considerable distance; it is a probability effect.   The *average* distance an electron moves between collisions is the mean free path.   Koller gives [10] an equation

$$\lambda = \frac{1}{(\pi N \sigma^2)} \tag{1-9}$$

for the mean free path λ in centimeters for an electron where there are N gas molecules per cubic centimeter having a molecular radius σ. He also includes in Table XIII, page 140, the values of λ in centimeters for Helium as 0.1259, Neon as 0.0787, and Argon as 0.0450.   These data were apparently determined at a pressure of 1 mm. of mercury and at 0° C., the same conditions as those given in Table II, page 11, since the two sets of data are in close agreement.

Ions exist in gas under normal conditions.   The exciting energy to produce them may come from a number of possible *natural* sources such as *first*, collisions with high-velocity electrons or with high-velocity positive particles emitted by nearby radio-active disintegrating substances such as radium, traces of which are present in all earth. *Second*, the ionizing energy may come from cosmic rays or from high-frequency radiations such as x-rays from radio-active substances, and to some extent x-rays and ultra-violet rays from the sun.   This natural ionization in *air* causes the production of about 2 ions per cubic centimeter per second at atmospheric pressure.   At the highest altitudes at which cosmic rays have been studied, the rate of ionization may be 100 times as great.[9]

If two metal electrodes are placed in a vessel containing gas, and if a voltage is impressed between these electrodes, the positive gas ions will be attracted to the negative electrode, and the negative ions to the positive electrode and a current of electricity will, therefore, flow across the gas. If it were not for the natural ionization, gas could be a perfect insulator because it would lack charged particles to "carry" the electric current between the electrodes.

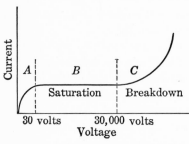

FIG. 1–6. The current which flows through normal air in regions A and B is due to the ions produced by natural ionizing agents. In region C, ionization by collision occurs. (This figure is not to scale.)

Suppose that two flat electrodes are spaced about one centimeter apart in air under normal conditions, and that a voltage impressed between these electrodes is gradually increased and the resulting current measured. From 0 to about 30 volts, the current will increase as shown by part A of Fig. 1–6 and then it becomes constant. This current flow is due to the free ions produced by natural ionizing sources.

A saturation current soon results, however, because as the voltage is increased region B is reached where the voltage takes the ions as fast as they are produced and thus uses all the available ions (due to natural ionization) to conduct current between the electrodes. At sea level the saturation current for air per centimeter cube is about 3×10^{-19} ampere.[9] This is explained in the following manner: If two ions are formed per cubic centimeter per second, and if all ions are being used, then since the charge on an electron is about 1.592×10^{-19} coulomb (page 2), and since one coulomb per second is one ampere, the current flow would be about $2 \times 1.592 \times 10^{-19}$ or 3×10^{-19} ampere.

If the voltage impressed on air (or other gas) is further increased, the current will remain constant as in region B until a voltage between the electrodes (one centimeter apart) is about 30,000 volts (for air). In region C the current through the air will increase rapidly until, with further increase in applied voltage, the air will break down completely, a spark will pass, and an arc will form between the electrodes.

The reason for this sudden increase in current and the resulting breakdown is briefly this: As shown by equation (1–5) an electron, if unimpeded in its flight, reaches the very high velocity of about 370 miles per second in the relatively weak electric field produced by only one volt. If it falls unimpeded through a difference of potential of 10,000 volts, the speed becomes [12] approximately 0.586×10^{10} centimeters per second, or about *36,400 miles per second.* Thus, if a high velocity electron * strikes a gas atom or molecule it may have sufficient energy to ionize the atom by knocking out one or more electrons. This process, which is cumulative, provides sufficient ions to carry currents of increasing magnitudes between the electrodes. If the ionization becomes sufficient, the current will increase to a high value, the electrodes will become hot, and an arc will form.

Recombination-Deionization.—An ionized gas contains positive and negative ions. Since these have opposite charges it is apparent that there will be a great tendency for **recombination** to take place and for the gas to **deionize.** As will be seen later (page 198) the **deionization time** in a gas tube is of great practical importance.

The probability of a positive ion meeting a negative ion in a given time is proportional to the number of *negative* ions present in the gas; similarly the probability of a negative ion meeting a positive ion is proportional to the number of *positive* ions present.[13] The rate of combination is, therefore, proportional to n^2, where n is the *total* number of positive and negative ions present per unit volume of gas. The rate of recombination is, therefore, equal to αn^2, where α is a constant for given conditions, and is known as the **coefficient of recombination.**

In addition to recombining, ions may be withdrawn from a gas by the action of magnetic or electric fields. They may also diffuse to the walls of a container. When electrons accumulate on the glass (insulating) walls of a vacuum tube they form a localized negative charge. This may produce a grid-like action on an electron beam, which is of special importance in x-ray tube and cathode-ray tube design.

Ion Sheaths.—The distribution of the ions may *not* be uniform in an ionized gas. This is especially true when a difference of potential is applied between the electrodes in a gas tube, in which case there is a tendency for ions to approach electrodes of opposite polarity. The non-uniformity is largely due to the fact that the electrons have a small mass and are much more mobile than the larger positive ions (atoms minus one or more electrons). The **mobility** of an ion is defined as the velocity in centimeters per second under the action of an electric field of one volt per centimeter. Ionic mobilities depend on the nature of the gas, and upon the pressure and temperature.

Equation (1–8) gave the molecular velocity in terms of the density and pressure of the gas. This velocity may also be expressed in the form

$$v = \left(\frac{3kT}{m} \right)^{1/2},$$
(1–10)

---

* Under usual conditions in gas-filled vacuum tubes the massive positive ions do not attain a velocity sufficient for ionization. See, however, § 7.

where v is the velocity in centimeters per second, T the absolute temperature, m the mass of the particle in grams, and k is the Boltzmann constant of 1.37×10^{-16} erg per degree.[14]   It is thus apparent that the velocities of ions vary inversely as the square roots of their masses. In mercury vapor,[10] which is extensively used in rectifier tubes, the square root of the ratio of the mass of the positive ion to that of an electron is 607 : 1.

To explain the formation of ion sheaths, assume that a body of ionized gas at uniform potential, containing approximately equal numbers of positive and negative ions, exists.   Such a uniform region in an ionized gas is called a **plasma**.   The ions are moving in random directions, and since their masses are different, the number of *electrons* which would pass, in a given time, through an imaginary plane surface in the gas would greatly exceed the number of *positive ions*.   In the absence of any disturbing field, 607 electrons would pass the surface for each positive ion.

Now suppose that a *negatively* charged electrode is placed in the ionized gas; it will attract positive ions and repel electrons with equal forces because the charges are equal.   The electrons move so readily however, and the positive ions so slowly, that there will be formed a region or sheath around the electrode in which a preponderance of positive ions exists.   These excess positive particles will neutralize the electric field from the negative electrode and thus largely prevent its penetration beyond the sheath into the ionized gas.   Any effect of a negative electrode in further controlling conditions in the tube is prevented; increasing the voltage merely changes the thickness of the sheath. This is an important effect in grid-controlled gas tubes (page 134). The thickness of the sheath can be calculated.[10, 14]   Sheaths also may be formed about a *positive* electrode.[10, 14]

7. Self-Maintained Discharges.—Discharges in gaseous space which conduct electricity under the influence of *the applied voltage alone*, and without any external ionizing agent contributing to any important extent to the production or introduction of ions within the space, are called **self-maintained**[15] or **self-sustaining**[16] **discharges.** Although external ionizing forces may assist in *starting* the discharge, once it is started, the *discharge itself* produces the required ions as fast as they are lost at the electrodes or otherwise neutralized.   External forces may assist in starting an arc in many ways; for example, natural ionization (page 13) producing free ions in air; or photoelectrically by visible light, ultra-violet light, or x-rays shining on the electrodes.   **Non-self-maintained** discharges are of the type encountered in gas-filled *thermionic* tubes.   These will be considered extensively throughout this book.

Self-maintained discharges include electric sparks, corona, glows, and arcs. The precise nature of the phenomena occurring in all these is not exactly known. Some of the complications involved in explaining such discharges are well stated [16] by Darrow as follows:

"In these the gas is swarming with free electrons and ionized atoms and excited neutral atoms and corpuscles of light, appearing and disappearing and changing state and interacting with one another and with the electrodes and the walls of the containing tube in such a tumultuous variety of ways that the phenomena are very difficult to understand."

The *self-maintained* discharge depends for its existence upon ionization by collision by *both* the positive ions and electrons; if only the electrons produce ionization, then such a discharge cannot exist.[15] The original investigation of this type of discharge was made by Townsend who derived [13] the mathematical relations applying.

The reason that *both* positive ions and electrons must produce ionization in a self-maintained discharge is shown in Fig. 1–7. Suppose that the voltage has just been applied between the two electrodes. The electrons (produced by natural ionizing agents) existing in the air or gas between the electrodes will travel toward the *positive* electrode, and the positive ions toward the *negative* electrode. Since the electrons will attain high velocity due to their small mass, these *electrons* will produce ionization by collision.

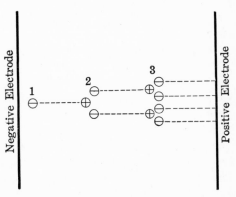

FIG. 1–7. Illustrating the fact that if the positive ions do not produce ionization by collision, a normal gas will soon be cleared of ions.

Assume that the voltage applied is *not* sufficient to give the massive positive ions enough energy for ionization by collision. Also assume that an electron starts from point 1 and travels to point 2 where it collides with a neutral atom and ionizes it. As a result of this collision, a new electron and a positive ion are produced. This *new* electron and the *initial* electron then move on toward the positive electrode. By the time they have reached position 3, they have the required ionizing energy, and upon impact will produce more ions as indicated.

If the illustration is studied, it is apparent that if the voltage is so low that the positive ions produce no electrons during their travel to the negative electrode, then the gas will soon be "cleaned up"; that is, cleared of ions. This is because the points where ionization occurs move successively closer and closer to the positive electrode, and soon there are no electrons left in the space between the electrodes, except of course as new ones are produced by external ionizing radiations. This means that the self-maintained discharge cannot exist except at a voltage sufficiently high for ionization by the positive ions to occur. Assuming that ions are lost only by neutralization at the electrodes, then the condition for a self-maintained discharge is that the *total* number of positive ions produced by an electron in moving from the cathode to the anode must regenerate one electron by the time those positive ions reach the cathode.[15] This means that the impressed voltage must be sufficient for ionization by the positive ions. Using the notations of Slepian and Mason, the Townsend equation is

$$\beta_2 = \beta \epsilon^{(\beta_2 - \beta)l}. \tag{1-11}$$

In this equation β_2 is the number of new ion *pairs* produced by an *electron* in traveling one centimeter in the direction of the uniform electric field, β is the number of new ion *pairs* produced by a positive ion traveling one centimeter in the opposite direction, and l is the separation in centimeters between the electrodes. Crowther states [13] that the ratio of β/β_2 is less than one per cent in air; that is, over 100 times as much ionization is produced in air by the easily accelerated electrons as by the massive positive ions. Conditions in a non-uniform field are treated in Reference 15.

Equation (1-11) expresses the conditions under which the discharge maintains itself.[15] If ionization conditions in the space between the electrodes is such that β_2 *is greater than* the term $\beta \epsilon^{(\beta_2 - \beta)l}$, the ions are not generated so fast as they are neutralized or lost at the electrodes; then the current-carrying ions disappear and the discharge stops. If, on the other hand, the value β_2 *is less than* the right hand term of equation (1-11), then ionization and the resulting current flow will increase *if the applied voltage and the resulting electric field is kept constant.*

A self-maintained discharge also may be obtained if the positive ions produce no ions *within the gas*, but knock out or otherwise produce electrons by impact upon the negative electrode, or cathode, to which they travel. This discharge will depend upon both the nature of the gas and the cathode material.[15]

Electric Sparks.—The most common form of self-sustained discharge, the electric spark, can be explained as follows: Suppose that

two large metal plane surfaces such as those shown in Fig. 1–8 are
spaced a distance d apart in air under ordinary conditions of temperature and pressure. If a constant
voltage E is applied as indicated,
the free electrons in the air between
the plates will be attracted to the
upper positive electrode, and any
positive ions will be attracted to the
lower negative plate. If the voltage is low, the ion current between
the plates, and thus the current I
from the source of voltage E, will be
very low, but appreciable.   After a
short time the current will reach a
constant value depending for its magnitude on the number of ions produced per unit time by natural ionizing forces.

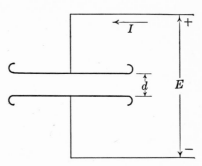

FIG. 1–8.   Parallel-plate spark gap.

If the voltage E is gradually increased, the current will not increase
(Fig. 1–6) until at a critical potential of *about* 30,000 volts per centimeter, when the air breaks down and a **spark** passes between the plates.
If the voltage is maintained, the spark may turn into an arc.   The spark
discharge differs from an arc only in its transient nature;[15] either the
supply voltage is not maintained *or* is instantaneously reduced so that
the spark is not continued.   The characteristics of the spark discharge
depend upon the nature of both the electrodes and the gas, and upon
the electrical supply circuit.   The spark is a self-maintained discharge,
but does not continue because the required voltage is not maintained.

The conditions for the passage of a spark are as given in equation
(1–11) and the preceding paragraphs.[15]   The voltage which, for a given
spacing, just satisfies this equation is the **sparking potential.**   In the
case of Fig. 1–8, the electric field between the plates is uniform before
the spark passes, and the **sparking gradient** would be the sparking
potential divided by the distance between the electrodes.   It is usually
expressed in volts per centimeter.

When the spark passes, an appreciable current flows because considerable ionization by collision has occurred.   Positive ions will accumulate at the negative electrode, and negative ions at the positive
electrode.   These cause an unequal **space charge** and an unequal
voltage distribution.   An unequal voltage gradient therefore exists
between electrodes.

Spark gaps are widely used to measure high voltages.[17]   **Needle gaps**
were formerly used but are not recommended for voltages above about
30,000 volts because of their erratic performance.   **Sphere spark gaps**

usually are employed for measuring high voltages. They should be constructed and used in accordance with the standards to which reference was made. They are reliable because their breakdown point is always the same, at least within narrow limits. Experiments [18, 19, 20] have shown, however, that for direct voltages and for transient impulses they do not perform the same as for alternating voltages.

Corona.—An unequal voltage gradient may be caused by the shapes of the electrodes and by their positions. If, at any region in a gas or

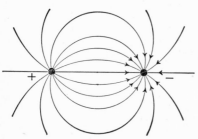

air, the critical voltage gradient is exceeded, then sufficient ionization will occur to cause a glow discharge at that region. To explain a typical case, consider the electrodes of Fig. 1–9 which represent the two parallel wires of a high-voltage transmission line.

The electric field between these two wires is concentrated at the surfaces of the wires. The lines of force per square centimeter are numerically equal to the voltage gradient,[21] and thus the air near the surface of the wire may be overstressed, although the air at some distance from the surface is not. If the voltage gradient near the surface equals the sparking gradient previously considered, then a self-maintained discharge called **corona** appears.

Fig. 1–9. The electric field is concentrated close to the surface of the two parallel wires.

When a wire (or other electrode) goes into corona, the region about it is ionized and is hence a conducting region. The corona discharge will, accordingly, expand about the wire until it reaches the proportions that the lines per square centimeter *at the surface of the corona* (and hence the voltage gradient) are such that the air beyond is no longer overstressed. This is, of course, only an approximate picture of the phenomenon, because actually the surface boundary is not sharply defined.

The light radiated by the corona discharge is due to recombination of ionized gas atoms or due to excited atoms returning to their normal state in accordance with the theory on page 11. Corona in air between parallel wires is influenced by the condition of surface of the wires, by geometrical configurations, and atmospheric conditions. It causes a loss of the transmitted power, and hence is a very important engineering consideration. Corona is fully discussed in such books as Reference 22.

Glow Discharges.—This discharge occurs between two *cold* electrodes at opposite ends of a tube containing air or gas at low pressure. The glow is a self-maintained discharge in which the current-carrying ions are supplied by the process itself. It has a practical application in the glow tubes used for electric signs. A typical glow discharge is illustrated in Fig. 1–10, and the corresponding voltage distribution curve is included. In the spark discharge previously considered, the voltage applied between the electrodes was uniform because the spark was a transient discharge of short duration. The glow discharge is a *con-*

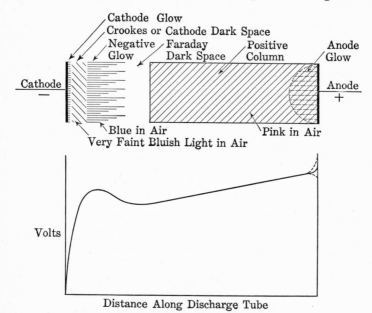

Fig. 1–10. Appearance, nomenclature, and potential distribution of the glow discharge. (Adapted from Reference 15.)

tinuous process, however, and space charges are set up within. This accounts for the peculiar shape of the voltage distribution curve.

The glow discharge tube has been extensively studied. It is treated in References 10, 13, 14, and 15 from which the following discussion is summarized. The separate regions in the glow are plainly marked on Fig. 1–10, and these will now be considered. It should be recognized that this discussion and the figure apply for a given type of gas—in this instance air—at a certain reduced pressure. Under operating conditions the (cold) *negative* cathode glows with a faint light called the **cathode glow.** Two types [15] of glow exist; the **normal glow,** in which the discharge does *not* completely cover the cathode; and the

abnormal or **anomalous glow,** in which the cathode is entirely covered. For the normal glow the cathode area covered increases and decreases in accordance with the total current flowing through the tube; this keeps the current density constant. As shown by comparison between the figure and the voltage distribution curve of Fig. 1–10, most of the voltage drop occurs in a short distance near the cathode in a region called the **Crookes** (cathode) **dark space.** This drop in potential between the cathode and the negative glow is called the **cathode fall.**[10] The magnitude of this voltage drop is substantially independent of the current until the current covers the entire cathode surface with the *abnormal glow* previously defined.[13] The voltage value of the *normal* cathode fall is a characteristic of the type of gas and the material of the electrode; it is practically independent of the pressure.[15] Typical values are given in Table III.

TABLE III

NORMAL CATHODE FALLS FOR CERTAIN GASES AND ELECTRODES
VALUES IN VOLTS

Values from Reference 15

TYPE OF CATHODE	AIR	HELIUM	NEON	ARGON
Platinum	277	160	152	131
Aluminum	229	141	120	100
Iron	269	161		131
Copper	252	177		131

When the cathode glow covers the entire cathode surface, then the fall changes from normal to the abnormal cathode fall. The characteristics of the abnormal cathode fall differ from those of the normal fall just discussed. The abnormal fall is greater than the normal fall and *increases* with an increase in current; this fall also increases with decreasing pressure.[15]

This suggests a possible scheme for rectification, which has been used to some extent. Thus, suppose that a circuit were arranged so that when one half of the alternating voltage cycle was impressed, the cathode glow would be normal, and that when the other half of the cycle was impressed the opposite electrode would be used and the discharge would be abnormal. Such a discharge would take place between a point and a plane in air. More current would flow in one direction than the other and rectification would result.[10]

The **negative glow** starts quite abruptly at the edge of the cathode or Crookes dark space, and gradually fades into the Faraday dark space. A potential maximum exists in this region.

The **Faraday dark space** exists between the gradually fading negative glow and the well-defined positive column. This space is not really dark, but appears so by contrast.

The **positive column** is independent of the phenomena at the cathode,[15] and no distinction exists between the positive columns of glows and arcs, either self maintaining or non-self maintaining. The positive column fills almost the whole of the length of the discharge tube; this is especially true in the neon tubes used for electric signs and in mercury vapor lamps.

As Fig. 1–10 indicates, the voltage drop across the positive column is very small compared with that of the cathode fall. In fact, the positive column can be almost eliminated without changing the characteristics of the rest of the tube. Thus, if it were possible to move the anode of Fig. 1–10 toward the cathode, the positive column would gradually disappear without appreciably altering the voltage distribution and hence the appearance of the rest of the discharge.

Regarding conditions at the positive electrode or anode, the potential drop may be large, small, or negative; it may or may not be accompanied by an additional visible glow. The anode drop will be small or even negative when the anode almost fills the tube; it will be large when the anode is small in area compared with the area of the tube.[15]

The phenomena which occur within the glow discharge tube are explained by Crowther in Reference 13 from which much of the following is summarized. The explanation applies to the tube under steady operating conditions.

Since it is a self-maintained discharge, the current-carrying ions come from collision with atoms or molecules of the residual gas. From preceding discussions, both positive and negative ions produce ionization. Some question exists regarding whether the electrons are liberated from the metal of the cathode or from ionization of the gas near the cathode or from both sources. Since the cathode fall depends on both the nature of the metal and the nature of the gas, it is possible that both effects exist, at least to some extent.

Most of the ionization occurs near the cathode. The electrons produced are rapidly accelerated and move away from the cathode leaving a space charge of the massive positive ions. This largely accounts for the high value of the cathode fall voltage.

The Crookes or cathode dark space represents the distance the electrons (which are produced near the cathode) must travel before they have sufficient energy to produce ionization by collision. This cathode dark space therefore terminates in the negative glow, a region in which gas atoms are excited and ionized, and from which light is emitted when excited atoms return to their normal state.

The excess positive charge in the Crookes or cathode dark space reduces the electric field in the negative glow and beyond as shown by the drop in the voltage distribution curve of Fig. 1–10. The electrons, therefore, soon lose their ionizing ability and the negative glow terminates in the Faraday dark space. The current in this dark space consists largely of electrons drawn from the negative glow. Since but few positive ions are in the negative glow, an increasing field exists between this portion of the discharge and the positive electrode. The electrons are again accelerated in this region and again attain enough energy to produce ionization by collision, causing the beginning of the positive column.

Ionization and excitation by collision from the electrons entering the positive column from the Faraday dark space occur all along the positive column, giving a uniform (in most commercial tubes) glowing column of light. The excess charges thus produced flow to the walls of the tube. Since the electrons diffuse more rapidly, the walls are a few volts negative *with respect to the axis* of the tube. This sets up an electric field, attracting positive ions to the walls. Energy is required for this process, and hence a voltage drop exists along the positive column.

To summarize, the electrons required for the self-maintained discharge are produced near the cathode through ionization (or an extraction process, or both) by the positive ions. In the dark portions the current is carried by electrons drawn from the luminous parts of the tube. The distribution of the applied voltage, and the nature of the ions in each region, have been studied [13, 15] by means of probe electrodes.

Arcs.—Two types of phenomena are commonly called **arcs**; first, the self-maintained discharge such as the arc used in welding; and second, the non-self-maintained discharge such as the arc in a gas tube with a *separately-heated* cathode (page 69). Only the *first type* will be considered at this time; the second will be considered in detail throughout this book.

The dividing line between an arc and a glow discharge is not always clear.[10] In an arc there is an emission of electrons from the cathode, and these electrons when accelerated by the positive anode cause ionization in the surrounding gas, thus producing positive and negative ions. The electrons are quickly withdrawn from this region, leaving an excess of positive ions and hence a positive space charge *near* the cathode.

The emission of electrons from the cathode appears to occur in two ways. *First*, the positive ions drawn to the cathode impart to it their energy and may keep the cathode at a temperature sufficient for *thermionic emission*. Second, the high positive space charge existing at the surface of the cathode may *pull electrons from it*, even when the metal is relatively cold. In arc discharges the total current carried between the two electrodes is largely supplied by electrons from the cathode; the *additional current carried by the gas ions is small*. Ionization is essential to produce the high positive space charge so that high currents may flow from the cathode at low voltages.

The arc in air is not surrounded by a tube, and hence there are no glass walls to which the ions diffuse and recombine as in the positive column of the glow discharge in neon tubes, for example. It is probable, however, that the cooler gases around the core of discharge serve the same function.[15] Recombination in the high temperature region at the core is negligible, but can occur in the cool surrounding gas. Energy must be put into the arc continually to supply the electrode losses, the losses due to recombination, and the loss due to radiation.

It is possible to express the relations in an arc by the empirical Ayrton equation as follows:

$$V = a + bl + \frac{(c + dl)}{i}. \qquad (1\text{–}12)$$

V is the arc voltage, i is the arc current, and l is the arc length. Although the values of the constants vary widely,[15] they are somewhat as given in Table IV, where V is in volts, i in amperes, and l in centimeters.

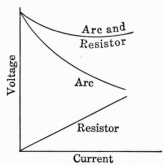

The arc has a negative current-voltage relation or **volt-ampere characteristic**. Thus, if values of the voltage required to maintain certain arc currents are plotted, a curve such as Fig. 1–11 is obtained. This means that the greater the current the *less the required voltage*.

FIG. 1–11. Voltage drop across a resistor, an arc in air, and the resistor and arc in series.

Thus an arc in air is unstable, and should be operated, therefore, in *series* with a fixed positive impedance, such as a resistance, if the

TABLE IV

CONSTANTS FOR THE AYRTON EQUATION FOR ELECTRIC ARCS

Carbon in air	$a = 38.5$	$b = 2.15$	$c = 54$	$d = 6.1$
Copper in air	$a = 60$	$b = 11.8$	$c = 0$	$d = 35.5$

voltage source is maintained constant. The volt-ampere characteristics of an arc alone, of a resistance alone, and of the arc and the resistance in series, are given in Fig. 1–11.

8. Electronic Phenomena in Solids.—The interior of a solid, such as a copper wire, may be thought of as consisting of rows upon rows of atoms arranged in three-dimensional lattice structures. The atoms of a metal may vibrate somewhat, but are fixed in position and they do not (in a solid) move about. Increasing the temperature of a metal is, however, thought to cause the atoms to vibrate more violently. Some information on the arrangements of atoms in a metal or other solid has been obtained by observing the photographic effects produced by x-rays directed on such bodies. This work started with the mathematical investigations of Laue in 1912 and the experimental studies [13] of Friedrich, Knipping, and W. L. Bragg.

It seems conclusive that the atoms of a metal are very closely packed together and that the orbits of the outer electrons may be actually *interlinked*. In a cubic centimeter of copper there are about 1700 times as many copper atoms as there are hydrogen atoms in a cubic centimeter of this gas at atmospheric pressure [4] and 0° C. Furthermore, the outer orbits of certain (good) metallic conductors contain only one or two electrons (page 9). Under such conditions the stability of these outer electrons seems to be affected by the presence of the other atoms.

The Classical Theory of Conduction.—A very simple theory of conduction was based on the concept of a metal as just given. This theory was accepted widely for many years, but is now seriously questioned.

It was thought that the spaces between the atoms in the lattice structure were filled with a "swarm" of **free electrons.** These electrons did not, necessarily, always remain free, but could be, and were, interchanged among the (vibrating) atoms. The spaces, however, always contained large quantities of *free* electrons, forming an **electron gas.** The velocities of the free electrons in a metal depended on the temperature of the metal.

If an electromotive force were applied to the two ends of a metallic conductor, that is, if one end were made positive and the other negative, then the free negative electrons would drift toward the positive terminal. This drift of electrons constituted the flow of an **electric current.** The electrons falling through the lattice spaces collided with the metal atoms. When they did this, they imparted energy to these atoms, causing them to vibrate more violently, and causing the wire to heat. A particular electron need not pass completely from one end of the conductor to the other. It might join an atom which had lost an electron. For alternating current, a resultant flow of electrons moves back and forth in the conductor.

In the materials generally classed as **insulators,** it was assumed that *very few* free electrons existed. The structure of the atoms was such that all the electrons were securely *bound* to the nucleus. The application of even a high voltage was merely able to deform the atom by stretching the bonds somewhat. Very high voltages were required to tear away these *bound electrons* and thus pass an appreciable current through an insulator. This classical theory was developed qualitatively by Riecke, Drude, and Lorentz [23, 24] in about 1900.

It is not proposed to go fully into the breakdown of the classical theory; the reader interested in more details should consult References 23 and 24. Very briefly however, the classical free electron theory required extensive modification when subjected to a quantitative analysis, especially in connection with the specific heats of metals.

Many new theories were postulated [23] to clear up the difficulties of the classical theory. The most promising analysis [24] seems to be that of Fermi, Pauli, and Sommerfeld, and is known as the **new quantum theory of free electrons,** or as the **Sommerfeld electron theory.**

The New Quantum Theory.—This theory is not so easily explained in simple terms as was the classical theory. This is not strange, in view of the fact that an electron is now considered to have the properties both of particles and waves. It is rather difficult to build up a physical picture on such a basis. The discussions here presented are largely based on the excellent article by Herzfeld.[24]

In the classical theory, if a negatively charged particle, such as an electron, comes into a region of high positive potential energy, it can pass on only if its *total energy* is greater than the highest value of the potential energy because (using the exact words of Herzfeld) "the total energy remains constant and the kinetic energy must be positive." In contrast, the *first important feature* of the new theory is this: Electrons behave like waves, and waves are not stopped *immediately* by a reflecting material, but can penetrate a *thin layer* and emerge with decreased intensity. A difference of potential (potential barrier) acts for electrons just as a reflecting material acts to light waves. Electrons can "penetrate" narrow potential ridges even if their energy is insufficient to carry them "over the top." This is called **quantum tunnelling.** This principle will be used later (page 46) to explain emission from cold bodies. Another point brought out by this theory is that even the free electrons in a metal are subject to forces exerted by the atoms of the metal lattice, rather than largely independent of these as in the classical theory.

In the classical theory, each particle of a system of particles can take on any value of a continuum of energies. In contrast, the *second important feature* of the new theory is this: Electrons can exist only in a finite set of discrete energy levels. Furthermore, the **Pauli exclusion principle** requires that not more than one electron can exist in any one energy level. This means that in a system of particles, not all of the particles can have zero energy. Thus the minimum energy of a gas is not zero but some finite value.

Using these features of the quantum theory as the basis for the statistics of the gas of free electrons, Sommerfeld succeeded in obtaining quantitative agreement with the experimental evidence even though he neglected the forces exerted by the atoms of the metal lattice.

According to Sommerfeld, in a metal there are one or more free electrons per atom. The average velocity of these electrons is very high, and *almost independent of temperature.* On the basis of the classical theory the average thermal energy of a free electron in a metal at room temperature is 1/25 of an electron volt (page 4). According to the Sommerfeld viewpoint the average thermal energy should be from 5 to 10 volts. These values are in reasonable agreement with experimental results for metals only.

Later developments have shown that this electron gas theory is the limit of the more general theory upon going from poor conductors to good conducters. This explains why it fits so closely the experimental results for metals.

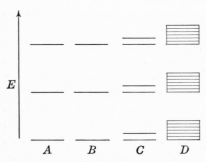

E

A   B   C   D

FIG. 1–12. Illustrating the origin of broad bands in crystals according to quantum theory. *A, B,* two free atoms; *C,* two atoms close together; *D,* crystal. (From Reference 24.)

In presenting these later developments, it seems advisable to quote directly from the article by Herzfeld.[24]

"It is well known that the quantum theory permits only a discrete number of states (orbits with given energies). Assume a number N of separate atoms, say, of silver. Then, for example, each atom will have 3 lowest possible states (the 'valence electron' can have 3 states of low energy). (Fig. 1–12.) All the atoms are alike, of course. If they are allowed to approach more and more, until they form a crystal, they will influence each other; this will lead to the result that instead of having the possibility of N identical lowest states, one for each atom, there are N different, but closely adjacent states. A similar effect is obtained if N identical radio-circuits are coupled; the system of circuits then will be found to have N different, although closely adjacent, radio frequencies.[25, 26]

"Each state of the free atom gives such a band containing aN states, where a is a small integer.

"According to Pauli no more than one electron can be in any particular state. If there are N electrons, they will of course fill the states of lowest energy in the lowest band. In case the number of electrons is just equal to the number of states in the lowest band, this band will be completely filled; there will be an equal number of electrons moving to the right and to the left, although how fast they get along will depend upon the height of the potential barriers within the crystal (between the atoms). Of course, because of the equal number going in each direction, there is no resultant current, and this will *not* change upon application of an external field. Such a field could generate a current only if it set more electrons moving, say, to the right. However, that is impossible because all states corresponding to motions to the right already are occupied, and because too much energy is required to put an electron into a higher band that is empty and where the electron therefore could get into a quantum state that corresponds to motion to the right. Therefore, we have an insulator. In a semiconductor, there are impurities that supply electrons into the empty bands of the surrounding medium and give rise to conduction. The same result is accomplished by the action of light of sufficiently short wavelength.

"If, however, the number of states in the lowest band is larger than the number of electrons present, empty states are available in the same band, and an external electric field has to raise the electrons only to a slightly higher energy to permit an excess of them to travel to one side. We have, therefore, an electronic conductor. There are, however, some electrons in the otherwise empty part of the band

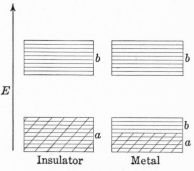

Fig. 1–13. Distinction between a metal and an insulator as explained by the quantum theory. *a*, full levels; *b*, empty levels. (From Reference 24.)

that lies above the completely filled part and below the top of the permitted band. The number of these electrons depends strongly upon the temperature.[26] See Fig. 1–13."

Those desiring more advanced or additional information on conduction in metals should consult References 27 and 28.

Thermal Agitation in Conductors.—According to accepted theory there are a large number of free electrons moving about in a conductor. Their velocities depend on the temperature of the conductor. This is a random motion, and at a given instant more electrons may be moving in one direction than in the other. This will result in the production of random voltage variations between the ends of the conductor.

The magnitude of the effective value of the voltage E produced by thermal agitation is derived [29] as

$$E = [4kTR(f_2 - f_1)]^{1/2}, \qquad (1\text{-}13)$$

where k is Boltzmann's constant (page 16), T is the temperature of the conductor in degrees Kelvin, R is the *effective resistance* of the conductor, and f_2 and f_1 are the limits of the frequency band being studied.

Terman [29] shows that the voltage E due to thermal agitation between the terminals of a 1/2 megohm resistor at 300 degrees Kelvin for a band 5000 cycles wide would be 6.4 microvolts. Such a voltage would be amplified and appear as noise in many communication circuits. Johnson [30] and others have studied this thermal agitation experimentally.

REFERENCES

1. Darrow, K. K. *The newly discovered elementary particles.* Electrical Engineering, Aug., 1935, Vol. 54, No. 8.
2. Kurie, F. N. D. *The cyclotron: A new research tool for physics and biology.* General Electric Review, June, 1937, Vol. 40, No. 6.
3. *American Standard Definitions of Electrical Terms*, A.I.E.E.
4. Hudson, R. G. *Electronics.* John Wiley & Sons.
5. Waterman, A. T. *Fundamental properties of the electron.* Electrical Engineering, Jan., 1934, Vol. 53, No. 1.
6. *Origin of the word electron.* Journal of the A.I.E.E., Oct., 1930, Vol. XLIX, No. 10.
7. Compton, A. H. *The corpuscular properties of light.* Physical Review Supplement, Review of Modern Physics, July and Oct., 1929, Vol. 1.
8. Tonks, L. *Electric discharges in gases.* Electrical Engineering, Feb., 1934, Vol. 53, No. 2.
9. Hull, A. W. *Fundamental electrical properties of mercury vapor and monatomic gases.* Electrical Engineering, Nov., 1934, Vol. 53, No. 11.
10. Koller, L. R. *The Physics of Electron Tubes.* McGraw-Hill Book Co.
11. Compton, K. T., and Langmuir, I. *Electrical discharges in gases.* Reviews of Modern Physics, Part I, April, 1930, Vol. 2, No. 2. Part II, April, 1931, Vol. 3, No. 2.
12. Henney, K. *The Radio Engineering Handbook.* McGraw-Hill Book Co.

13. Crowther, J. A. *Ions, Electrons, and Ionizing Radiations.* Longmans, Green & Co.
14. McArthur, E. D. *Electronics and Electron Tubes.* John Wiley & Sons.
15. Slepian, J., and Mason, R. C. *Electric discharges in gases.* Electrical Engineering, April, 1934, Vol. 53, No. 4.
16. Darrow, K. K. *Electric discharges in gases.* Electrical Engineering, March, 1934, Vol. 53, No. 3.
17. *AIEE Standards for Measurement of Test Voltages in Dielectric Tests.* These are summarized in Electrical Handbooks.
18. McMillan, F. O., and Starr, E. C. *The influence of polarity on high voltage discharges.* Transactions AIEE, 1931, Vol. 50.
19. Meador, J. R. *Calibration of the sphere gap.* Electrical Engineering, June, 1934, Vol. 50, No. 6.
20. Bellaschi, P. L., and McAuley, P. H. *Impulse calibration of sphere gaps.* Electrical Journal, June, 1934.
21. Albert, A. L. *The Fundamental Theory of Electrical Engineering.* Ginn & Co.
22. Peek, F. W. *High Voltage Engineering.* McGraw-Hill Book Co.
23. Hughes, A. L., and DuBridge, L. A. *Photoelectric Phenomena.* McGraw-Hill Book Co.
24. Herzfeld, K. F. *The present theory of electric conduction.* Electrical Engineering, April, 1934, Vol. 53, No. 4.
25. Herzfeld, K. F. *On the atomic properties which make an element a metal.* Physical Review, 1926, Vol. 29, page 701.
26. Slater, J. C. *Cohesion in monovalent metals.* Physical Review, 1930, Vol. 35, page 509.
27. Darrow, K. K. *Statistical theories of matter, radiation, and electricity.* Physical Review Supplement, July, 1929, Vol. 1.
28. Seitz, F., and Johnson, R. P. *Modern theory of solids.* Journal of Applied Physics, February and March, 1937, Vol. 8, Nos. 2 and 3.
29. Terman, F. E. *Radio Engineering.* McGraw-Hill Book Co.
30. Johnson, J. B. *Thermal agitation of electric charge in conductors.* Physical Review, July, 1928. Also Bell System Monograph B-334.

NOTE: A book entitled *Fundamentals of Engineering Electronics* by W. G. Dow (published by John Wiley & Sons) contains valuable information on the subjects discussed in this and the following chapters.

SUGGESTED ASSIGNMENTS

1. List the elementary particles mentioned on page 1, and briefly describe each particle.
2. Calculate the data for, and plot a curve showing the variations in the apparent mass of an electron at different velocities.
3. Calculate the data for, and plot a curve showing the velocity of an electron at various voltages. What is an important factor influencing the reliability of the calculated values?
4. A cathode-ray tube (Chap. 14) is being operated so that the electrons are accelerated by a potential of 1000 volts. Calculate the force acting on the electron beam when the tube is exposed to the magnetic field

of the earth.   Repeat for an accelerating voltage of 200 volts.   What conclusions can be drawn from these results regarding the practical operation of cathode-ray tubes?

5. Assume values typical to some commercial application, and calculate the voltage required to maintain a carbon arc in air.   Does this value agree with observation?

6. What are the theories advanced for the fact that sphere gaps may not spark over for the same voltage values when alternating, direct, or transient voltages are being measured?

Additional problems applicable to this chapter will be found in Reference 10.

CHAPTER 2

EMISSION OF ELECTRONS

In the preceding chapter the basic laws of electronics were considered. Stress was placed on two important subjects, electronic phenomena in gases, and electronic phenomena in solids. The third division, electronic phenomena in liquids, was not discussed because it is not now of primary importance in vacuum-tube practice.

The operation of electronic equipment, such as vacuum tubes, depends largely on electrons which have been emitted *from* solids. The emission of electrons is, accordingly, a very important subject, and this chapter will be devoted to its consideration.

The crystals of a metal consist of ions spaced in a lattice, the spaces between being occupied by the so-called free electrons. The potential due to these charges varies between lattice centers but is practically uniform when it is averaged over a space containing about ten ions, unless these ions are at the surface of the crystal. At the surface of the crystal, the outermost charge consists always of electrons. These electrons give rise to a shell of negative potential over the surface of the metal. For an electron to get out of the metal it must therefore gain enough energy to surmount this potential barrier at the surface. Electrons can gain this necessary energy and thus be liberated from metals in any one of at least five ways. These are as follows:

1. *Photoelectric Emission.* By directing a beam of suitable light on certain metals, electrons are liberated.
2. *Thermionic Emission.* When a suitable conductor is sufficiently heated, electrons are given off.
3. *Secondary Emission.* Directing a beam of high velocity electrons against a metal causes **secondary electrons** to be liberated.
4. *Cold Cathode Emission.* If a metal is subjected to a very intense electric field, electrons are emitted, even at room temperatures. This is sometimes called **autoelectronic emission.**[1]
5. *Emission by Chemical Action.* This is discussed on page 46.

9. Photoelectric Emission.—Emission of electrons occurs when light rays of the proper wavelength (or frequency) fall on certain photo-sensitive metal * surfaces.

* To be strictly correct, the term electromagnetic radiation should be used instead of light rays, and photoelectric emission occurs from *all* matter, even occurring to some small extent from insulators.[2]

The discovery of this effect is attributed to Hertz in about 1887. While studying electromagnetic waves to check Maxwell's predictions, he observed that a spark gap in air broke down more readily when it was illuminated by ultraviolet light. He showed that the light must fall on the metal gap terminals (and not merely in the space between), that they should be clean and smooth, and that illuminating the negative terminal was most effective.[3]

This discovery by Hertz was studied further by Hallwachs who experimented with freshly polished zinc plates, and with other metals. His experiments were also performed in air.

Elster and Geitel are credited [4] with developing the predecessor of the modern phototube consisting of the active material in an *evacuated* glass bulb. They found that the output of a phototube is proportional to the intensity of the illumination.

Photoelectric emission was put to little practical use until about 1928 when the **phototube** [5] was developed for sound motion-picture work. As good tubes became available commercially, the applications multiplied rapidly.

The exact nature of the mechanism by which electrons are ejected from a metal when it is exposed to radiation of the proper wavelength is not definitely known. Theories have been proposed, have been accepted for a time, and then rejected.

Repeated experiments have shown that pure photoelectric emission is *independent of temperature,* at least over *very* wide limits. If, as the classical theory stated, a metal contained an "electron gas" of free electrons, and if the velocities of these electrons depended on the temperature, it should be expected that temperature would influence photoelectric emission *if the photoelectric current came from the free electrons.* It can be shown by simple calculations (Reference 6, page 31) that it would take hours for an electron *to absorb* enough energy from a beam of light to make possible its escape from the metal.

The next assumption was that the photoelectric currents *did not come* from the *free* electrons, but from the *bound* electrons in the outer orbits of the atoms. Such a theory agreed with the Bohr atom models. The elements which had one electron in the outer orbit, and were accordingly somewhat unstable, were found to give the largest photoelectric currents. It was assumed that a photon or quantum of radiation "reached" into the atom and by some trigger-like action gave its energy to, and *released,* a bound electron.

If photoelectric cells or phototubes are so designed that the results are not influenced by spurious effects, it will be found that the *number of electrons* or **photoelectrons** *emitted varies directly with the intensity of* *the light striking the active material.* (This relation may not hold for all commercial phototubes.[7]) This is in agreement with the quantum theory of light since the number of photoelectrons released is directly proportional to the number of quanta of light falling on the surface of the metal.

It has also been found that the *velocity of the photoelectrons is independent of the intensity of the light falling on the surface of the metal.* If a feeble beam of light comes from a distant star and falls on a photoelectric surface the *velocity* (but of course not the number) of the electrons emitted *is the same* as the velocity of the photoelectrons produced by a powerful light beam of the same wavelength. As one author states,[7] "the ejection of a photoelectron is, so to speak, a private affair between the electron and the quantum concerned in ejecting it."

According to the quantum viewpoint, the corpuscles or photons of light contain different amounts of energy. Thus, photons of red light (of a long wavelength and low frequency) contain relatively small amounts of energy $h\nu$ (page 6), but photons of shorter wavelength and higher frequency (for instance violet) contain more energy. From a theoretical viewpoint it appears, therefore, that there should be a relation between the velocity of photoelectrons and the frequency of the light. It has been found experimentally that this is true and that *the velocity of the ejected photoelectrons increases directly with the frequency of the light* (or radiation).

Einstein's Equation for Photoelectric Emission.—Based upon the then-existing knowledge of photoelectric emission, Einstein proposed, in 1905, a most revolutionary concept. He stated [2, 4, 7] that the emission process could be represented by the equation

$$\frac{1}{2} mv^2 = h\nu - p. \tag{2-1}$$

An explanation of this equation is as follows: According to the quantum theory, each photon or corpuscle of light or radiation contains a quantum of energy equal to $h\nu$, where h is Planck's constant (page 6) and ν is the frequency of the radiation. In the photoemissive process, this energy is expended in two ways: *first,* a certain amount is required to separate the photoelectron from the metal, and *second,* the remainder is imparted as kinetic energy to the photoelectron. That is, the kinetic energy $mv^2/2$ which the liberated electron has, will equal the energy of the photon $h\nu$ minus the **surface work** p.

If there were no forces at the surface of the metal tending to prevent electrons from escaping, then any radiation, no matter how low its frequency, could liberate electrons. As shown, however, when a negative electron leaves a metal, it must do work to overcome the potential barrier at the surface of the metal.

From these relations and from equation (2–1) it might be inferred that for a given radiation all photoelectrons are ejected from a metal *with the same velocity*, since p is a constant for a metal and $h\nu$ is a constant for radiation of a given wavelenth. This is not true, however, because all electrons do not have the same initial energy. Thus, an electron from deep down under the surface will suffer many collisions on its way out, and will therefore emerge with less energy and a lower velocity.[2]

Equation (2–1) gives, therefore, the relations for the *maximum* velocity with which a photoelectron is ejected. The remainder of the electrons have velocities between this value and zero. The value of $h\nu$ which will *just enable* an electron to escape with *zero velocity* from the surface (instead of deep down) gives the frequency of the light of the longest wavelength which can possibly cause photoemission from a given material. This frequency is sometimes called the **photoelectric threshold**. These relations are shown by Fig. 2–1. If light of a definite wavelength and frequency ν is used, the velocities of the photoelectrons will be distributed between zero and a maximum value

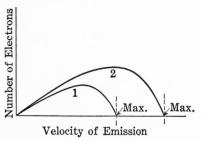

FIG. 2–1. Velocity distribution of photoelectrons. Curve 2 is for a radiation of higher frequency than curve 1.

somewhat according to curve 1 of Fig. 2–1. If light of a shorter wavelength and higher frequency ν' is used, the quanta will contain more energy and the velocity distribution of the photoelectrons will be as indicated by curve 2. For a complete analysis, Reference 4 should be consulted.

Recent Theories of Photoemission.—These theories of photoemission, based on the *classical* free electron viewpoint or on the Bohr-atom model, are not accepted as being entirely satisfactory. In fact, it appears that no simple and complete picture of the process of photoemission is available. The best evidence indicates that the *same* group of electrons in a metal produce both photoelectric and thermionic emission. Many of the older effects which were thought to indicate otherwise have been disproved.[3]

Fowler predicted that a *slight* shift with temperature should exist in the photoelectric threshold frequency or minimum radiation at which photoemission occurred.[7] This was based on the concept of Pauli, proposed in 1927, that electrons in a metal had far greater energies than given by the classical electron gas theories. Fowler's predictions were verified by DuBridge.[7]

Although the frequency versus sensitivity characteristics of photo-electric emission are not clearly understood, the proportionality between the quantity of light of one wavelength and the number of electrons photoelectrically emitted from a surface is one of the most steadfast laws of physics. It is this fundamental principle which has made possible many of the applications of the phototube.

10. Characteristics of Photo-emitters.—Suppose that a circuit is arranged somewhat as in Fig. 2–2. The surface of the *positive* metal plate P is illuminated by passing light through the *negative* grid G. Of the photoelectrons ejected from the plate P, some will have a maximum velocity corresponding to the maximum kinetic energy given by equation (2–1). When an electron falls through a difference of potential, the gain (or loss) in energy is Ve, where V is the voltage and e is the electronic charge (page 2). If the maximum kinetic energy $mv^2/2$ *exceeds* Ve, some of the photoelectrons from the plate will reach the negative grid against the effect of the opposing voltage V. When $mv^2/2$ *is less than* Ve, then even the fastest electrons will be unable to reach the grid. When $mv^2/2$ *equals* Ve, the velocities of the *fastest* electrons are such that they are just able to reach the negative grid.

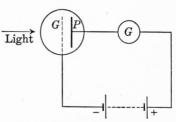

FIG. 2–2. Simplified circuit for studying photoelectron stopping potential.

The *negative* voltage which, when applied to the grid of Fig. 2–2, is just sufficient to prevent all electrons from reaching the grid is known as the **stopping potential.** Since for this condition Ve just equals $mv^2/2$, the velocity of the fastest photoelectrons emitted can be calculated. The stopping potential *depends on the wavelength* (it is proportional to the frequency) of the radiation, but is independent of the intensity. These relations were proved experimentally by Millikan.

If the wavelength of the light striking plate P of Fig. 2–2 is increased (the frequency decreased toward ν_0), a condition will be approached where the number of electrons emitted approaches zero, and their velocities of emission approach zero. Hence equation (2–1) now becomes

$$h\nu_0 = p, \qquad (2\text{–}2)$$

that is, *all* the energy is required to overcome the surface work of the metal.

The surface work p is the product of two factors,[2] the **photoelectric work function,** ϕ, of the metal and e, the electronic charge. Hence from equation (2–2)

$$hv_0 = p = \phi e \qquad \text{and} \qquad \phi = \frac{hv_0}{e}, \qquad (2\text{–}3)$$

where ϕ is expressed in volts. The photoelectric work function also is given by the relation [2, 4]

$$\phi = \frac{12{,}336}{\lambda_0}, \qquad (2\text{–}4)$$

where ϕ is in volts when λ_0 (corresponding to v_0) is the long wave limit at which electrons are emitted from a given material.

TABLE V

VALUES OF THE LONGEST WAVELENGTH λ_0 AT WHICH PHOTOELECTRIC EMISSION OCCURS FROM CERTAIN ELEMENTS, AND CORRESPONDING VALUES OF THE PHOTOELECTRIC WORK FUNCTION ϕ

(Data from Reference 4)

ELEMENT	LONGEST WAVELENGTH λ_0 IN MILLIMICRONS (mμ)	SURFACE WORK FUNCTION ϕ IN VOLTS
Silver	261	4.73
Platinum	196	6.30
Nickel	246	5.01
Tungsten	265	4.58
Lithium	540 *	2.1 to 2.9
Sodium	500 *	1.90 to 2.46
Potassium	550 *	1.76 to 2.25
Rubidium	570 *	1.8 to 2.2
Caesium	660 *	1.9

* Thin films.

Detailed values of the photoelectric work function are given by Hughes and DuBridge.[4] The values of Table V in **bold faced type** are those listed as the most reliable. All values were taken after extended outgassing (page 67). It is interesting to compare the values of the last five of the elements listed with the discussion on page 35.

It is probable that the values in Table V are the most reliable available. They may not agree entirely with tables given in other books for several reasons. The removal of occluded gases from the surface may change the value of the photoelectric work function as much as 30 per cent. Differences in the degree of outgassing will have pronounced effects. The exact condition of the surface is, therefore, important.   Other factors such as the accumulation of electrons on the glass tube walls, and the formation of transparent films of active metals on these walls,[7] may also influence the photoelectric work function.   Extreme care in the determination of the exact wavelength is important.

Determination of Photoelectric Work Function.—For the various methods of determining this constant, Reference 4 should be consulted. Briefly, some of these methods are the **stopping-potential method,** the **spectral distribution curve method,** and the " complete " **photoelectric emission method.**[4]

In the stopping-potential method, the stopping potentials of the ejected photoelectrons are measured for a given metal at several different wavelengths of mono-chromatic light (light of one wavelength).   When these values of stopping potential are plotted as ordinates with light fre-quency as abscissas, a straight line is obtained (see Reference 4, page 21).   When the data are corrected for errors (due to contact differences of poten-tial), the line intercepts the X axis (Fig. 2–3) at the value ν_0 from which the longest wave-

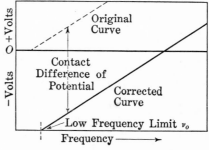

FIG. 2–3.   Illustrating the verification of Einstein's equation.

length value λ_0 (Table V) can be obtained.   This method was used by Millikan in verifying Einstein's equation.

For determining the photoelectric work function by the second method, the **photoelectric yield** (see Reference 4, page 51), or the rate at which electrons are ejected by unit intensity of absorbed light, is plotted for various frequencies against values of wavelength.   The intercept on the wavelength axis gives the longest wavelength λ_0 (Table V) at which emission occurs.

Color Sensitivity.—As is well known, the active material in a photo-tube is more responsive to light of certain wavelengths.   The relative responsiveness of a photosensitive material (or phototube) to radiation of various wavelengths is called its **color sensitivity** or **spectral sensitivity.**

The color sensitivity curves for the alkali metals are shown in Fig. 2–4.   These curves bring out two important points: [9] *First,* the wave-length of maximum sensitivity *increases* in the same order as the atomic number of the elements increases; and *second,* the relative number of the photoelectrons emitted and hence the magnitude of the photoelectric current *decrease* as the atomic number of the element increases. These relations should be compared with the atom-model theory on page 7.

The Selective Photoelectric Effect.—If curves for the metals of Fig. 2–4 are taken with plane-polarized light instead of unresolved light, it will be found that the spectral sensitivity curves are changed in part. For certain types of polarized light and for certain angles of incidence the photoelectric emission is more pronounced; that is, a selective

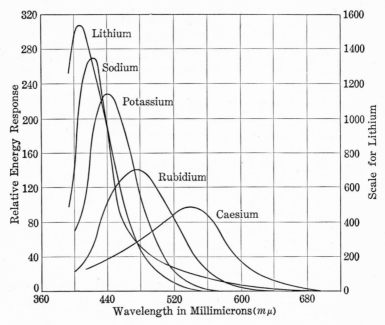

Fig. 2–4.   Color sensitivity curves for certain metals.   (Data by Miss Seiler, Astrophysical Jour., Vol. 52, 1920.)

effect, determined by the atomic structure, exists.   For additional information consult References 4 and 7.

Photoemission from Composite Films.—Although it has been shown that the spectral sensitivity characteristics depend solely on the nature of the photoactive metal, this is strictly true for thick layers only. The emission curves from various substances are greatly modified if they are studied in very thin layers only a few atoms thick.[2, 4]   It has been shown [2] by Ives that for thin sodium films deposited on polished platinum, the photoelectric current increases with increasing thickness of films.   The spectral characteristics also vary.

Composite films have been studied only recently, and such studies have been *very* encouraging. The caesium-oxygen-silver type of photosensitive surface has largely replaced the pure-metal types previously used. Information regarding these cells will be found in Chap. 13. It is significant to observe that great developments may be expected in phototubes with composite cathodes.

11. Thermionic Emission.—In **thermionic emission,** the energy required for liberating the electrons from the metal comes from the energy source used to *heat* the metal. As the name implies, the electron emission is thermal in nature. This subject is so important that only certain theoretical aspects will be discussed in this chapter; the following chapter will consider thermionic emission in detail.

Thermionic effects date back at least to 1725 when DuFay discovered that the *space* in the vicinity of a red hot body is a conductor of electricity.[10] Little additional theoretical information on thermionics was obtained until 1887 when Elster and Geitel found that an electric charge could be made to pass from a hot body through a vacuum to another body in its vicinity.

The basic principle of the thermionic vacuum tube was discovered by Edison in 1883. In investigating the failure of incandescent lamp filaments, in which he found that the filament burnouts nearly all occurred at the positive end, Edison arranged a special lamp in a circuit as shown in Fig. 2–5. He observed that when the cold electrode was connected through the galvanometer to the *positive* battery terminal, a current flowed; when connected to the *negative* terminal, no current flowed.

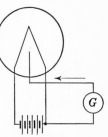

FIG. 2–5. Edison observed that a current (conventional) flowed when the auxiliary electrode was positive, but that no current flowed when it was negative.

This so-called **Edison effect** was not explained until 1903 when Richardson developed his equations (page 54) expressing the relation between electron emission and temperature. Entirely new industries such as radio and sound motion pictures have been developed as a result of the investigations on the emission and control of electrons.

In discussing the theory of thermionic emission it is generally assumed that there is a large number of free electrons in a metal, and that these electrons are in rapid motion among the metal atoms. The older "classical" viewpoint gave these electrons lower velocities and energies than the later Sommerfeld theory (page 27).

These electrons are thought to move in random directions with various velocities. A few move very slowly and a few very rapidly.

The higher the temperature, the larger will be the percentage of the rapidly moving electrons. If these electrons have sufficient energy they may escape through the surface of the metal and into the region (vacuum) beyond. For this to occur, the velocity of the escaping electrons must be such that the kinetic energy $mv^2/2$ must equal or exceed a value W which is a given value for each emitting surface. That is, for an electron to escape,

$$\frac{1}{2} mv^2 \geqq W, \tag{2-5}$$

where W represents the work done by a single electron in escaping from the surface of a metal.

This value of W is equal to the product of the electron charge e and an electromotive force ϕ and hence, for an electron which is just able to escape with zero velocity,

$$\frac{1}{2} mv^2 = W = \phi e. \tag{2-6}$$

In this expression ϕ is called the **work function** of a metal and is expressed in *volts* (page 4).

It is evident that strong forces must exist at the surface of a metal. If this were not true, small voltages would pull large currents from metals. These forces have been explained as due to electrical images.[2, 4] The work function ϕ is the potential difference through which an electron must pass in leaving the surface of a metal. It is apparent that when a negative electron leaves a metal, the metal is made *positive* with respect to the electron and the space it occupies. Thus, work must be done to remove an electron from a metal surface. Since the region within a conducting metal must be one of constant potential, this potential difference or surface *potential barrier* must be very thin. Thus, conditions may be pictured as in Fig. 2–6.

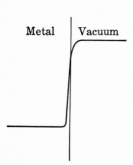

Metal | Vacuum

Fig. 2–6. The potential difference or potential barrier at the surface of a metal is confined to a very thin layer.

The thermionic work function ϕ is of the same nature and is identical in value with the photoelectric work function ϕ, page 38. (Values of ϕ for thermionic materials will be found on page 56.) In fact, there are reasons for regarding thermionic emission as a photoelectric effect. Thus, thermionic emission may be a photoelectric phenomenon, due to the action of the temperature radiation within the hot metal on itself.[4]

The emission of electrons from a hot filament is analogous to the evaporation of a liquid.   Just as heat energy is required to evaporate a liquid, so is heat energy required to "evaporate" electrons, and the emission of electrons causes cooling of the metal.   Thus, Davisson and Germer measured the work function of tungsten by observing this effect.   By measuring the electrical energy input to a filament when the plate was *negative* (so that no current left the filament) and when it was *positive*, they were able to determine the heat required for electron evaporation and thus the work function.[2]   Extensive additional information on thermionic emission will be found in the following chapter.

12. Secondary Emission.—If an electron moving with high velocity strikes a metal plate, the energy of impact may be sufficient to knock out or release **secondary electrons** from the surface of the metal. The number of secondary electrons thus produced depends on (1) the number of the bombarding or **primary electrons;** (2) upon the velocities of the primary electrons; (3) the type of material used for the bombarded surface; and (4) the physical condition of the surface.

Secondary emission is nearly independent of temperature, except as a high temperature may change the nature of the surface by changing the structure or by releasing *adsorbed* gas.*   A knowledge of secondary emission has existed for over thirty years,[11] but little practical use has been made of the phenomenon until recently.

To study secondary emission the simple circuit of Fig. **2–7** is satisfactory. A conventional three-electrode vacuum tube may be used.   The grid is made *more positive* than the plate.   When the plate is at zero potential with respect to the filament, as shown in Fig. **2–7**, the grid will collect all the electron current flowing from the filament or cathode. As the plate potential is made positive by moving the contact along the battery, the *plate* begins to collect electrons which pass through the wires of the grid.

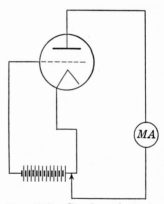

Fig. 2–7. Simple circuit for studying secondary emission.

As the plate is made more positive, some of the electrons attracted by it are accelerated to such a degree that they have sufficient kinetic energy to cause *secondary emission* from the metal plate by knocking

---

* A distinction is made between gases *ab*sorbed within the body of a metal and gases *ad*sorbed on the surface.[4]

electrons out of it.   This occurs at point *A* of Fig. 2–8.   As the plate voltage is made more positive, the plate current *decreases* to point *B*. The reason is as follows: Although the plate potential is sufficiently positive to accelerate further the electrons passing through the grid until they are able to cause secondary emission when they strike the plate, the plate is unable to capture these secondary electrons because they are pulled away from the region of the plate by the grid, which is more positive.   Thus at point *B* the net current in the plate circuit is zero.   Just as many *secondary* electrons are produced and lost to the grid as there are primary electrons striking the plate.

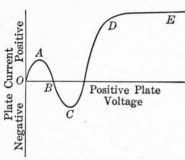

FIG. 2–8.   Secondary emission from the plate of the tube of Fig. 2–7 will cause the plate current to vary as shown.

If the plate is made more positive, the net electron current to it reverses in direction and goes to point *C*, because *more secondary electrons are produced than there are primary electrons striking the plate.* Hence, some of the high-speed primary electrons are producing *more than one* secondary electron.   But, as the plate is made *more* positive approaching the potential of the grid, the plate is able to attract the secondary electrons back to it and the plate current then becomes positive and flattens off due to saturation (page 77) between *D* and *E*. It is interesting to note that secondary emission occurs in thermionic vacuum tubes under usual operating conditions.   Since the plate is the only *positive* electrode within the structure, however, the effect is not apparent * in small tubes.

Very little is known regarding the exact nature of secondary emission.   In some way it appears that the primary or bombarding electrons impart energy to the electrons of the metal, thus permitting them to escape through the surface forces as secondary electrons.   The most complete theoretical treatment of secondary emission is due to Fröhlich in 1932.   He concluded that metals with a crystal structure having large lattice spacings and which had a low work function should be the best secondary emitters.[11]   This applies only to simple surfaces such as pure metals.

The secondary emission from composite surfaces is higher than from simple surfaces.   One article [11] states that many investigations have been made of composite surfaces consisting of surface layers of sodium,

* It affects the value of current flow to the negative grid in the larger tubes.

potassium, rubidium, or caesium on base metals such as silver, nickel, aluminum, or tungsten. Of these, the best surface layer found is caesium. A curve for a caesium-caesium oxide-silver surface is shown in Fig. 2–9. The method of preparing this surface is given in Reference 11. Additional information on secondary emission will be found in Reference 2.

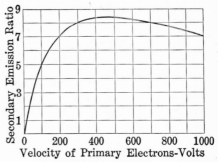

FIG. 2–9. Ratio of secondary to primary electrons for caesium-caesium oxide-silver surface. (From Reference 11.)

The important facts [8, 11] regarding secondary emission may be summarized as follows: Secondary emission depends on the surface treatment. Emission increases from a low value, rises to a maximum for primary electrons having energies equivalent to several hundred volts, and then decreases slowly. The *maximum* ratio of secondary to primary electrons is about 1.5 for well degassed ordinary metals, about 4 for metals not specially treated, and as high as 10 for films of alkali metal on oxidized metal surfaces. The velocities of the secondary electrons are quite small, usually being only a few volts even for primary electrons of a thousand volts.

Electrons may also be released by positive ion bombardment, and in other ways.[8] Recent developments indicate that amplifier tubes operating on secondary emission will soon be available commercially.

13. Cold Cathode Emission.—As has been shown, the free electrons are held in a metal by a surface force or potential barrier and are thus prevented from escaping easily into the surrounding air. This potential barrier was illustrated by Fig. 2–6. For the photosensitive metals, the photons of light give the electrons sufficient energy to escape across this barrier. In thermionic emission the heat which is supplied to the filament imparts to the electrons the necessary energy.

It has been found that very strong electric fields will also cause an emission of electrons from a metal which is *not photosensitive* even when held at room temperature. One author states [1] that very intense fields having a voltage gradient of 10^6 or 10^7 volts per centimeter at the surface of a metal will draw electrons out of the metal at room temperature. This is called a **cold cathode effect,** or **autoelectronic emission.** It occurs in a circuit such as Fig. 2–10. A fine point is used as a *cathode* and emission occurs at moderate voltages of 1000 to

10,000 volts.* It has been found that the emission varies exponentially with the field strength.[1]

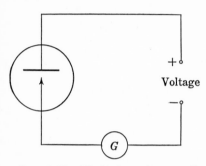

FIG. 2–10. Moderate voltages will cause very intense fields when a fine point is located close to a plane. In a vacuum, 1000 to 10,000 volts may be sufficient to pull electrons out of the point.

Attempts to explain this type of emission are summarized in References 1, 4, and 12. On the basis of the classical theory, only those electrons can escape from a metal which have sufficient energy to pass over the peak of the potential barrier.[4] The number of such electrons should show a strong dependence on temperature. The currents extracted from metals by strong electric fields are, however, independent of temperature (until a point is reached where thermionic emission becomes appreciable).

Considered from the more recent viewpoints, which attribute to the free electrons higher initial velocities and the characteristics of waves (page 10), the electrons are able to "tunnel" through the potential barrier without "passing over" the entire potential difference. The strong electric field is thought to *decrease the width* of the potential barrier making it possible for even those electrons having low kinetic energies to tunnel the barrier. The probability of the occurrence of this phenomenon increases rapidly with electric field strength and it is possible to obtain emission at room temperatures.[1]

The potential difference at the surface is of the order of 15 volts, and the maximum kinetic energy of the free electrons in the metal corresponds to about 10 volts, leaving a difference of 5 volts preventing their leaving the metal. The strong external electric field so limits the barrier to a thin layer at the surface that the electrons can penetrate or tunnel it as explained in Reference 12.

14. Emission by Chemical Action.—This type of emission was listed but not discussed on page 33. Such emission often occurs, especially where care has not been taken to remove impurities, gases, etc. In vacuum tubes it can usually be regarded as an unwanted effect.

Examples of emission by chemical action listed [8] in one article are as follows: Air, especially when moist, when in contact with phosphorus is charged with both positive and negative ions of low mobility.

* Voltage gradient is volts per unit distance. Thus, a relatively small voltage with electrodes at close spacing will cause high gradients. Also, electric fields are concentrated at points, thus increasing greatly the voltage gradient at the surface of the metal point.

Hot platinum in contact with phosphorous vapor emits positive ions but no appreciable negative ions or electrons.   Instances of the chemical reactions of various gases on electropositive * metals such as sodium, potassium, etc., in causing emission are also recorded.

15. The Photovoltaic Effect.—There are two sets of phenomena which, while not strictly classifiable as electronic emission, are so closely allied that they must be discussed to give a complete picture of electron phenomena occurring in solids when activated by outside sources of energy.   These are the *photovoltaic* and *photoconductive* effects observed when electromagnetic waves (usually in the visible or near visible spectrum) impinge on certain metallic substances.

Light shining on certain metallic contacts causes an electromotive force to be generated and a *voltage* to exist between the two substances. These experimental facts are called **photovoltaic effects.**   The discovery of this effect was made by Becquerel in 1839.   He was experimenting [4] with two similar platinum electrodes immersed in a dilute sulfuric acid solution and observed a potential difference between the terminals when *one* electrode was illuminated.

The early types of photovoltaic cells were also electrolytic cells.   In 1930 liquid cells with copper-oxide electrodes in a bakelite container having a glass window for admitting light were available commercially. These cells did not experience wide use.   The photovoltaic cells most widely used today do not contain a liquid but are of the dry disk type. *Two* types are in general use, the **iron-selenium type** or Photronic cell, and the **copper-oxide type** such as the Photox cell.

In 1876, Adams and Day observed that if a selenium rod were connected to a circuit by platinum-wire electrodes, a current would flow through the circuit if either selenium-platinum junction were illuminated.[4, 13]   Fritts, in 1883, deposited selenium on metal discs.   Such cells were found to cause currents to flow through connected circuits. Lamb and Bartlett further developed this principle producing the selenium-on-iron cell, a device having excellent characteristics.

The oxide photocell was discovered by Grondahl, who noticed that the performance of a copper-oxide rectifier was influenced by illumination.[4]   Lange, in 1930, developed a commercial form of the cell.

Although the dry-disc cells are sometimes classed as photoemissive cells, they are *usually* classed as photovoltaic devices.   Since these cells generate electromotive forces and therefore produce a potential difference between their terminals when light falls upon them, it seems advisable to class them as photovoltaic cells, since no ex-

---

* Electropositive metals are those which lose *electrons* readily such as photosensitive materials.   That is, they are metals having low work functions.

ternal sources of electromotive force need be applied as for the photoemissive tubes.

The theory of the copper-cuprous-oxide * photovoltaic cell is discussed in References 2, 7, and in great detail in Reference 4. Before considering these theories it will be necessary to describe briefly the construction of the cells.

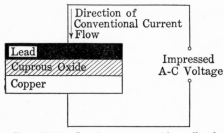

FIG. 2–11. In the copper-oxide cell, the electrons flow more readily from the copper to the oxide. When used as a rectifier, the rectified (conventional) current flows as indicated.

The units for *rectifiers* are made somewhat as in Fig. 2–11. The units are held in close contact by an insulated bolt.[14] The cuprous oxide (Cu_2O) is formed on the copper by heating under controlled conditions. The lead serves only as a current-collecting electrode to make a good contact with the oxide, and other metals may be used instead. When used as a rectifier with an alternating voltage impressed as indicated, *electrons* pass *from the copper to the oxide readily*, but it is difficult for them to pass in the opposite direction.[2, 14] The device, therefore, permits a rectified current to flow.

When used as a photocell, a thin film of a semitransparent metal is deposited (by evaporation or by sputtering) on the cuprous oxide, or, a metal grid is pressed against the oxide, to serve as a current-collecting electrode. The light shines through this collecting electrode and into the very thin layer of oxide. When the circuit is arranged as in Fig. 2–12, and when the cell is illuminated, an *electron* current flows as indicated. No batteries or other source of energy need be applied; the

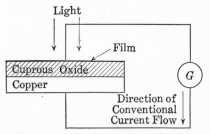

FIG. 2–12. In the copper-oxide photocell, a semi-transparent metallic film admits light to the oxide. The electrons absorb energy from the light, and pass from the oxide to the copper.

energy of the light is converted by the cell into electrical energy. Note that the electrons flow *from the oxide to the copper*. This may be unexpected because when the cell is used as a rectifier, *this is the high-resistance direction*.

---

* Although either copper-cuprous-oxide or cuprous-oxide is correct, the cells usually are called copper-oxide cells in engineering literature.

This type of photoelectric effect is explained by assuming the existence of a very thin "barrier" or "blocking" layer,[2, 4, 7] at the interface between the cuprous oxide and copper. The effect at this interface may be regarded as either the generation of an electromotive force, or the "emission" of electrons and the production of a current.[4, 7] The work of Auwers and Kerschbaum (summarized in Reference 4) favors the current viewpoint and the photoemissive classification.

It appears that each quantum of light sets free an electron from the oxide. Their kinetic energy is sufficient to carry them across the interface, in the direction in which the cell is a poor conductor (and has high resistance), as explained in the paragraph on rectifier action. This

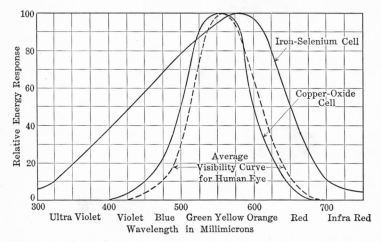

FIG. 2–13. Spectral sensitivity curves. (Data from References 10 and 13.)

kinetic energy must also be sufficient to send some of the electrons on around the circuit as indicated by Fig. 2–12, since no other source of energy is available. Other electrons flow back to the oxide across the barrier layer, in which direction the cell offers little resistance, as explained when rectifier action was considered.

The tendency for some electrons to flow on around an external circuit is equivalent to saying that the cell generates an electromotive force, and hence leads to the photovoltaic classification. The resistance of this external circuit should be low, as will be explained in Chap. 13. The current output of these cells is directly proportional to the light intensity for zero-resistance external circuits, and nearly so for low resistance values. The spectral sensitivity curve for a copperoxide cell is shown in Fig. 2–13. In addition to the sources already listed, further information will be found in Reference 15.

Physically, the selenium-on-iron photocell is similar to the copper-oxide cell just described. Furthermore, it appears to function—qualitatively at least—in the same manner. It is probable that its electronic action is similar to that of the oxide cell. A spectral sensitivity curve is included in Fig. 2–13.

16. The Photoconductive Effect.—In 1873 Smith found that the resistance of selenium resistors which he was using changed when

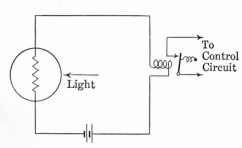

light fell on the resistors. This phenomenon has been named the **photoconductive effect.** Selenium cells, the resistance of which varies with the illumination, have been developed for photoelectric control purposes. Thus, if the illumination on the cell of Fig.

FIG. 2–14. Control circuit using a selenium cell.

2–14 increases, the resistance of the cell decreases; the current from the battery is increased; and the relay is operated, thus providing photoelectric control.

Selenium is a poorly conducting element "between" the conductors and the insulators. In the periodic table of the elements it is between the metal tellurium and the non-metal sulphur.[9] In a gray crystalline form it shows photoconductive effects. Substances other than selenium are photoconductive; among these is a thallium oxysulphide compound developed by Case. This has been used in the Thalofide cell. The commercial forms of the photoconductive cells will be considered in Chap. 13.

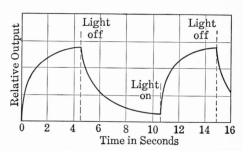

FIG. 2–15. With intermittent illumination, the output of the ordinary selenium cell lags behind light changes. (From Reference 9.)

The change in resistance lags considerably behind the illumination for the photoconductive cells. This is especially true for those using selenium as illustrated by Fig. 2–15. This is an important factor limiting the use of such cells, although it appears that the characteristics of the Thalofide cell were sufficiently good in this respect to permit of its use in early sound motion picture systems.

Each of the various photoconductive cells has its particular spectral response, depending on the type of photoconductive material used.

Theories of the photoconductive effect are treated in detail in Reference 4. Although the photoconductive effect has been known since an early date and has been the object of much experimentation, little information was available regarding its *exact* nature until recently. The reason is that certain secondary effects within the metal obscure the true photoelectric current. Much credit is due Gudden and Pohl for revealing this fact and for determining the true nature of the photoconductive effects now to be considered.

It appears that the photons or light quanta release electrons *within* the conductor from the crystals of the selenium or other substance. This is a **volume photoelectric effect** and the resulting current caused to flow by the difference of potential connected to the terminals is called the **primary photoelectric current.**[4] The many secondary effects caused by this primary current flow may completely obscure the true nature of the primary current. It is stated [4] that these secondary effects are caused by the fact that the passage of the primary current more or less temporarily lowers the natural resistance of the material.

In order to study the volume photoelectric effect successfully the smallest possible primary photoelectric currents are used. When such precautions are followed and crystals of diamond or zinc blende are used, the photoelectric current is found to be *directly proportional* to the intensity of the light.[7] Furthermore, it *starts and stops* instantly with the light. (This is certainly not in accordance with Fig. 2–15, but it should be remembered that this figure represents the characteristics of a commercial selenium cell and includes both the primary and the secondary currents.) It has also been found that, for these crystals, the number of photoelectrons released is very nearly identical with the number of quanta absorbed in the crystal.

REFERENCES

1. Dushman, Saul. *Electron emission.* Electrical Engineering, July, 1934, Vol. 53, No. 7.
2. Koller, L. R. *The Physics of Electron Tubes.* McGraw-Hill Book Co.
3. Richtmyer, F. K. *Introduction to Modern Physics.* McGraw-Hill Book Co.
4. Hughes, A. L., and DuBridge, L. A. *Photoelectric Phenomena.* McGraw-Hill Book Co.
5. Institute of Radio Engineers. *Reports of the Standards Committee.*
6. Morecroft, J. H. *Electron Tubes and Their Application.* John Wiley & Sons.
7. Hughes, A. L. *Fundamental laws of photoelectricity.* Electrical Engineering, Aug., 1934, Vol. 53, No. 8.

8. Compton, K. T., and Langmuir, I. *Electrical discharges in gases.* Rev. of Modern Physics, April, 1930, Vol. 2, No. 2.

9. Zworykin, V. K., and Wilson, E. D. *Photocells and Their Application.* John Wiley & Sons.

10. Westinghouse Electric and Mfg. Co. *Industrial Electronic Tubes.* Course No. 25.

11. Zworykin, V. K., Morton, G. A., and Malter, L. *The secondary emission multiplier—A new electronic device.* Proc. I.R.E., March, 1936, Vol. 24, No. 3.

12. Herzfeld, K. F. *The present theory of electric conduction.* Electrical Engineering, April, 1934, Vol. 53, No. 4.

13. Weston Electric Instrument Corp. *The Photronic Photoelectric Cell.* Monograph B-8.

14. Grondahl, L. O., and Geiger, P. H. *A new electronic rectifier.* Jl. of the A.I.E.E., March, 1927, Vol. 46, No. 3.

15. Grondahl, L. O. *Cuprous oxide rectifier and photoelectric cell.* Rev. of Modern Physics, 1933, Vol. 5.

SUGGESTED ASSIGNMENTS

1. Referring to the first four elements of Table V, assume that the long wave limit is determined experimentally and calculate the corresponding values of the surface work function.

2. Fully explain Hertz's photoelectric experiments in the light of modern photoelectric knowledge.

3. Compare the surface work function of the elements with the surface work function of a composite caesium-oxygen-silver light-sensitive electrode (consult Chap. 13).

4. Explain the theory of the barrier or blocking layer in the copper-oxide photovoltaic cell.

5. Enumerate the reasons sometimes advanced for regarding the selenium-iron photocell, and the copper-oxide photocell as photoemissive instead of photovoltaic cells. Do you regard these as valid?

CHAPTER 3

THERMIONIC CATHODES

The emission of electrons was considered in the preceding chapter. It was shown that electrons were released by photons of light striking certain metals; by heating the metals to high temperatures; by directing streams of rapidly moving electrons against metals; by subjecting the surface of a metal to strong electric fields; and by chemical action.

Of these effects, the first two are in extensive commercial use, and the third shows promise of early practical applications. The second effect, *thermionic emission* at high temperatures, is so very important that this chapter will be devoted to it.

Certain theoretical aspects of thermionic emission were considered in the preceding chapter. It was pointed out that the free electrons available in a metal for electrical conduction are also the electrons emitted when the metal is heated. Although called "free electrons," in all probability the individual electrons are only temporarily free.

These free electrons move about within the metal of a filament (for example) at various velocities depending on the temperature. At room temperature the electrons cannot pass out through the surface due to the surface forces which they encounter. At higher temperatures, however, many of the electrons have energies sufficient to enable them to pass through the surface and thus escape from the filament into the region surrounding it.

17. Equations of Electron Emission.—According to equation (2–6), an electron can just escape with zero velocity from a surface when the kinetic energy of the electron equals the surface work W required, that is, when

$$\frac{1}{2} mv^2 = W = \phi e, \qquad (3\text{--}1)$$

where v is the velocity of the electron, m is its mass, e is the electronic charge, and ϕ is the **thermionic work function** (page 42).

The nature of *thermionic* work function is the same as that of the *photoelectric* work function; they both represent the potential barrier effect at the surface tending to keep the free electrons within the metal. In photoelectric emission, the light photons give the free electrons the energy required for passing through this barrier. In thermionic emission this energy is imparted to the electrons by heating the filament.

53

Numerical values for these constants should, therefore, be identical for both photoelectric and thermionic emission, and such is often the case (see Table 3–2, page 75, Reference 1). Variations in samples, test methods, and measurement errors, however, prevent such data from being always in agreement. Values of the thermionic work function ϕ_0 are included in Table VII. (The notation ϕ_0 instead of ϕ is used with Dushman's equation, page 55.)

Richardson's Emission Equation.—In 1903 Richardson developed an equation that the relation between electron emission and temperature is [2, 3, 4]

$$N = n \left(\frac{kT}{2\pi m} \right)^{1/2} \epsilon^{-W/kT} \tag{3-2}$$

where N is the number of electrons emitted per unit area per unit time; n is the number of electrons per unit volume in a metal; $k = 1.371 \times 10^{-16}$ erg per degree (Boltzmann gas constant); T is the absolute temperature (degrees Kelvin, or degrees centigrade plus 273); m is the mass of the electron (9.00×10^{-28} gram); ϵ is the base of the natural logarithms (2.718); and W is the energy in *electron volts* which an electron must have to be able to escape from the metal filament.

The *current I* (or quantity per unit time) of electricity emitted by *unit area* of a filament is equal to the product Ne, where e is the charge on an electron. Furthermore, n is a constant for any metal and is independent of T. Combining all the constants into two values a and b, equation (3–2) can be written

$$I_T = aT^{1/2}\epsilon^{-b/T}. \tag{3-3}$$

In this expression, I_T is the *saturation current*, or the maximum current which an anode or plate voltage of any (reasonably) high value can take from the heated filament at a given temperature. For further information regarding the derivation of this equation consult References 3, 4, and 5, or Richardson's own writings, Reference 6.

From equations (3–1), (3–2), and (3–3), it follows [3] that $b = W/k$, that $W = bk$, and that $W = bk = \phi e$. Hence,

$$\phi = \left(\frac{k}{e} \right) b = \frac{1.371 \times 10^{-16} \times 300}{4.774 \times 10^{-10}} b = 8.61 \times 10^{-5} b \text{ (volts)}. \tag{3-4}$$

In this substitution, the numerical values of the Boltzmann constant k, and the electronic charge e (page 2) are substituted. The factor 300 is to express ϕ in volts instead of electrostatic volts. The reciprocal relation $b = \phi \times 11{,}600$ also holds.

The values of a and b in equation **3–3** are constant for given materials. These are listed in Table VI, the data being taken from References 2 and 7 in which the original sources are given.

TABLE VI

VALUES OF CONSTANTS FOR EQUATION 3

ELEMENT	a	b	T, DEGREES K
Carbon	2.37×10^6	48,700	2000
Calcium	1.74×10^4	36,500	
Molybdenum	2.1×10^7	50,000	2000
Nickel	4.61×10^6	34,000	
Platinum	1.195×10^7	49,300	1600
Tantalum	4.3×10^2	44,200	2000
Tungsten	1.05×10^7	53,000	2000

The derivation of Richardson's equation was based on the *classical* electron theory of metals. Reimann in Reference 5 points out that since this theory is no longer accepted, any formula based on it must be inaccurate. He also states, however, that as an *empirical* formula, equation (**3–3**) is satisfactory and has been used successfully for many years. Richardson's equation is of much historical importance since it probably represents the first attempt to express electronic phenomena *quantitatively*.

Accepted Emission Equation.—Richardson showed that an equation of the form

$$I_T = A T^2 \epsilon^{-b_0/T} \tag{3–5}$$

would be in accordance with *observed* emission data. M. v. Laue, in 1918, and Dushman, in 1922, independently derived this equation.[3] Equation (**3–5**) is often referred to as Dushman's equation, and is more widely used at present than equation (**3–3**), although the results obtained by either equation are substantially the same.

In this equation A is a universal constant defined by the relation [3]

$$A = \frac{2\pi e m k^2}{h^3}, \tag{3–6}$$

where h is Planck's constant equal[3] to 6.547×10^{-27} erg sec., and e, m, and k have the values given on page 54. (This value for h is slightly different from the value given on page 6. It is corrected from time to time as more accurate data are available, the value given by Reference 7 being 6.558 ± 0.009.) Using these constants in equation (**3–6**), A equals[3] the value 60.2 amp/cm² deg². It is often stated[4] that this value applies to *all pure metals*.

It has recently been shown, on the basis of the new electron theory of conduction (page 27), that the value of A in equation (3–5) should be multiplied [3] by the factor 2; that is, the constant should be 120.4 instead of 60.2. A detailed discussion of this will be found in Reference 2.

At present, the matter seems to be uncertain. Theory indicates that a constant of 120.4 should be used. Actual emission for several pure metals gives A approximately equal to 60.2. Other values both greater and less than this have been found. For composite surfaces, such as thoriated tungsten and oxide-coated cathodes, A is not even of the same *order of magnitude* as this theoretical value (pages 63 and 65).

It has been suggested that the difference between the experimental and the theoretical values of A is due to a reflection coefficient r modifying the equation,[3] but Brattain and Becker point [8] out that r is probably very small and suggest that the discrepancy is due to a temperature coefficient for the work function.

Values of A and b_0 for use in equation (3–5) are included in Table VII. These data are from References 2 and 3. The values of the work function ϕ_0 are computed by equation (3–4), these relations also applying to the constants of equation (3–5). The value I_T is the emission current in amperes per square centimeter, and T is the temperature in degrees Kelvin.

TABLE VII

VALUES OF THE CONSTANTS FOR EQUATION (3–5)

ELEMENT	A	b_0	ϕ_0	I_T	T
Carbon	5.93	45,700	3.93	2.84×10^{-3}	2000
Calcium	60.2	26,000	2.24	4×10^{-3}	1100
Caesium	162	21,000	1.81	2.5×10^{-11}	500
Molybdenum	60.2	50,900	4.38	2.34×10^{-3}	2000
Nickel	26.8	32,100	2.77		
Platinum	1.7×10^4	72,500	6.27	9.2×10^{-10}	1600
Tantalum	60.2	47,200	4.07	1.38×10^{-2}	2000
Thorium	60.2	38,900	3.35	4.3×10^{-3}	1600
Tungsten	60.2	52,400	4.52	1×10^{-3}	2000

Early thermionic data were for use in the $T^{1/2}$ expression, equation (3–3). At present, most data are for use in the T^2 expression, equation (3–5). For these reasons, the data will be found expressed as a, b, and ϕ, or as A, b_0, and ϕ_0. For the numerical relations between these various units, the reader should consult Reference 4 or 5.

18. Determination of Emission Constants.—Many early investigators believed that electron emission phenomena were due to residual gases, and that emission could not occur in a perfect vacuum.   Langmuir is credited [3] with proving that emission did occur in a vacuum, and for establishing certain important laws regarding the phenomena. In his work he developed a technique of producing a high vacuum, and demonstrated the importance of a *clean* surface for obtaining reproducible results.

In 1913, Langmuir found [3] that the electron current passing from a heated filament (cathode) to a positive plate (anode) in a vacuum depended on, *first*, the voltage of the anode, and *second*, the temperature of the cathode.   With the cathode at a constant high temperature, the electron current flowing to the anode, as the anode voltage V was increased, varied *at first* according to the "three halves power law," following the relation

$$i = cV^{3/2}, \tag{3-7}$$

where c is a constant depending on the type (physical shape and dimensions) of tube used.   Over this region the electron current is limited by the space charge effect caused by the electrons already between the electrodes repelling the electrons as they are emitted from the cathode (see page 77).

After the positive anode voltage V was increased to a certain value, however, the voltage was largely able to overcome the space charge and to take all the electrons emitted from the cathode at a *given temperature*. The current then became substantially constant.   This is the **saturation current** I_T which is given by equations (3-3) and (3-5).

Values of the constants for these two equations can be determined by measuring the *saturation* currents for given cathodes at various temperatures, and by plotting these values.[3, 4, 9]   If $\log (I/T^2)$ is plotted against values of $1/T$, a straight line such as Fig. 3-1 is obtained.   The values of b_0 are obtained from the slopes of the curves, and A is determined from the intercept on the Y axis for $1/T = 0$. Values of b and a for equation (3-3) are obtained similarly.

The Schottky Effect.—The positive anode voltage produces an electric field between the anode and cathode; it is this field which causes the emitted electrons to flow over to the anode.   This electric field also has a slight effect on the work an electron must do to *escape* from the surface of the metal filament; that is, the field *lowers* the thermionic work function very slightly.   This effect is usually negligible for low voltages, but in some instances it is of importance, especially from a theoretical standpoint.

Schottky, in 1914, explained this effect, and derived the equation [3],[4]

$$i_v = i_0 \epsilon^{4.39\sqrt{E/T}}.$$ (3–8)

In this expression i_v is the emission occurring at any field strength E due to an anode voltage V, and i_0 is the emission which would occur at zero field strength. (Emission occurs in a tube even with no applied anode voltage.) The current i_0 is the value to which the emission equations (3–3) and (3–5) apply. It is, therefore, necessary to correct observed emission data [3],[4] before using such data for determining the constants for those equations.

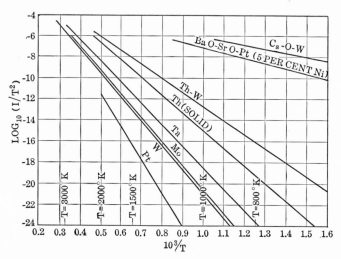

Fig. 3–1. Comparison of emission from coated filaments with that from pure metals. (From Reference 3.)

Temperature Determination.—In studying thermionic emission it is necessary to have accurate measurements of the cathode temperature. Although optical pyrometry is the most accurate method of determining temperature,[4] it is often difficult or entirely impossible to see the cathode of a vacuum tube. A method based on the energy radiated by the cathode is usually employed.

If a cathode having a resistance of R ohms carries a current of I amperes, the heat developed is I^2R. This will cause the temperature of the wire to increase until equilibrium is reached and the heat generated is equal to the heat lost. Since the cathode is often a slender filament in a vacuum, very little heat will be conducted away by the leads, and no convection can occur. Most of the heat loss is due to radiation, largely in the infra-red.

The energy radiated from a filament depends on two factors, *first*, the nature of the surface, and *second*, the temperature. These relations are expressed by the fourth power law

$$\eta = e_t\sigma T^4, \tag{3-9}$$

where η is the energy radiated by a surface of **emissivity** e_t, σ is the Stefan-Boltzmann constant (5.722×10^{-5} erg per sq. cm. per sec. per deg.), and T is the absolute temperature. The value of e_t is always less than unity except for a perfect black body radiator. (A very interesting application of radiation theory will be given on page 71.) The total radiation emissivity for several materials at various temperatures is given in Table VIII. These data are from Reference 7.

TABLE VIII

TOTAL RADIATION EMISSIVITY, e_t

METAL	TEMPERATURE		
	1000° K	1500° K	2000° K
Tungsten	0.114	0.192	0.260
Platinum	0.134	0.192	
Molybdenum	0.096	0.157	0.210

If e_t and σ are known, the total energy radiated from unit area of filament surface at a temperature T can be calculated. Knowing the surface area, the total energy input can be found. The process can then be reversed, and the temperature at which a filament is operating can then be determined from the energy input. Curves are given in Reference 4, page 78, for such determinations. This reference also gives many examples of useful filament calculations and comparisons.

The entire filament does not operate at a uniform temperature but is cooler near the ends where at least *some* heat is conducted away by the lead wires. Therefore, the resistance of the filament is less over the end sections; the voltage drop across the filament is less; and this drop is not uniform as compared with an evenly heated filament. Furthermore, the brightness and the emission of electrons are less than for an ideal filament, and these are also non-uniform along the filament. Curves showing these relations are included in Reference 4, page 79.

19. Cathode Materials.—The filaments of the tubes used by the early investigators were made of metals such as platinum, and of carbon. Wehnelt, in 1905, investigated emission from metallic oxides, such as those of barium, calcium, and strontium coated on a platinum wire, and found these to be excellent emitters. In 1913 Langmuir and Rogers discovered [3] that if a tungsten wire containing 1 or 2 per cent of thorium oxide were properly heat treated the emission would greatly exceed that of pure tungsten.

Cathodes used as a source of electrons in modern thermionic tubes are of three types: *first*, pure metals, usually tungsten; *second*, oxide-coated filaments; and *third*, thoriated-tungsten filaments. Each of these is best adapted to tubes for certain specific uses.

Tungsten Filaments.—This material is used almost exclusively for the source of electrons in the *large* high-vacuum tubes. This includes the types used for signal or speech purposes, those for high-voltage rectification, and for x-ray tubes. The reason for this use is that tungsten has excellent mechanical properties and has no active surface layer (such as an oxide coating) which would be damaged by positive ion bombardment. Also, the filament will withstand high overloads. As will be seen, however, tungsten is not so efficient an electron emitter as are the other cathodes.

The constants of tungsten are given in Table VII. Although the work function of tungsten is comparatively high (4.52), the melting point is also high (about 3600° K); therefore it can be operated at the high temperature of about 2500° K, thus providing copious electron emission. During operation the tungsten slowly evaporates, reducing the size of the filament and eventually lowering the emission so that the tube must be replaced.

Much experimental work has been done, largely by Langmuir and his associates,[10] in determining the characteristics of tungsten and the effect on it of certain gases. These and other data are summarized in Reference 11. The emission of tungsten in comparison with other materials is shown in Fig. 3–2.

Oxide-Coated Cathodes.—Filaments of this type were first used in the tubes for early speech amplifiers or repeaters installed in long-distance telephone lines. Much credit is due H. D. Arnold and his associates for their pioneer work with oxide-coated filaments for commercial tubes, and for other contributions to the development of vacuum tubes. This type of filament is the most efficient thus far developed *commercially*. The oxide-coated filament is a rather complex structure and is accordingly difficult to study.

Platinum or platinum-iridium wire was used as the core in the early oxide-coated filament. Later, nickel, tungsten, and molybdenum were employed. At present, **Konal** (formerly spelled Konel), an alloy of nickel, cobalt, iron, and titanium, is widely used in radio receiving tubes.[12] It is the view of some (as will be seen later) that the nature of the core has little or no effect on the emission; others hold that it does.

Many methods [4, 11] have been used for preparing the oxide coatings. One method is to pass the core wire through a paste of the proper type, and then bake the mixture on the surface at a comparatively low temperature.   Another method is to dip the filament wire into an aqueous solution containing about 3 per cent of barium nitrate, and then evaporate the water by heating in an atmosphere of carbon dioxide.   The filament is then dipped into a strontium nitrate solution and heated in carbon dioxide.   This cycle is repeated many times.

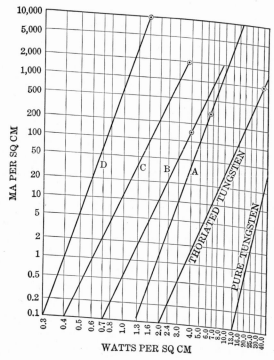

FIG. 3–2.   Emission from coated filaments as a function of power input. (From Reference 3.)

These are, naturally, trade processes, and will not be considered further.

The strontium is added largely to improve the mechanical characteristics of the coating; coatings containing strontium adhere to the core better, and have a longer life.   A mixture of 3 parts barium to 2 parts strontium is used.[4]   In referring to such coatings the word "barium" is usually used, when a combination of barium and strontium is really meant.

The oxide-coated filament or cathode must be activated before it shows appreciable electron emission. The exact procedure depends on the type of coating. In general the method consists of heating the filament in the evacuated tube for several minutes at a temperature of 1000° to 1500° K, well above the normal operating range.[4] The filament is then operated at a lower temperature for a longer period of time with anode (plate) voltage applied. During this process the emission increases rapidly to its maximum value.

In the procedure just considered, the applied voltage is essential for activation. In other processes, such as where Konal metal is used, the activation seems to be entirely thermal.[4] It should be recognized that these processes are being improved continuously.

As Koller states,[4] "The theory of the behavior of coated filaments is in a very unsatisfactory state." There are many reasons for this: *First,* coated filaments of many types have been used; *second,* even with one type of coated filament it is difficult to get reproducible results; *third,* although some have found that the core metal does not affect the emission, there is strong evidence that with Konal metal it does.[3]

The most probable explanation of emission from oxide-coated filaments has been given by J. A. Becker and is summarized in Reference 3. An excellent article by this authority will be found in Reference 13, and more recent article in Reference 14.

According to Becker, if a clean platinum surface and a platinum surface covered with a single layer of barium atoms are held at the same temperature, *one hundred million* times as much emission will occur from the barium surface as from the one of platinum. The active layer is at the outer oxide surface. This active material consists of metallic barium produced at the surface either by electrolysis of the oxide during the activation process or by chemical reaction between the oxide and the core material. The barium diffuses to the surface through the oxide and forms a very thin layer of ionized barium atoms called **adions.** These adions lower the thermionic work function of emission of electrons which come from the oxide layer beneath.

During operation, the oxide-coated filament burns at the low temperature of about 900° K to 1100° K. At these low temperatures the filament is a dull red, and is scarcely noticeable.

Emission curves of oxide-coated filaments are shown as *A, B, C,* and *D* of Fig. 3–2. These curves are reproduced from Reference 3. Dushman states that curve *A* is for coated filaments produced by the Western Electric Company in 1923 (see Reference 15), curve *B* is for filaments produced by the same company in 1928, and the curves *C* and D are for filaments made by RCA Radiotron Company and used in 1934. The progress in the art is evident.

Various oxides other than barium and strontium have been used for oxide-coated filaments. The values of the constants for these will be found in References 2, 3, and 7. For barium and strontium oxides (probably on platinum alloy), the second reference lists the following values to be used in equation (3–5): $A = 0.01$, $b_0 = 11,600$, $\phi_0 = 1.00$, and $I_T = 0.092$ ampere per square centimeter. These data are for a temperature of $1000°$ K.

As previously mentioned the oxide-coated cathode is the most efficient emitter used *commercially*, although the **caesiated-tungsten cathode** is the most efficient type known.[3, 4] In addition to the high efficiency of the oxide-coated cathode, the vacuum requirements are less rigorous than for the thoriated-tungsten type to be discussed in the following section. The oxide-coated cathode works well in gas-filled tubes, and is well adapted to heat-shielded type cathode construction (page 70).

Thoriated-Tungsten Filaments.—In the development of ductile tungsten wire for lamp filaments, it was discovered that the addition of a small amount of thorium oxide or thoria (Th O_2) would prevent the "slipping" or "offsetting" of the tungsten crystals at right angles to the length of the filament when such filaments were heated by alternating currents.[2] In 1913 Langmuir and Rogers found that if such filaments were properly heat treated, a much higher electron emission could be obtained than for tungsten alone. Much of the subsequent work in this field is due to Langmuir.

The melting point of tungsten is about $3600°$ K, and its work function is 4.52. The melting point of thorium is about $2100°$ K, and its work function is 3.35. Tungsten will *adsorb* a layer of thorium on its surface and will hold it there at high temperatures, even above the point where pure thorium would melt and evaporate.[4] Such a filament has the desirable mechanical properties of tungsten, and has emission characteristics far better than pure tungsten. This combination provides an excellent filament material for small and medium-sized tubes, and carbonized thoriated-tungsten filaments (page 65) are now being used in the smaller *power* tubes. At present it is used largely in this latter type. These filaments are operated at a yellow heat of about $1500°$ K.

Koller states[4] that thoriated-tungsten filaments usually contain about 1.5 per cent thoria (by weight). Chaffee bring out the point that only about 0.7 per cent is left in the finished wire.[11] This wire must be activated before high emission is obtained.

This is done only after the wire is mounted in the tube. As the tube is exhausted, the glass and all metal parts are heated to free occluded gases by baking the tube in an oven, and by further heating the electrodes with a high-frequency induction furnace. This heating process "flashes" a getter composed of an active chemical substance such as magnesium, and this absorbs the residual gas and further *produces* and *maintains* a high vacuum.

During the activation process, two steps are included.[3] *First*, the filament is burned for a minute or two at a temperature higher than 2700° K. This high temperature cleans the surface of the tungsten and reduces some of the thoria inside the filament to metallic thorium. At this high temperature any thorium atoms that diffuse to the surface are immediately evaporated there, and the emission is substantially the same as for pure tungsten. *Second*, the temperature is decreased to from 2000–2200° K. The rate of diffusion to the surface is still high, but the rate of evaporation is lowered so that an adsorbed layer of thorium atoms accumulates on the surface. The emission gradually builds up until it is about 1000 times that of pure tungsten at the same temperature.

The metallic thorium diffuses to the surface along the grain boundaries of the tungsten particles and then spreads out over the surface. The grain size is therefore important; a fairly small grain structure should exist. If the grains are too large, the number of paths available for the metallic thorium to pass to the surface would be so reduced that the surface of the filament would not be covered adequately, thus reducing the emission.

The thorium spreads along the filament surface in a monatomic layer (one atom thick). The formation of a complete layer on the surface of the filament is a critical process.[3, 4] The work function of a monatomic layer of thorium on tungsten is *lower* than for pure thorium alone. The action of the monatomic layer is to lower the surface work function so that electrons from the interior of the filament more readily pass through.

During normal operation the layer of thorium atoms slowly evaporates from the filament surface, and this layer is continuously replenished by thorium atoms from within. If the tube is mistreated (for example by raising the filament to an excessive temperature) the thorium layer may be completely evaporated. The emission will then be greatly decreased, and the filament must be reactivated.

Several methods have been recommended for reactivating thoriated-tungsten filaments. In one method the filament is burned or "flashed" at a high temperature by impressing about $3\frac{1}{2}$ times normal voltage across the filament for 10 to 20 seconds. The filament is then operated at about 1½ times normal voltage for 1 to 2 hours. During both operations *no voltage* is applied to the plate. If this treatment does not return the filament to normal operating condition, the thorium content of the filament has probably been exhausted, and the emission characteristics permanently altered.

The emission characteristics of thoriated-tungsten filaments must depend on the fraction θ of the surface covered by thorium. It was formerly assumed that maximum emission occurred when $\theta = 1$. Recent studies [3] indicate that maximum emission occurs when $\theta = 0.7$ (approximately).

So many variables enter that it is difficult to include data for A and b_0 of equation (3–5) for thoriated-tungsten filaments. For a comprehensive list of such data, Reference 7 should be consulted. The values $A = 3.0$, $b_0 = 30,500$, $\phi_0 = 2.63$ volts, and $I_T = 0.04$ ampere per square centimeter for a thoriated-tungsten filament at 1600° K are given in this reference.

It should be mentioned that other elements such as cerium, zirconium, lanthanum, yttrium, uranium, calcium, magnesium, strontium, and barium have been combined with tungsten, but none of these has been so satisfactory as thorium.[4]

A process of **carbonization** [4] has been developed which greatly improves thoriated-tungsten filaments. The filament is heated in napthalene (or other suitable) vapor. Carbon from this vapor diffuses into the tungsten forming a surface layer of tungsten carbide. With a properly carbonized filament the rate of evaporation of the thorium layer is about 1/6 that of the non-carbonized type, and its characteristics are in general improved. Carbonized thoriated-tungsten filaments are supplanting pure tungsten filaments in the smaller power tubes.

Although the thoriated-tungsten filament is a more efficient emitter than pure tungsten, it is not so good as an oxide-coated filament. Furthermore, the thoriated-tungsten is very sensitive to small amounts of residual gas, and must, therefore, be operated in a high vacuum and cannot be used in gas tubes as can the oxide-coated type. It can be operated at temperatures much below that required for tungsten, and has, therefore, a much longer life.

20. The Schroteffekt.—Translated, this means *small-shot effect*, and is due to the fact that the electron flow from the cathode to the plate consists of discrete charges. Furthermore, the emission of electrons at a given instant may be greater or less than the average emission over a given interval. Hence, the emission and the electron flow to the plate resemble a "rain of small shot." Such an effect results in irregularities in the output of a thermionic tube and causes noise in a loud speaker connected to a vacuum-tube amplifier.

This generated noise is one of the factors limiting the amount of amplification which can be used satisfactorily. For example, if the speech or signal strength impressed on an amplifier is so low that it is about the same magnitude as the variations due to the shot effect, then both the useful signal and the noise would be about the same strength in the output of the amplifier. To overcome this trouble, it would be necessary to use a higher signal strength so that the signal-to-noise ratio would be high.

For maximum shot effect, a tube must be operated so that the space current to the plate is limited by *temperature*. If the space current is limited by the *space charge*, then this accumulation of electrons "damps out" the variations due to shot-effect irregularities in emission. A very complete discussion of this subject is included in Reference 16.

21. Residual Gas.—As was outlined briefly on page 64, extreme care is taken in the manufacture of thermionic tubes to remove all possible traces of residual gas. Three important effects [3, 4] are caused by gases: *First*, they may form monomolecular or monatomic films on the surface of the emitting cathode; this may greatly lower the emission. *Second*, if gas is present it may be ionized by collision, resulting in the formation of massive *positive* ions. These will travel toward the negative cathode, and if the voltage gradient is sufficient, they will attain a velocity sufficient to sputter atoms off the cathode surface. *Third*, the accumulation of positive ions may neutralize, in part, the negative space charge, thus interfering with the normal operation of a tube.

This positive ion bombardment on a pure metal filament such as tungsten has little, if any, effect on the electron emission; it does, however, disintegrate the filament and reduce its life. With thoriated-tungsten and oxide-coated filaments, the bombardment tends to disintegrate the active surface layer, thus greatly lowering the emission.

In the manufacture of tubes, gases are driven out of the glass walls by heating the glass in a flame to a temperature of from 360° C to 500° C depending on the type of glass.* The metal parts are treated

---

* Certain details of vacuum-tube manufacture are discussed in this and in other sections because of the theoretical principles involved. *Glass-enclosed*, instead of metal-enclosed tubes, have been used as illustrations. This may appear questionable because the so-called all-metal tube is a more recent development. The basic electronic principles of the two types are essentially the same, however, and they differ largely in the mechanical details of manufacture. While it is not the purpose of this book to set forth arguments as to the commercial advantages and disadvantages of glass versus metal, it is of importance to note that the industry itself has not decided to what extent (if at all) metal eventually will replace glass for enclosing the elements of vacuum tubes. (See Electronics, October, 1937, page 11.)

both before assembly and during exhaust to remove gases. The materials most widely used for the tube structures are tungsten, molybdenum, nickel, iron, and graphite; special treatments [4] have been developed for these.

After assembly and during exhaust, the metal parts are heated to high temperatures by a high-frequency induction furnace. The filament is burned at a high temperature to remove occluded gases. Even with such care, some residual gas remains, and this is "cleaned up" by a getter, and also by electrical means.

Substances such as phosphorus, calcium, magnesium, barium, strontium, aluminum, and alloys and mixtures of these are used for getters. An alloy of barium and magnesium produces excellent results.[17] The getters are placed in some convenient form in the tube and are flashed or vaporized by the heat of the high-frequency induction furnace just before the tube is sealed from the vacuum pumps. The gas reacts chemically with the getter and also is absorbed and held as a monatomic layer on the surface of the getter.[4] Furthermore, a good getter continues to absorb gases as they are released in the tube during operation.

The electrical method of assisting with the clean-up process consists of drawing an electron current from the cathode to the anode at from 100 to 200 volts. The residual gas is ionized by these currents and these ions acquire velocities sufficient to *drive* them into the walls of the tube and the electrodes. This action can take place without the presence of a getter, but is facilitated by a layer of the getter on the surfaces.[4]

There are at least two sources of *positive* ions in thermionic vacuum tubes. The *first* of these is the formation of positive ions through ionization by collision of the electrons (flowing to the plate) and residual gas atoms. The *second* is the emission of positive ions by the filament. These positive ions are charged particles of the filament material.

22. Emission Efficiency.—Many factors enter into the selection of the best material for a filament or cathode. Included among these are the mechanical characteristics, the emission characteristics, and the radiation characteristics discussed briefly on page 59. The rate at which heat is *radiated* depends on the temperature and the (heat) radiation **emissivity** of the surface. The radiation emissivity is determined by the chemical nature of the surface and by its physical condition.

Values for the emissivity of certain pure metals are given in Table VIII. For an oxide-coated filament, the *average* value is 0.70. The emissivity of a thoriated-tungsten filament is about the same as for pure tungsten, but for a carbonized thoriated-tungsten filament it is about 1.2 times greater.[4]

All other factors being equal, the ideal filament is one having a very low emissivity; that is, it is a poor heat radiator. Since the emissivity is different for various materials, the electron emission per unit area for filaments *at the same temperature* cannot be taken as a basis for comparing cathodes. Thermionic emitters should be compared as to the current emission *per watt* of input at the same value of watts input *per unit area*. Interesting calculations illustrating this principle are given by Koller in Reference 4, page 84.

The total emission current from a filament is approximately given by the relation

$$I_T = CP^n, \tag{3-10}$$

where C is a constant depending on the surface of the emitter, P is the electrical power supplied to heat the filament, and n is a constant depending on the type of emitter.

Figure 3-2 gave the emission per square centimeter as a function of the power input in watts per square centimeter. It is, therefore, a comparison of the relative efficiencies of various emitters. The special system of curvilinear coordinates was developed by Davisson. When plotted on these power emission charts, the emission curves should be almost straight lines.[18]

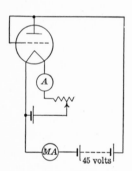

The emission characteristics of thermionic vacuum tubes of the broadcast receiver type can be determined with a circuit arranged as in Fig. 3-3. The filament (or heater) is energized in the usual manner, but the grid and plate (and the other grids if it is a multi-electrode tube) are connected together and made about 45 volts positive with respect to the filament.

FIG. 3-3. Circuit for obtaining the emission efficiency.

The values of filament current *must be low* or the tube may be permanently damaged. The filament current and thus the power input should be varied and the resulting values of the emission current (not exceeding normal plate current) determined by reading the anode milliammeter. These curves can be easily extended to give emission at normal operating conditions. The power input in watts (or watts per square centimeter if the dimensions are known) is then plotted on the X axis and the emission current (or current per square centimeter) plotted on the Y axis. If the dimensions are not known, so that the curves cannot be plotted in terms of power and emission *per square centimeter*, the results may be misinterpreted.

If an emission curve is not substantially a straight line when plotted on a power emission chart but bends *downward*, the departure may be due to any one of several causes.[18]   *First*, the rate of cooling may not be according to the Stefan-Boltzmann law, equation (3–9).   *Second*, the anode voltage may be too low to draw off all the emitted electrons. *Third*, there may be considerable cooling due to the evaporation of the electrons (page 43).   If the curve bends *upward*, the reasons may be, *first*, residual gas (poor vacuum) or *second*, heating of the electrodes by the electron current.

For the methods and precautions to be used in testing tubes Reference 18 should be consulted.

23. Mechanical Structure of the Cathode.—The electron-emitting cathodes used in *thermionic tubes* are often ribbon *filaments* arranged in one of the forms of Fig. **3–4**.   These are especially suited for operation from con- tinuous sources of power such as batteries. When filament-type tubes are heated with alternating current, hum may result in the radio sets or amplifiers.   They are un- suited for the amplification of weak signals.

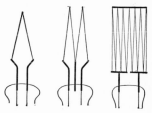

FIG. 3–4.   Directly-heated cathodes of the filament type.

One source of this hum is the varia- tions in temperature caused by the alter- nating current changes.   When the cur- rent is maximum in either direction, the power supplied and the resulting temperature is greatest, and hence the hum produced from these variations has *twice* the fundamental frequency.   This effect is minimized, *first*, by making the filament massive so that the temperature variations are small, and *second*, by using a material which will supply *large* quantities of electrons even if the tempera- ture is lowered somewhat.

Filament-type cathodes are used in some amplifier tubes designed for the power output stages where the speech or signal level is high. Such filaments must be capable of emitting large electron currents. The series-parallel combination of the third filament of Fig. 3–4 pro- vides a large emitting surface for power output tubes.   Filament type cathodes are also used in many rectifier tubes.

Indirectly-Heated Cathodes.—This type cathode was developed so that tubes heated with alternating current could be used where the signal strength was low, such as in the early stages of a radio set or a speech amplifier.   A heater wire is enclosed in a metal cylinder (often of nickel or of Konal) covered with an oxide-coated emitting surface. This cylinder is massive, and hence its temperature does not change appreciably due to the alternating-current variations. Also, this cylindrical cathode is all at the same electrical potential, and this equipotential surface is also necessary for low noise.

The heater wire within the coated cylinder is usually of tungsten. This wire must be insulated electrically from the cylinder walls. Two general methods are used. The *first* of these is to separate the heater from the metal cylinder by some electrically insulating but heat-conducting refractory material; the *second* is to arrange the heater wire so that it is always held away from the cylinder *without* the use of the re-fractory material. The first type heats more slowly because of the large mass of material which must be brought up to temperature. This was particularly bothersome in the early tubes.

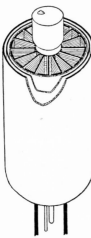

For the quick-heating tubes, the heater is usually a "hairpin" of wire wound into a double helical coil. The hairpin arrangement must be used so that the two wires carrying the heating current in opposite directions are close together and produce no resultant magnetic field. The helical-coil construction is to give a spring-like effect to the heater so that it can be suspended under tension from insulating plugs in the ends of the cylinder. This tension holds it in position under all conditions. The heater wires are sometimes coated with an insulating surface layer. For a discussion of this process and for much additional information on indirectly-heated cathodes, References 19 and 20 should be consulted.

FIG. 3–5. Special heat-shielded cathode. Electrons emerge from open end. The heat required is only 1/24 as much as for a filament of same electron-emitting area. (Courtesy General Electric Co.)

Heat-Shielded Cathodes.—As was mentioned on page 58, most of the heat losses from the cathode are due to radiation. Values for the (heat) radiation emissivity for certain pure metals were given in Table VIII, and for thoriated-tungsten and oxide-coated cathodes on page 67. It is evident that an oxide-coated cathode with an average radiation emissivity of 0.70 will radiate heat at a high rate, and that this is an undesired characteristic for a thermionic cathode. Nevertheless, the need for high electron emission, and the other desirable characteristics of the oxide-coated cathode (such as its ability to operate in a gas) necessitate its use in tubes for handling large power currents such as in gas and vapor rectifiers.

Koller in Reference 4, page 82, explains how oxide-coated cathodes are designed so that both the electron emission and the thermal efficiency are high. Owing to the importance of this principle, his illustration will be summarized.

Assume that to obtain the needed electron emission the oxide coating is applied to a nickel cylinder (emissivity of nickel is 0.15) of total end area 0.1 of the total area, and of side area 0.9 of the total. Assume that the ends have an emissivity of 1.0 and the coated side of 0.75. Then, the heat radiated would be $(0.1 \times 1) + (0.9 \times 0.75) = 0.775$ unit. Now suppose that the oxide coating is applied to the *inside* of the cylinder instead of the outside. The heat radiation will now be $(0.1 \times 1) + (0.9 \times 0.15) = 0.235$ unit, or about 1/3 the former value.

Oxide coatings may also be applied to the vanes extending out to the cylinder. Also, additional non-coated cylinders, as shown in Fig. 3–5,

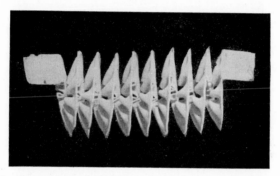

Fig. 3–6. Type of heat-shielded cathode used by one manufacturer. Adjacent turns act as heat shields. Such cathodes can only be used in gas tubes. (Courtesy Westinghouse Electric and Mfg. Co.)

reflect heat back to the emitting elements. Holes are often placed in these cylinders to facilitate the passage of the electrons. Koller states [4] that three such cylinders reduce the radial heat flow to 4 per cent that of a coated surface. This saving is of *great* importance where tubes are designed to rectify large amounts of power.

There are other methods of decreasing radiation. Thus if oxide coated ribbons are wound on edge to form a spiral as in Fig. 3–6, or if they are folded "accordion fashion," adjacent turns will act as heat shields and the radiation will be greatly reduced.[12] These structures, and the cathode discussed in the preceding paragraph are suited only for gas-filled tubes in which positive ions are produced by collision. If these positive ions are not present to neutralize the electrons which accumulate in the deep slots and holes, this accumulation of electrons will form a strong negative space charge, and will prevent electrons from flowing out the slots and holes to the positive anode or plate.

REFERENCES

1. Hughes, A. L., and DuBridge, L. A. *Photoelectric Phenomena.* McGraw-Hill Book Co.
2. Dushman, Saul. *Thermionic emission.* Reviews of Modern Physics, Oct., 1930, Vol. 2, No. 4.
3. Dushman, Saul. *Electron emission.* Electrical Engineering, July, 1934, Vol. 53, No. 7.
4. Koller, L. R. *The Physics of Electron Tubes.* McGraw-Hill Book Co.
5. Reimann, A. L. *Thermionic Emission.* John Wiley & Sons.
6. Richardson, O. W. *The Emission of Electricity from Hot Bodies.* Longmans, Green & Co.
7. *International Critical Tables.* McGraw-Hill Book Co.
8. Brattain, W. H., and Becker, J. A. *Thermionic and adsorption characteristics of tungsten on thorium.* Physical Review, March 15, 1933.
9. Henney, Keith. *Radio Engineering Handbook.* McGraw-Hill Book Co.
10. Jones, H. A., and Langmuir, I. *The characteristics of tungsten filaments as functions of temperature.* General Electric Review, 1927, Vol. 30.
11. Chaffee, E. L. *Theory of Thermionic Vacuum Tubes.* McGraw-Hill Book Co.
12. Lowry, E. F. *Thermionic cathodes for gas-filled tubes.* Electronics, Oct., 1933, Vol. 6, No. 10.
13. Becker, J. A. *The role of barium in vacuum tubes.* Electronics, Nov., 1930, Vol. 1, No. 8.
14. Becker, J. A. *Thermionic electron emission.* Bell System Technical Journal, July, 1935, Vol. 14, No. 3.
15. King, R. W. *Thermionic vacuum tubes and their applications.* Bell System Technical Journal, Oct., 1923, Vol. 2, No. 4.
16. Pearson, G. L. *Fluctuation noise in vacuum tubes.* Bell System Technical Journal, Oct., 1934, Vol. 13, No. 4.
17. Wagner, E. R. *Processes in vacuum tube manufacture.* Electronics, July, 1934, Vol. 7, No. 7.
18. Institute of Radio Engineers. *Reports of the Standards Committees.*
19. O'Neill, G. D. *Indirectly-heated cathodes.* Radio Engineering, June, 1936, Vol. 16, No. 6.
20. Klemperer, H. *Heater-cathode insulation performance.* Electrical Engineering, Sept., 1936, Vol. 55, No. 9.

SUGGESTED ASSIGNMENTS

(Certain of these problems are based on an excellent list given [4] by Koller.)

1. Calculate the required velocity and the work done when an electron is emitted from a tungsten filament.
2. Referring to Table VI, page 55, calculate the corresponding value of ϕ for each element listed.

3. Determine or assume the dimensions of a typical tungsten filament and calculate the emission current at operating temperature.
4. Prepare a list of references and a short discussion on the work of H. D. Arnold and his associates in developing the oxide-coated filament and the vacuum tube for commercial telephone purposes for Bell System long lines.
5. Assuming that each is operated at the optimum temperature, calculate the emission current per unit area for tungsten, thoriated-tungsten, and oxide-coated filaments. Compare these three when so operated as to their heating power requirements.

CHAPTER 4

TWO-ELECTRODE THERMIONIC VACUUM TUBES

In the preceding chapters the basic theories regarding electrons and their emission from solids have been presented. Also, the electronic phenomena occurring in gases have been discussed. This chapter will consider the application of these principles to the two-electrode thermionic vacuum tube or **diode**. The diode is defined [1] as a "two-electrode vacuum tube containing an anode and a cathode."

These diodes include both the **high-vacuum** and the **gas** tubes. A high-vacuum tube is defined [1] as a "vacuum tube evacuated to such a degree that its electrical characteristics are essentially unaffected by gaseous ionization." A gas tube [1] is a "vacuum tube in which the pressure of the contained gas or vapor is such as to affect substantially the electrical characteristics of the tube."

Although Edison discovered the rectifying properties of the vacuum tube in 1883, little, if any, practical use was made of the principle until 1904, when Fleming adapted the diode for use as a **demodulator** or **detector** [2] of radio-telegraph signals.

The diode was used for this purpose for some years, but was supplanted (for a time) by the three-electrode tube or triode. The diode as a detector has again come into favor, and is now almost universally used in modern radio-receiving sets. The diode is also suitable for alternating-current power rectification, and has achieved wide use for this purpose. It is used for rectifying large amounts of power in industrial equipment, and also for supplying direct current to small devices such as radio-receiving sets.

As a power rectifier, the diode has two forms. The first of these is the *high-vacuum* tube, and the second is the *gas* tube. The *theory* of these tubes will be considered in this chapter, and their applications in Chapter 7. The use of the diode as a detector in radio-receiving sets will be considered in Chapter 12.

24. Ratings of Rectifier Tubes.—Probably the greatest use of high-vacuum and gas diodes is for rectifiers of alternating current. A simple half-wave rectifier is shown in Fig. 4–1. Before discussing the tubes themselves, it is advisable to consider briefly their use as rectifiers and certain of the ratings applying, leaving the detailed consideration to Chapter 7, page 177.

When a diode is used as a rectifier of alternating current, the voltage between the cathode and anode or plate is *positive* during one half of the cycle, and *negative* during the other half. For the part of the cycle that the anode is positive, current flows. For the other half, no current flows. The rectifier tube, therefore, is alternately a *conductor* and an *insulator*. There is, however, much more to rectification than this statement indicates.

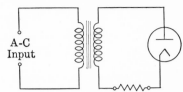

Fig. 4–1. During the negative half cycle, no current flows in the secondary circuit, and the full secondary voltage exists across the tube.

When the tube conducts, voltage drops occur in the secondary of the transformer, the load, and across the tube. During the negative half cycle, no drops occur; the tube now acts as an insulator, and the *full secondary voltage is impressed between the electrodes*.

It is important that a tube does not "flash back" or arc across during the part of the cycle it is acting as an insulator. The maximum voltage that a tube will safely stand between the cathode and plate (with the plate negative) is known as the **maximum peak inverse voltage.** Although under normal operating conditions this voltage is merely the peak of the transformer secondary voltage, under transient conditions this value may be greatly exceeded.

Under normal operation an electron current is drawn from the cathode to the anode. These electrons are emitted by the cathode. The **maximum peak anode current** is an indication of the available electron emission. This value should not be exceeded in gas tubes. If it is, the filament may be damaged permanently.

During normal operation, heat is evolved at the anode or plate. This depends on the **maximum average anode current** of the rectified direct current flowing. An excessive current may overheat and permanently damage a tube.

25. The High-Vacuum Diode.*—This consists of an electron-emitting cathode, usually in the form of a filament, and an electron-collecting anode or plate. The plate is made positive with respect to the filament so that electrons will flow to the plate. These elements are in a glass or metal container which is highly evacuated.

---

* Various commercial names have been applied by the different manufacturers to vacuum tubes, especially those used for the so-called industrial purposes as distinguished from communication uses. It was proposed (Electrical Engineering, February, 1937, page 284) to accept certain of these terms as standard tube nomenclature, but this probably will not be done. For a book of this nature, it seems advisable to use the terminology now generally accepted and which will probably be made standard. Although somewhat longer, these terms are more descriptive.

Suppose that the circuit connections are as in Fig. 4–2.   The "A" battery supplies the current I_f for heating the filament.   The desired positive potential E_p impressed on the plate is obtained by selecting with the **voltage divider** [2] the portion of the "B" battery voltage desired. The electron current I_p flowing to the plate is measured by a milliammeter placed as shown.   In studying tubes, the negative filament terminal (or the cathode if it has an indirectly-heated cathode) is taken as the point of reference.[1]   This terminal may be grounded if desired.

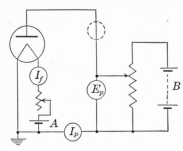

Fig. 4–2.   Circuit for studying a diode.

It will be noted that the plate-circuit milliammeter for measuring the current I_p is shown near the common (grounded) terminal.   It is sometimes placed in the dotted position, but this dotted position is at a higher potential than the one shown.   For safety to personnel, and to equipment, the position indicated should be used if possible, especially in testing high-voltage tubes.

Diode Characteristics.—Suppose that the voltage on the plate is held constant at E_p volts and that the filament current I_f is varied. The values of the plate current I_p when plotted give a curve such as E_p of Fig. 4–3. Now suppose that the plate voltage is held at a new value $E_p{}'$ and the filament current is varied as before.   A new curve $E_p{}'$ will result.

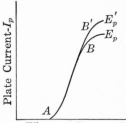

Fig. 4–3.   Variations in diode plate current with filament current for two different plate voltages E_p and $E_p{}'$.   The flattening is due to temperature saturation.

No electrons are emitted by the filament and hence no current can flow to the plate until a certain temperature corresponding to the current at point A is reached.   After this, the plate current increases very rapidly until the region B, where the curve gradually flattens.   This levelling in region B (sometimes referred to as a *point*) is called **temperature saturation.**   Here, the electrons are being taken by the positive plate at a constant rate independent of the filament temperature, the limiting factor being **space charge** (page 77).   If the plate voltage is increased to $E_p{}'$, then the plate is more positive, more electrons can be taken, and the levelling off occurs at a higher value of plate current.

Now suppose that the filament current I_f is held constant at some value providing normal emission, and that the plate voltage E_p is reduced to zero. It will be found that even with zero potential some current, I_p, *will flow* to the plate, and that the plate voltage must be made *negative* to stop this current. This current flow with zero plate voltage is due to the fact that *some* of the emitted electrons *have sufficient energy* to carry them to the plate and on around the circuit, even with zero plate voltage or with a slightly *negative* plate voltage. This is illustrated in Fig. 4–4.

With the filament current I_f still held constant, the plate current I_p will vary as shown with increasing values of plate voltage E_p. The plate current reaches a constant value some-what as in Fig. 4–4, but this time due to **voltage saturation.** If the filament is oper-ated at a higher temperature by increasing the filament current to I_f', the saturation plate current will be higher as indicated. When the region of voltage saturation is reached, the plate is at a positive potential sufficient to attract substantially *all* the electrons to it as they are emitted. Thus, increasing the temperature provides *more emission*, and a larger plate current results. Although the plate-current curve is almost

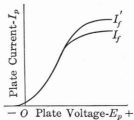

FIG. 4–4. Variations in diode plate current with plate voltage at two fila-ment temperatures. The flattening is due to voltage saturation.

flat after voltage saturation is reached, it usually rises slightly. One reason for this is the Schottky effect (page 57).

It is evident that the operating voltage chosen should be below the voltage saturation region if the operation of the tube is to be inde-pendent of filament current and temperature. This is very important in tubes used as amplifiers and for similar purposes.

The electrons are drawn to the plate by the positive potential E_p, supplied in Fig. 4–2 by the "B" battery. This potential imparts energy to the electrons, the energy being supplied by the battery. When they suddenly strike the plate, they give it most of their energy, causing the plate to heat. This loss is in the nature of an $I_p^2 R_p$ loss, where R_p is the direct (as distinguished from alternating) **plate resistance.**

Space Charge.—The presence of the electrons in the space between the filament and plate has a very important effect on the operation of a vacuum tube, and this effect will now be considered. Although ex-plained for diodes, the principles apply to triodes and to the various multi-electrode tubes as well.

First consider conditions in a diode when the filament is at operating temperature, and the *plate voltage is zero.* Neglecting the few high-velocity electrons which cross to the plate, there are few electrons in the vicinity of the plate. Most of the emitted electrons hover about the filament in a dense cloud. As many electrons return to it during a given time as are emitted by it.

Now consider conditions in the same tube when the filament is at operating temperature, and the *plate voltage is highly positive* so that *voltage saturation* has been reached. Under these conditions the electrons are almost all taken by the plate *as fast as they are emitted,* and there is *no longer* a dense cloud around the filament. Above voltage saturation, the electron current is limited by the cathode temperature as explained on page 54.

These negative electrons are charges in space and so constitute a **negative space charge** in the region between the filament and plate. In the first instance, with *zero plate voltage,* the space charge was concentrated about the filament. In the second, *after voltage saturation* had been reached, the negative space charge was *more* uniformly distributed throughout the space between the electrodes. This statement needs further explanation, because it might appear that it *would be* uniformly distributed, an assumption which is incorrect. Assuming a uniform current flow from filament to plate (that is, suppose a current of 20 milliamperes is flowing through the tube) more electrons must be moving near the cathode, where they have low velocities, than near the plate where their velocities are higher.[3] There is, accordingly, a higher electron density near the cathode even after voltage saturation.

The negative space charge *actually extends throughout the space* between the filament and plate. For *ordinary radio receiver tubes* under *normal* operating conditions the density of the charges is relatively so very much greater near the filament (or cathode) surface, that it is well to assume that the space charge is confined to a thin sheath about the filament varying in thickness from a few thousandths to a few hundredths of a centimeter.[4] This sheath of negative charges produces a field near the surface of the filament which tends to force emitted electrons back into the filament. The positive plate potential tends to draw electrons out of this negative sheath to the plate. The plate current (from a very low value to the region of voltage saturation) of Fig. 4–4 is determined largely by the extent to which the positive electric field produced by the plate neutralizes the negative electric field produced near the filament by the negative space charge.

Potential Distribution between Electrodes.—The influence of the negative space charge alters greatly the distribution of the voltage applied between the filament and the plate. Thus, Fig. **4–5** represents a parallel plane cathode and a positive anode respectively. Further, assume that distance and voltage are plotted as indicated. Several conditions will now be investigated.

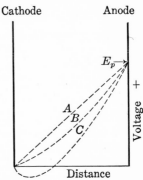

First, with a voltage E_p applied between the two (plane) electrodes, and with the cathode *cold*, the distribution of the voltage between the electrodes will be as shown by curve A. Since there is no emission, there are no electrons and hence *no space charge* between the cathode and anode. *Second*, with the cathode *heated* and with a positive voltage E_p applied to the anode, but *assuming* all the electrons are emitted with zero velocity, there will be a space charge, and the voltage distribution will

Fig. 4–5. Showing the voltage distribution between the cathode and anode or plate in a high-vacuum diode.

be as shown by B. But electrons are *not* all emitted with zero velocity: many of them have velocities sufficient to carry them far out into the space between the electrodes. The *third* condition, curve C, represents the *actual* voltage distribution in a thermionic vacuum tube operated *well below voltage saturation* as is normally done in radio receiver and similar tubes.

Curve C is exaggerated somewhat because in reality the negative space charge in a thermionic vacuum tube usually is a thin sheath *close* to the filament. Nevertheless, the negative space charge region is at a potential *lower* (more negative) than the filament, and hence the space charge tends to repel electrons back to the filament. The plate, therefore, draws the plate current from the negative space charge region. For further information, Reference 5 should be consulted.

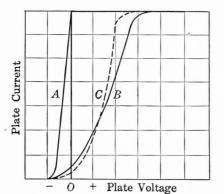

Fig. 4–6. Illustrating the effect of space charge on plate current. Curve A, no space charge; curve B, space charge in high vacuum; and curve C, space charge and residual gas. (Adapted from Reference 6.)

Effect of Space Charge on Plate Current.—Typical plate current-plate voltage curves for a diode were shown in Fig. 4–4. Note the effect of the space charge on this plate current as represented in Fig. **4–6**.

If some of the electrons *had* small initial velocities, but if *no space-charge effect existed,* some plate current would flow as shown by *A,* even for *negative* plate potentials.   As soon as the plate became just slightly positive it would take *all* the electrons emitted.   But with space charge, the positive plate is not able to do this until it is sufficiently positive to overcome the negative space charge effects as shown in *B.* In the practical case there are three parts to a curve such as *B.*   The *first* part is determined by the initial velocity of the electrons; the *second* part by the space charge; and the *third* part by the filament emission.[5]

The knee of the curve where the current is no longer determined by space charge, but where saturation is reached, would be very abrupt but for several reasons.[6]   *First,* the electrons have different initial velocities, and thus the applied plate voltage does not affect each the same.   *Second,* there is an *IR* drop along the filament; thus when saturation is reached for the negative end, it has not been reached for the positive end.

After saturation is reached, increasing the plate voltage does not increase the plate current.   Such a tube is therefore a *constant-current* device, and can be inserted in *series* in a circuit to hold the current constant for wide voltage fluctuations.

The space charge offers opposition to the flow of electron current from the filament or cathode to the plate.   There is, therefore, a relatively high voltage drop between these electrodes.   This is in contrast with the low voltage drop in the gas tubes (Fig. 4–11, page 87).

Equations for Plate Current.—Langmuir derived the equation for the theoretical relation between the voltage applied between a pair of electrodes and the resulting electron current between them when in a high vacuum.   Child had previously derived the same formula for currents carried by positive ions in low-pressure arcs.[6, 7]

Excluding the first and the last parts of curve *B* of Fig. 4–6, and considering *only the central portion,* where the plate current is controlled by the *space charge,* and with the filament at a constant temperature, the current over this central portion is given by the so-called theoretical **three-halves power law,**

$$I_p = KE_p^{3/2}. \qquad (4\text{--}1)$$

In this expression I_p is the plate current flowing, K is a constant determined by the spacing and geometrical dimensions of the electrodes,[7] and E_p is the voltage between the anode or plate and the cathode.

It should be recognized that the three-halves power law is based on theoretical considerations.   In a thermionic vacuum tube the initial velocities of the emitted electrons and contact differences of potential between the electrodes modify this law.[8] Furthermore, the type of cathode used has an influence. For example, with a filament cathode, a drop of potential occurs along its length, and hence all parts are not at the same potential with respect to the plate. As a result, the voltage E_p of equation (4–1) will be different for each part of the filament. These and other effects cause deviations from the theoretical law.

For two infinite parallel plane electrodes, the equation applying is [7]

$$I_p = \frac{(2.33 \times 10^{-6} E_p{}^{3/2})}{x^2}, \qquad (4\text{--}2)$$

where I_p is the plate current in amperes per square centimeter, where E_p is in volts, and x is the spacing between the filament and plate in centimeters.

For a straight, single-wire cathode of radius a, placed at the axis of a cylindrical anode of radius r, the equation for the anode current is (where r/a is greater than 10)

$$I_p = \frac{(14.65 \times 10^{-6} E_p{}^{3/2})}{r}, \qquad (4\text{--}3)$$

where E_p is in volts, and r is in centimeters.

From these two equations it is evident that the distance between the filament and plate should be as small as practicable if large currents are desired.

Effect of Residual Gas.—As has been mentioned previously, extreme care is taken to remove all traces of gas from a high-vacuum thermionic tube. Although in a good high-vacuum tube the residual gas is removed to such a degree that it has no appreciable effect on the performance, it is of interest to investigate influence of residual gas on the *plate current.* This is illustrated by curve C of Fig. 4–6.

If the velocity of the emitted electrons in traveling to the anode or plate is sufficient, they may collide with and ionize atoms of the residual gas. The resulting positive ions have a very pronounced effect on the space charge and hence on the plate current. Thus, the effect of residual gas on the plate current (aside from possible effects on emission) is largely confined to anode voltages above the ionization potential of the residual gas. For this reason, curve C of Fig. 4–6 follows curve B (for a high vacuum) very closely until ionization by collision begins and positive ions are produced. For a discussion of the minor effects occurring at low plate voltages, consult Reference 8.

In studying the effect of the positive ions, it will be recalled (page 16) that they are massive and move very slowly compared to the electrons. As an illustration, Koller shows [6] that for mercury vapor, the positive ion has a mass 360,000 times the mass of an electron. From equation (1–10), page 15, the relative velocities for positive ions and electrons having the same kinetic energies (as would be approximately true in the same electric field) will be determined by the square roots of the masses, or 1 : 607. Hence a positive mercury ion will remain in the electric field between a filament or plate about 607 *times as long* as an electron.

This means that although a positive ion can neutralize the electric field of only one electron *at a given time*, the *time interval* that the positive ion spends in the field is relatively so much greater, that in effect the positive ion neutralizes the negative field (space charge) produced between the electrodes by many electrons. This neutralizing effect greatly increases the flow of electrons to the plate; that is, the plate current.

The important effect is *not* due to the additional current which the positive ions carry (which is a factor, but a negligible one), but is due almost entirely to space-charge neutralization. The *magnitude* of the saturation currents as given by the maximum value of curves *B* and *C*, Fig. 4–6, is, therefore, about the same for a well-evacuated tube as for one containing a small amount of residual gas.

26. Types of High-Vacuum Diodes.—These will be but briefly described; detailed information will be found in the trade catalogues and pamphlets issued by the various manufacturers. It is interesting to note, however, that high-vacuum diodes are constructed in many sizes, from those capable of handling a few milliamperes at low voltages to those passing many amperes at voltages of many thousands of volts. The emission is usually obtained from *directly-heated* tungsten filaments.

The anodes or plates of such tubes tend to become very hot, and this is one of the important factors limiting the amount of current they can pass at given voltages. This heating is due largely to the energy imparted by the rapidly moving electrons to the positive plate and to the energy received by radiation from the filament. The power dissi-

Fig. 4–7. In large power vacuum tubes the plate or anode is immersed in water. A copper-glass seal connects the plate to the glass envelope. (Courtesy Western Electric Co.)

pated by the electrons is equal to E_pI_p, where E_p is the voltage applied between the *plate* and *filament*. Two general methods are used for cooling the plates. *First,* the tube is cooled by the air surrounding the glass or the metal (for all-metal tubes) envelope. *Second,* some of the large tubes are cooled by circulating water.

Water cooling of the plate is made possible by a copper-glass seal developed [9] by Housekeeper. The copper plate also forms part of the outside envelope of the tube as illustrated in Fig. 4–7. This plate is immersed in circulating cooling water, and must be insulated from the filament or cathode. This is the function of the glass portion of the envelope through which the filament leads enter the tube.

Several forms of the seal are possible, one being illustrated in Fig. 4–8. The copper is drawn out to a very thin "feather edge," and by a special process the glass is *sealed* to it. The glass and metal are so proportioned that the stresses produced when the tube is heated or cooled will not be sufficient to crack the glass container or break the copper-glass seal. The glass and copper *do not* have the same coefficients of expansion, but on heating or cooling the very thin copper edge "gives" enough to prevent breaking the seal. This ingenious development has been very satisfactory and has made possible the operation of tubes at very high power

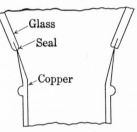

Fig. 4–8. Illustrating a method of making a copper-glass seal.

levels since the plate can be maintained at a low operating temperature.

Vacuum diodes are made to rectify currents at very high voltages. Tubes capable of passing 8 amperes maximum peak plate current and designed for maximum peak inverse voltages of 50,000 volts are quite common. Other tubes are available commercially for peak currents of 1 ampere and inverse voltages of 150,000 volts or more.

Before leaving the subject of high-vacuum diodes, a word (see footnote on page 75) should be said about the trade names used. Unfortunately, the standards applying to vacuum tubes are not complete. The various manufacturers have developed certain trade names which are sometimes used especially for power, as distinguished from communication, purposes. Thus one company uses the trade name **Kenotron** to denote *any* two-electrode high-vacuum tube. In common practice, however, the word Kenotron (when used at all) usually implies a *high-voltage* high-vacuum diode. Also, these are often called **valves.**

27. Gas Tubes.—These were defined on page 74. A small amount of suitable gas is introduced into an evacuated tube to give the operat-

ing characteristics desired.   The discharge occurring is usually classified as an *arc*, because of the low value of cathode fall.[10]   As men-

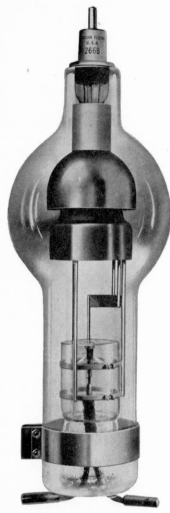

tioned on page 24, the arc is a non-
self-maintained discharge since the
electrons required are furnished by a
heated cathode.   This cathode is usually
of the oxide-coated type, may be either
directly or *indirectly* heated, and is often
heat shielded (page 70).

The effect of *residual* gas in a tube
was discussed in a preceding section of
this chapter.   It was shown that the
positive ions, resulting from collisions
of the electrons with the gas atoms,
neutralized the negative space charge
and thereby permitted a large plate
current to flow.   The phenomena occurring in a gas tube are similar.
This general subject was also discussed
on page 16.

The gas tubes used as rectifiers,
which are the types treated in the following pages, consist essentially of a
hot cathode which emits electrons and
a positive anode to which these electrons are attracted.   These electrodes
are enclosed in a glass or metal tube
and gas at a low pressure is introduced.
The gases used are neon, helium, argon,
and mercury vapor, the last two being
most common.   In the mercury vapor
tube (one form of a gas tube) [1] a small
amount of mercury is introduced.   At
the low pressure, and at the operating

A half-wave, thermionic, mercury-vapor rectifier.   Rating as follows: Filament, 42 amperes at 5
volts; anode-cathode drop, 15 volts;
maximum peak anode current, 20
amperes; maximum peak inverse
potential, 20,000 volts.   (Courtesy
Western Electric Co.)

temperatures, the tube becomes filled
with mercury vapor.

Assume that the cathode of a mercury-vapor tube is at operating temperature, but that the positive anode
voltage is *not* applied.   The tube is
now filled with *neutral* mercury atoms.

When the anode-circuit switch is closed, electrons are drawn to the

positive anode, and are accelerated to high velocities. These electrons collide with, and ionize the neutral mercury atoms. The electrons
produced by this action are mobile and are *quickly* drawn to the anode;
they add slightly to the anode (or plate) current, but this is unimportant.
The *massive* positive ions are (relatively) *slowly* drawn to the negative
cathode, and it is these ions which largely determine the operating
characteristics of the tube.

As shown on page 16, a positive mercury ion remains in the interelectrode space 607 times as long as an electron. These ions form a
sheath about the cathode, and the *positive* electric field of this sheath
neutralizes, to a large extent, the *negative* electric field of the space
charge.

Voltage Distribution in Gas Tubes.—The effect of the space charge
on the voltage distribution in a high-vacuum thermionic tube was
discussed on page 79 and represented by Fig. 4–5. Similar curves for
a mercury-vapor tube are shown in Fig. 4–9. Most of the drop in

potential, and hence most of the
acceleration the electrons receive, is in the region very close
to the cathode where they are
emitted. Regarding this cathode drop or "fall" in gas tubes
with hot cathodes, one article [10]
states the following: "Since
the condition for a self-maintained discharge does not have
to be met at the cathode, the
cathode fall is much less than
in the true glow. It is only
necessary that the cathode fall
be sufficient for the emitted

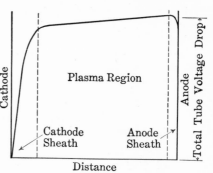

FIG. 4–9. In the gas or vapor tube, most
of the voltage drop occurs in a thin sheath
near the cathode. Compare with Fig. 4–5.
(Distances not to scale.)

electrons to produce positive ions necessary for the neutralization of
the electron space charge. This requirement seems to be met in many
cases by a cathode fall equal to the lowest excitation potential (page
11) of the gas. This requirement seems to be met in many cases by a
cathode fall equal to the lowest excitation potential of the gas."

After the drop in potential occurring in the cathode sheath, the
voltage remains substantially constant across the plasma region consisting (page 16) of a region in which the number of positive and
negative ions is substantially the same. There is a slight *change* in
potential across the sheath near the anode; this is usually a slight drop
in potential.

Additional information on the theory of gas tubes will be found in References 3 and 11. These also list many references giving detailed explanations and data on the phenomena occurring.

A full-wave argon-filled rectifier tube. Ratings as follows: Filament, 15 amperes at 2.5 volts; anode-cathode drop, 8 volts; maximum peak anode current, 6 amperes; maximum peak potential between electrodes, 100 volts. (Courtesy Western Electric Co.)

The characteristic of a gas tube of great practical importance is this: The gas (or mercury vapor) tube will pass *large* currents with a *low internal voltage drop* between the cathode and anode. This low voltage drop is substantially the same for both small and large gas tubes, but for mercury vapor tubes it varies with the temperature of the condensed mercury determined by the bulb temperature, as shown in Fig. 4–10. This low drop results in *high efficiency*. Furthermore, this small voltage drop is almost *constant* over the entire operating range. This makes possible a rectifier with *good regulation;* that is, the output voltage varies little with the magnitude of the load current. These characteristics for high-vacuum and gas tubes of comparative sizes are shown in Fig. 4–11.

A circuit for studying the operation of a gas diode can be arranged as in Fig. 4–12. The curve of Fig. 4–11 can be obtained by varying the anode current I_p by changing the voltage divider, and by measuring the corresponding voltage drop E_p. For determining the curve of Fig. 4–10, the temperature of the rectifier bulb must be varied. This can be accomplished by mounting the tube in a temperature-controlled oil bath. For values below room temperature, cooling water can be piped through the oil.

Operation of Gas Tubes.—Greater care must be used in the operation of gas tubes than is needed for high-vacuum tubes. There are at least two important rules to follow. These will be explained for mercury-vapor tubes, but also apply to similar tubes using argon and other gases.

First, the cathode should reach operating temperature before the anode voltage is applied. This is *very important* in the larger tubes. These tubes have massive oxide-coated cathodes (which may be heat shielded) and come up to operating temperature very slowly, often requiring several minutes or more.   Suppose that the anode voltage is applied *before* the electrons are emitted.   Then there will be no drop in voltage outside the tube (Fig. 4–1, page 75), and the entire secondary

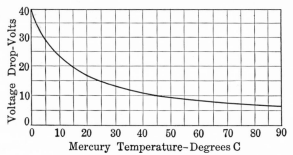

FIG. 4–10.   Effect of temperature on the voltage drop in a mercury-vapor diode at constant current.   (Data from Reference 3.)

voltage will be impressed across the tube.   As a few electrons are emitted, ionization by collision occurs and positive ions are produced. Owing to the high voltage still existing across the tube, these massive positive ions are drawn to the cathode with high velocities, and when

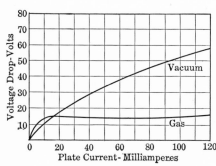

FIG. 4–11.   Internal voltage drops between cathode and anode (or plate) for comparable gas and vacuum rectifier tubes.

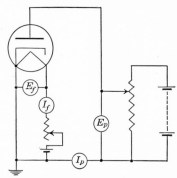

FIG. 4–12.   A circuit for testing a gas diode.   In some tubes the cathode is internally connected to the filament.   In others external connections must be made.

they strike the cathode, they will knock off the active material and permanently injure the cathode.

The ionizing potential for mercury vapor is only 10.4 volts.   The total drop in the tube (Fig. 4–11) is only about 14 volts.   The potential drop across the tube which will accelerate the massive positive ions sufficiently to cause disintegration is approximately 22 volts. Thus, in operation, the voltage across a mercury vapor tube should never be allowed to approach closely this value. In commercial circuits, slow-operating relays are used to delay the application of the anode voltage until cathode operating temperature is reached.

Second, the maximum peak anode current should not be exceeded. This value of current is determined by the maximum emission from the cathode and by the heat- dissipating characteristics of the tube. If this current is exceeded the voltage drop within the tube may be sufficient to cause cathode disintegration by positive ion bombardment; also, the tube may be overheated, causing damage to the electrodes.

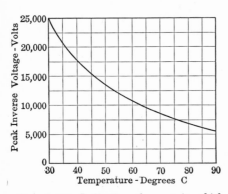

Fig. 4–13. Indicating the way in which the peak inverse plate voltage a mercury-vapor tube will stand varies with temperature. (Data from Reference 3.)

Of course, the maximum peak inverse voltage should not be exceeded, or the tube may arc back, permanently damaging it. The inverse voltage which a mercury vapor tube will stand depends on the temperature as shown by Fig. 4–13. This is because the vapor pressure *depends on* the temperature of the tube, and the vapor pressure determines the vapor density and hence the operating characteristics.

28. Types of Gas Diodes.—As for the high-vacuum tubes, gas diodes are made in many sizes ranging from those passing a few hundred milliamperes (Type 82, for example) to those passing *hundreds* of amperes and capable of withstanding inverse voltages of *thousands* of volts. Thus, the mercury-vapor tubes used at one of the large broadcast stations have the following ratings: [12]

Cathode heater voltage	5.0 volts
Cathode heater current	65.0 amperes
Peak anode current	450.0 amperes
Average anode current	75.0 amperes
Peak inverse voltage	16,000.0 volts

A schematic diagram of this tube is shown in Fig. 4–14. The cathode is a stack of oxide-coated disks enclosed by heat shields. These are indirectly heated by a coiled tungsten heater wire running co-axially through the center of the disks. This cathode is capable of supplying a peak emission current of 1.25 amperes per watt of heating power in comparison with the usual 0.05 ampere per watt for an open-ribbon filament.[12]

It should be recalled (page 71) that the heat-shielded cathode can be used only in gas tubes. In these, the positive ions neutralize the space charge which would otherwise prevent the electrons from flowing out through the holes provided in the heat shields. Stated another way, in a high-vacuum tube the heat shields would also act as electrostatic shields and would prevent the positive electric field of the plate from reaching the emitted electrons.

The slow heating time required by the heat-shielded cathode of the large mercury-vapor tube previously discussed is illustrated by Fig. 4–15. As indicated, a higher voltage may be initially impressed (and then reduced) to lower the heating time required before the anode voltage can be applied.

Air cooling is always used for gas diodes, and is sufficient because the losses are relatively low. Forced air is used for the large tubes.[12]

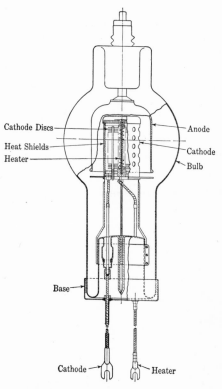

Fig. 4–14. Cross-section of a large hot-cathode mercury-vapor diode. (Courtesy R.C.A. Manufacturing Co.)

As for the high-vacuum tube, trade names are sometimes used in denoting gas tubes. Thus, the **Phanotron** has been applied by one company to any gas diode.

29. Comparison of High-Vacuum and Gas Diodes as Power Rectifiers.—Briefly, the operating characteristics of two comparative types of diodes are somewhat as follows: *First*, much more power is required to heat the tungsten filament of the high-vacuum tube than is required by the heat-shielded cathode of the gas tube. *Second*, the voltage drop across the high-vacuum tube is much greater than that across the gas diode; also, the drop across the former increases with increase in current, while that across the latter is substantially constant. *Third*, the efficiency of the high-vacuum diode is lower than

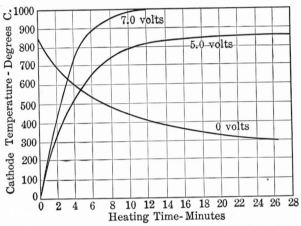

Fig. 4–15. Heating and cooling curves for the heat-shielded cathode of a large mercury-vapor rectifier tube. Heater voltages shown; 5.0 volts is normal. (From Reference 12.)

for the gas tube. This is very important for tubes handling large amounts of power, but of little consequence for such applications as rectifiers for radio receiving sets.

The high-vacuum diode has certain characteristics which make its use highly desirable. *First*, it is rugged and not so easily damaged by misuse. A momentary short circuit, which would ruin a gas tube, would probably merely overheat the plate of a high-vacuum tube. *Second*, variations in the voltage of the filament supply for a high-vacuum tube will affect only the magnitude of the anode or plate current flowing. The gas tube, however, is very critical as to filament supply. Thus, one manufacturer states that for a vapor tube rated at 2.5 volts on the filament, the voltage should be maintained within 5 per cent of this value. If the filament is operated above 2.5 volts the life of the tube will be greatly reduced, and if operated at voltages below the lower limit the tube may fail immediately. *Third*, the high-vacuum tube does not produce radio interference, but the gas diode does. *Fourth*, the high-vacuum diode has been developed to withstand much higher maximum peak inverse plate voltages, and will, therefore, rectify much higher alternating voltages.

30. High-Pressure Gas Diodes.—These tubes are used extensively for charging automobile storage batteries. They are known by the trade names **Tungar** and **Rectigon.**

The essential elements of these tubes are a short, heavy tungsten filament cathode located close to a heavy graphite anode. Argon gas at the relatively high pressure of about 5 centimeters of mercury is introduced into the tube. This argon gas serves two purposes.

First, through ionization by collision, the argon gas provides positive ions for reducing the space charge, thereby permitting large currents to flow. *Second*, the argon gas at this high pressure largely prevents evaporation of the tungsten. This is extremely important because the cathode is operated at a *very high* temperature to provide the required electrons from a simple cathode structure.

As an example of the protective action of the gas, one author states [13] that in similar "Tungar" tubes using a barium-coated nickel cylinder for a cathode, the life of the filament was 4000 hours when in mercury vapor at 1 to 3 millimeters pressure, but was only 20 hours when the vapor pressure was 0.01 millimeter. In each instance the tube was passing 5 amperes. Thus, the presence of the gas largely prevented destructive evaporation of the filament.

These high-pressure gas diodes can be used *only* at low voltages because the maximum peak inverse anode voltage they will stand is about 200 volts. If higher voltages are used they will arc across on the negative half cycle when the anode is negative and the cathode is positive. This limits the use of these tubes to such applications as automobile storage battery chargers. These tubes are made in several sizes, the largest being designed to pass 6 amperes continuously.

After the tube has been started (that is, once the gas is ionized), it will continue to operate without filament heating current. When used in this manner, the current may become concentrated at one point on the filament, and may weaken it causing failure. For commercial purposes it is not advisable to operate the tube in this way. For further information on these rectifier tubes, Reference 14 should be consulted.

31. X-Ray Tubes.—A form of electromagnetic radiation commonly known as x-rays is emitted when a rapidly moving stream of electrons is suddenly stopped by striking a metal electrode. They are also known [2] as **Roentgen** rays, named after the scientist who discovered the phenomena in 1895. The first x-ray tubes consisted essentially of a metal cathode and anode in a glass tube containing traces of residual gas. No heated filament was used, the initial current starting from the free ions present. This tube was not entirely satisfactory largely because of its erratic performance and lack of control.

A high-vacuum, hot-cathode, x-ray tube [2] with a heated filament as the source of electrons was invented by Coolidge in 1913. This tube is constant in operation and the quality of the rays is readily controllable. A simplified circuit of this tube is shown in Fig. 4–16.

The construction of the tube depends on the use to which it is to be put. The cathode is usually a tungsten filament surrounded by a small metal cylinder connected electrically to the filament. The metal

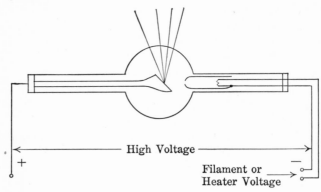

High Voltage

+ Filament or –
Heater Voltage

FIG. 4–16. Simplified circuit arrangement for an x-ray tube.

cylinder assists in focusing the electron beam on the anode or **target** (also called an anti-cathode). The target is defined [2] as "the electrode on which cathode rays are focused and from which roentgen rays are emitted." The target * often contains a tungsten insert in a massive copper electrode.

Tungsten is used because it will withstand the electron bombardment, and copper is often employed because of its high heat conducting ability. In this connection it should be remembered that the target is in a high vacuum; therefore, the heat generated by the impinging electrons must be conducted away largely through the body of the metal electrode. Cooling fins are often placed on the end of the positive electrode exposed to the air. Also, this electrode is sometimes water cooled. X-ray tubes have been designed with a target which is rotated rapidly to prevent pitting.

In the medical profession x-rays are used in many ways, generally familiar to all. *First*, because of their penetrating power, x-rays can be used with fluorescent screens (which emit *visible* light when struck by *invisible* x-rays) to study the body. *Second*, since x-rays affect photographic films, they can be used to penetrate the body and photograph conditions therein. *Third*, x-rays not only penetrate, but pro-

---

* The tungsten insert is often referred to as the *target*, and the complete positive electrode structure as the *anode*. It should also be added that while many medical authorities prefer the term *roentgen rays*, the term x-rays is generally preferred by physicists and engineers.

duce important effects on living tissue. They can be used, therefore, for treatment of certain diseases such as cancer and diseases of the skin.

The uses enumerated above, and the many others omitted, have an important bearing on x-ray tube design. In general, each special use requires rays of a different **hardness** or quality. The hardness of x-rays is defined [2] as "the attribute which determines the penetrating ability." Long x-rays do not penetrate readily, but the shorter the wavelength, the *harder* the rays, and the greater their penetrating ability. Medical science ordinarily is interested in x-rays of from 0.1 to 1 Angstrom unit, an Angstrom unit equalling 10^{-8} centimeter.[15]

The control of the x-ray radiation from a Coolidge tube is relatively simple. The *hardness* (that is, the wavelength or frequency) of the radiation depends on the *voltage applied between the cathode and target*, since this voltage determines the velocity and the energy of the impinging electrons. The *quantity* of the radiation of any degree of hardness, that is, the "amount" of radiation of a given type, is determined by the *filament current*, because the tube is a diode and is operated at high voltage, and at these high voltages voltage saturation has been reached. The current is *not* limited by the space charge, but by the number of electrons emitted; that is, by the *temperature of the filament*. Increasing the temperature increases the emission and thus the electron current to the target. An increased current to the target gives greater x-ray radiation.

In addition to uses by the medical profession, x-rays are now utilized extensively by engineers. Among these uses [15] is the x-ray examination of welds and castings.

32. Glow Lamps (**Neon Tubes**).—These consist of two electrodes mounted close together in a bulb filled with an inert gas, usually neon, argon, or helium gas, or with combinations of these gases. The type of gas and the pressure are determined by the results desired and the purpose

Shockproof oil immersed deep therapy x-ray tube. The anode is hollow and cooled by pumping oil into the pipe at the upper end of the tube. This x-ray tube is approximately 18″ long and 4″ in diameter. It is used primarily for cancer treatment and industrial radiography. Rating, 200,000 volts, 25 milliamperes. (Courtesy Westinghouse Electric and Manufacturing Co.)

for which the tube is to be used.   The shapes of the electrodes are similarly determined.

When the lamp is connected to a direct voltage and the voltage is gradually increased, a point will be reached where the gas suddenly ionizes and the *negative* electrode glows. When connected to an alternating source, *both* electrodes glow.

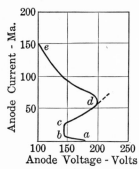

FIG. 4–17. Characteristics of a glow lamp. (Adapted from Reference 11.)

The characteristics of a typical glow lamp are shown in Fig. 4–17, and are explained [11] as follows.   Suppose that a glow lamp is connected in series with a rheostat as shown in Fig. 4–18.   If the constant applied battery voltage exceeds the critical value necessary to ionize the gas, the gas immediately breaks down and a small current flows.   If the voltage is below this value, the lamp remains an insulator.

If, after breakdown, the current is increased, by reducing the series resistance of the rheostat, a faint luminosity appears at the negative electrode (cathode).   If the series resistance is further *decreased*, more current flows, and the voltage drop across the tube *decreases* to point b. As the resistance is further decreased, the glow increases until the cathode is entirely covered.   The voltage drop remains constant along the line b–c, this being the normal cathode drop of potential (page 22).

If the series resistance is again decreased, the cathode drop in potential increases along the line c–d since the cathode is now covered with an abnormal glow (page 22).   The cathode becomes heated by the bombardment of positive ions, and may emit electrons.   As the resistance is further decreased the glow discharge turns into an arc with *negative resistance characteristics*.   The current *increases* as indicated and the voltage *decreases* along the line d–e.

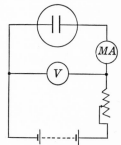

FIG. 4–18.   Circuit for determining the glow lamp characteristic of Fig. 4–17.

Glow lamps are often operated from constant sources of potential such as 110-volt circuits.   If so, they have sufficient resistance in series to limit operation to the region b–c of Fig. 4–17.

Such lamps have been used successfully in one system of television.[16] In these lamps, both the negative and positive electrodes were flat metal plates several inches square, and separated about one milli-meter. Under proper conditions the negative electrode (cathode) is covered with a glow, the brightness of which is *directly proportional to the current* flowing through the tube. This tube, when viewed through a rotating scanning disk, makes possible the reproduction of television images. By using three similar lamps, one containing neon and two containing argon, television *in colors* has been successfully demon-strated.[17]

Neon lamps are now commercially available in many sizes and are widely used for dim sources of illumination, and for many other pur-poses such as in stroboscopes. Oscillators using discharge tubes (neon lamps) have been described.[18, 19] For a complete classification of gaseous tube lamps, and for a historical development of the subject Reference 20 should be consulted.

The tubular glow lamps so widely used for advertising signs are usually referred to as **neon tubes** although other gases are often em-ployed. These tubes were developed commercially by Claude. They were discussed in an article [21] by Kober, from which the following is largely summarized.

A simple neon tube consists essentially of an electrode in each end of a *long* glass tube filled with an inert gas, such as neon. Before ionization the gas is a good insulator and no current flows. When a high voltage is impressed, however, the gas becomes ionized, current flows, and a self-maintained glow discharge is established. The illu-mination comes largely from the positive column instead of the cathode as in the glow tube having the electrodes close together. This phe-nomenon was discussed on page 23, and a drawing of the glow dis-charge and a voltage distribution curve given on page 21.

A high-voltage drop exists at the cathode which cannot be neutral-ized as in hot cathode gas tubes. This results in an opposition to cur-rent flow, causing energy loss, and also sputtering. This effect is caused by the massive positive ions being drawn to the cathode with high velocity. They knock metal atoms off the cathode, causing its gradual disintegration. This can be minimized by proper design so that the current per unit area is low. Claude found [21] that for cathode areas in excess of 1.5 square decimeters per ampere, the cathode drop reaches a minimum value.

Disintegration of the cathode by sputtering largely determines the life of the tube. The sputtering also affects the tube in another way. A thin metallic film is formed on the inside of the tube near the cathode. As this film is deposited, the useful gas of the tube is occluded, *dimin-ishing* the gas pressure and *increasing* the mean free path of the positive ions. The voltage required to operate the tube gradually increases, and this further increases the sputtering. The voltage required to operate the tube becomes greater than that supplied by the transformer, the tube begins to flicker, and eventually ceases to operate.

The potential gradient in volts per centimeter for a neon tube is shown in Fig. 4–19. This curve shows that the voltage drop is high at

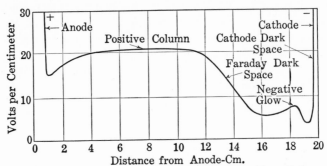

FIG. 4–19. Potential gradient for a typical neon tube. (From Reference 21.)

the anode and cathode, and that it is constant along the positive column (see page 21).

The volt-ampere characteristic of a neon tube is shown in Fig. 4–20. Regarding this curve, Kober states [21] as follows: "As may be noted, from A to B the curve has a negative slope. This is due to the fact that the cathode drop remains normal up to point B while the voltage of the positive column, having a negative characteristic, decreases with the current. At point B (zero slope) the cathode drop becomes abnormal and just balances the positive-column drop. From B to C, the abnormal cathode drop with an increase in current, increases more rapidly than the positive column decreases; this explains the positive slope."

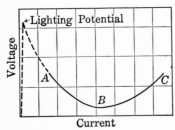

FIG. 4–20. Ideal volt-ampere characteristic for a neon tube. (From Reference 21.)

For a discussion of normal and abnormal cathode drops refer to page 21.

Glow discharge lamps, or tubes, are being extensively used for illuminating purposes in addition to sign advertising. Thus, the sodium-vapor lamp is proving very satisfactory for highway and bridge illumination. Dushman has written two articles (Reference 22) dealing in great detail with both the radiation and conduction phenomena in gaseous discharge lamps, and the reading of these articles is highly recommended.

Operation of Neon Tubes.—Neon tubes require a high voltage to produce the initial discharge, but need only a relatively low voltage (depending on the length) to maintain the discharge.   Thus, the transformers used should have good *current* regulation, but poor *voltage* regulation, just the opposite from power-system transformers.   Shell-type transformers with a magnetic shunt inserted between the primary and secondary coils, to give high leakage reactance, are used to step up from 110 or 220 volts to the operating voltage of the tube. Since this voltage may be as high as 15,000 volts, the proper design of the insulation is important.

The operating characteristics of a typical neon tube are summarized in Table IX, taken from Reference 21.

TABLE IX

SPECIFICATIONS FOR A TYPICAL NEON SIGN INSTALLATION
(From Reference 21)

Tube	
Diameter	15 mm
Length	60 ft. (4 tubes)
Gas	Neon
Transformer	
Primary volts	110
Secondary volts (open)	15,000
Secondary volts (with load)	depends on tube length (max. 10,000)
Secondary milliamperes	25
Load watts	210
Volts per ft.	130
Watts per ft.	1.5
Lumens per ft.	36
Lumens per ft.-watt	24
Power factor	0.40 to 0.60
Life	10,000 to 15,000 hr.
Electrode drop per tube	250–300 volts

Several excellent papers [23, 24, 25] have been published which explain in detail the operation of neon tubes and their transformers. These include many oscillograms and other valuable data.

33. Mercury Arc Tubes.—The history of the mercury arc lamp dates back to at least 1860 when Way discovered that if an electric circuit were opened by a mercury contact, a long brilliant arc was formed.[11]   In 1890, Hewitt began developing mercury arc lamps with the arc enclosed in an evacuated glass tube.

The Hewitt mercury lamp was commercialized about 1901.   In its simple form it consists of a long glass tube with a metallic electrode at one end and a mercury pool as an electrode at the other end.   The lamp is usually mounted at an angle with the horizontal, and with the mercury pool below the other electrode.   The arc is started by tipping the tube until a thin filament of mercury connects with the metal electrode, and then suddenly breaking the mercury path by restoring the tube to the operating position.   Ions are released by the arc formed when the current is interrupted, and an arc is established within the tube.

Mercury arc lamps are well adapted for uses as in industrial shops.   The source is large and the light well diffused.   The peculiar greenish-blue color of the mercury arc is excellent for high visibility.

Mercury Arc Rectifiers.—Hewitt also is credited with inventing the mercury arc rectifier.[11]   This device is so widely used and well known that it needs no further introduction. It is covered extensively in the technical literature.   Three books, References 14, 26, and 27, contain much information on the subject.

A simplified circuit of a single-phase mercury arc rectifier of conventional design is shown in Fig. **4–21**. The arc is started by closing the starting switch, tipping the bulb so that the mercury pool makes contact with the starting electrode, and then suddenly restoring the bulb to the upright position, thus breaking the mercury connection and establishing an arc.   This arc forms the **cathode spot** on the mercury pool and produces initial ionization so that current can then flow to the main electrodes.

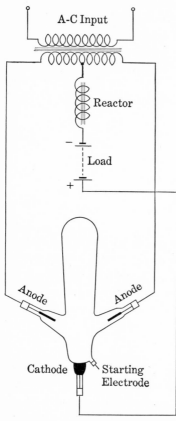

Fig. 4–21.   Simplified circuit of a small single-phase mercury-arc rectifier.

These electrodes are often of graphite.   They serve only as collectors of electrons from the arc stream.   They are so connected to the transformer that they are alternately positive and negative.   When an electrode is positive it draws electrons from the ionized mercury vapor. A rectified current will therefore flow through the load, represented in Fig. **4–21** by a battery to be charged.

If the mercury arc stops for any reason, recombination occurs, the vapor in the tube deionizes, and the arc will not start again until the tube is tipped as previously explained. The reactor in series with the battery to be charged (or other load) is to prevent the arc from stopping when the applied alternating voltage wave passes through zero. The inductive reactance prevents the current to one anode from dying out until the current to the other has been estab-lished within the tube. In rectifiers of larger sizes, two auxiliary "keep alive" electrodes are provided as shown in Fig. 4–22. These are similar to the main anodes, but are arranged to conduct a current of at least 5 amperes at all times, thus assuring continuous operation of the arc.

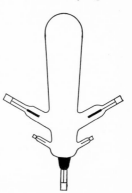

FIG. 4–22. Mercury-arc rectifier with keep-alive electrodes.

The vaporized mercury condenses on walls of the tube and flows back into the mercury pool. The temperature at which the bulb operates determines the point at which con-densation occurs. This in turn determines the vapor pressure in the tube and thus temper-ature influences the operating conditions.

Theory of Operation of Mercury Arc.—This is very simple as ex-plained above, but when the *exact nature* of the way the electrons are drawn out of the mercury pool is considered, differences of opinion exist. The mercury arc is a non-self-maintained discharge, and thus electrons must be supplied by the cathode (page 16).

Some favor the viewpoint that the electrons are obtained by a thermionic process from the very hot cathode spot, and statements are often made that the temperature of this spot may reach 2000° C. In all probability, however, the temperature is only a few hundred degrees, far below the point of thermionic emission.

Ionization by collision occurs within the mercury-arc rectifier tube. The mobile *electrons* so released are quickly withdrawn to the anodes, adding but little to the total current flow (page 16). The massive positive ions travel relatively slowly to the negative mercury pool cathode, where they form a very intense *positive* space charge over the surface of the mercury.

It was suggested [10] by Langmuir that this high-intensity field ex-tracts electrons from the relatively cold mercury in accordance with the *cold cathode effect* discussed on page 45. Experiments show that fields of about 10^6 volts per centimeter are required to produce electron emission from metals at low temperature. Since the cathode drop is only about 10 volts, the positive space charge film would need to be of the order of 10^{-5} centimeter thick.[14]

The pressure of the mercury vapor immediately over the cathode spot is quite high, and it is assumed that the electrons need to travel but a short distance before they encounter and ionize a mercury atom. This action provides positive ions for pulling the electrons from the surface of the mercury.

Although the mercury-arc rectifier is one of the oldest of electrical devices, exact data regarding it are meager.   Reference 14 quotes certain data from the work of Guntherschulze, some of which will be mentioned here.   The area of the cathode spot is about 2.5×10^{-4} square centimeter.   Mercury is evaporated at the rate of 7.2×10^{-3} gram per second per ampere.   The cathode drop is 9 volts, which is less than 10.4 volts, the ionizing potential of mercury, but this may be justified on the basis of cumulative ionizing effects (page 12).   In the sheath above the cathode spot 56 per cent of the current passing through the tube is due to electrons leaving the mercury pool, and 44 per cent is due to positive ions entering the mercury from the ionized vapor.

Arc-Back.—Referring to Fig. 4–21, it is evident that the electron current flows from the mercury pool to the electrode on the right when this electrode is *positive*, and to the one on the left during the part of the cycle that the left one is *positive*.   Under normal operating conditions, very little reverse (electron) current flows in the opposite direction; that is, from either of the current-collecting electrodes, when they are negative, to the more positive mercury pool.

If the tube is overloaded, however, then the temperature of the mercury vapor will be increased, and the vapor pressure will also increase.   This lowers the insulating properties of the mercury vapor, and decreases the inverse or back voltage a tube will stand between the electrode, negative at a given instant, and the mercury pool.   The tube then has a tendency to **arc back** or **backfire** which may permanently damage the tube.[14, 28]

Shields or **grids** surrounding each of the current-collecting electrodes (or anodes) are used to prevent arc back.   These assist in several ways.[11]   *First,* they protect the anodes from particles and drops of condensed mercury, and from blasts of mercury vapor.   Drops of mercury on an anode might have "cathode spots" formed on their surface, tending to cause reverse-current flow.   *Second*, the grids decrease the deionizing time, tending to keep the ion density lower and the insulating properties higher.   *Third,* the grids "even out" the voltage distribution at the anodes, avoiding strong fields which might pull electrons from the anode surfaces.

These characteristics are shown in Fig. 4–23. The total drop in voltage is less than 25 volts. This drop is higher than in rectifiers *without* a grid. The fact that mercury-arc rectifiers have a low internal voltage drop and no cathode to heat makes them very efficient.

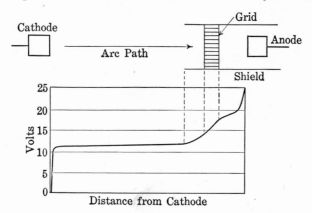

FIG. 4–23. When the anode is shielded as indicated, the voltage is distributed as shown.

Commercial Forms of Mercury Arc Tubes.—In the smaller sizes, mercury-arc rectifier tubes are made of glass. Various shapes and electrode positions have been used.[14] Also, various electrode materials have been tried experimentally.

In the larger sizes, the electrodes are mounted in steel tanks, parts of which may be water cooled. The design of these tanks involves special insulation studies. Owing to the difficulty of maintaining a high vacuum, evacuating pumps are continuously connected during operation. Further information on mercury-arc rectifiers will be found in Chapter 7.

34. The Ignitron.—This is the trade name of a newly developed rectifier. Although it has a third "igniting" electrode it is so closely related to the conventional mercury-arc rectifier that its theory will be considered in this chapter. Further information will be found on page 198.

The tendency to arc back or backfire has always been a limiting factor in the design and application of the conventional mercury-arc rectifier. Bent anode arms and grids as discussed in the preceding section are used to reduce this arcing. Both of these increase the length of the arc path, and increase the voltage drop, which reduces the efficiency. Also, in the mercury-arc rectifier, an *arc* and the *cathode spot* must both be maintained at all times, or the device must be restarted.   This means that both anodes must be in one bulb, and that when the inverse voltage is on an electrode, *it is in an ionized gas,* thus increasing the tendency to arc back.   If continuous operation must be assured, auxiliary electrodes continuously passing at least 5 amperes must be used, and this loss lowers the overall efficiency.

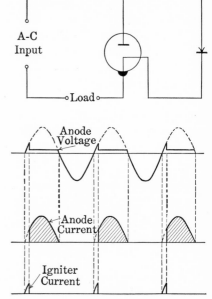

An Ignitron rectifier tube.   The igniting electrode is shown at the right.   (Courtesy Westinghouse Electric and Manufacturing Co.)

FIG. 4–24.   Showing a simple Ignitron rectifier circuit which starts to conduct at the beginning of each cycle.

An **Ignitron** consists essentially of a graphite anode about an inch or more above a mercury pool, and with a third igniter electrode in the mercury pool as shown in Fig. 4–24.   The electrodes are placed in a glass bulb in the small sizes, and in steel enclosures for the large sizes. The Ignitron is due to Slepian and Ludwig who developed the igniter principle [29] of starting the arc.   The igniter is often a crystal of carborundum.

The operation of the Ignitron is very simple,[30, 31] and is illustrated by Fig. 4–24.   When the voltage applied to the circuit makes the anode positive, current flows through the rectifier to the igniter, and when the current is sufficient, a cathode spot is formed about the igniter in the mercury pool.   At this point, the arc forms to the anode and the igniter current drops to zero.   The voltage drop across the tube is then only about 10 volts, giving a very efficient rectifier.   When the applied voltage reverses, making the anode negative, the arc goes out and the tube deionizes.   The cathode spot is not started again because the rectifier prevents current flow to the igniter.   Each Ignitron is a half-wave rectifier.

Many advantages are at once apparent; among these are the following: *First,* arc-back or backfire is largely prevented because when the inverse voltage is on the tube, the vapor is deionized.   *Second,* the anode may be close to the mercury pool, giving a low internal voltage drop.   *Third,* the arc is fired at will, giving a control feature (page 198) not present in the conventional mercury-arc rectifier.   *Fourth,* no "keep-alive" electrodes are needed.   *Fifth,* the Ignitron has an advantage over thermionic gas tubes in that the excellent features of the mercury pool cathode instead of a thermionic cathode are obtained. Indications are that the Ignitron should prove a useful device.

REFERENCES

1. Institute of Radio Engineers.   *Reports of the Standards Committees.*
2. American Institute of Electrical Engineers.   *American Standard Definitions of Electrical Terms.*
3. McArthur, E. D.   *Electronics and Electron Tubes.*   John Wiley & Sons. See also articles in General Electric Review, March–Sept., Nov., Dec., 1933.
4. Pidgeon, H. A.   *Simple theory of the three-electrode vacuum tube.*   Journal of the Society of Motion Picture Engineers, Feb., 1935, Vol. 24. Also, Bell Telephone System Monograph B-852.
5. Langmuir, I., and Compton, K. T.   *Electrical discharges in gases.* Reviews of Modern Physics, April, 1931, Vol. 3, No. 2.
6. Koller, L. R.   *The Physics of Electron Tubes.*   McGraw-Hill Book Co.
7. Dushman, Saul.   *Electron emission.*   Electrical Engineering, July, 1934, Vol. 53, No. 7.
8. Chaffee, E. L.   *Theory of Thermionic Vacuum Tubes.*   McGraw-Hill Book Co.
9. Wilson, W.   *A new type of high power vacuum tube.*   Bell System Technical Journal, July, 1922, Vol. 1, No. 1.
10. Slepian, J., and Mason, R. C.   *Electric discharges in gases.*   Electrical Engineering, April, 1934, Vol. 53, No. 4.
11. Westinghouse Electric and Mfg. Co.   *Industrial Electronic Tubes.* Course 25.
12. Steiner, H. C.   *Hot-cathode mercury rectifier tubes for high power broadcast transmitters.*   Proceedings of the Institute of Radio Engineers, Feb., 1935, Vol. 23, No. 2.
13. Hull, A. W.   *Gas-filled thermionic tubes.*   Transactions of American Institute of Electrical Engineers, July, 1928, Vol. 47.

14. Prince, D. C., and Vogdes, F. B. *Principles of Mercury Arc Rectifiers and Their Circuits.* McGraw-Hill Book Co.

15. Clark, G. L. *X-rays—What should we know about them?* Electrical Engineering, Jan., 1935, Vol. 54, No. 1.

16. Gray, F., Horton, J. W., and Mathes, R. C. *The production and utilization of television signals.* Transactions of the American Institute of Electrical Engineers, Vol. 46, 1927. Bell System Technical Journal, Oct., 1927, Vol. 6.

17. Ives, H. E., and Johnsrud, A. L. *Television in colors by a beam scanning method.* Journal of the Optical Society of America, Jan., 1930, Vol. 20. Also, Bell Telephone System Monograph No. B-448.

18. Kock, W. E. *Generating sine waves with gas discharge tubes.* Electronics, March, 1935, Vol. 8, No. 3.

19. Kock, W. E. *Filter-coupled glow discharge oscillators.* Radio Engineering, June, 1936, Vol. 16, No. 6.

20. Moore, D. F. *Development of gaseous-tube lighting.* Electrical Engineering, Aug., 1931, Vol. 50, No. 8.

21. Kober, P. A. *Neon tube sign lighting.* Electrical Engineering, Aug., 1931, Vol. 50, No. 8.

22. Dushman, Saul. *Low pressure gaseous discharge lamps.* Electrical Engineering, Aug. and Sept., 1934, Vol. 53, Nos. 8 and 9.

23. McMillan, F. O., and Starr, E. C. *High-voltage gaseous-conductor lamps.* Journal of the American Institute of Electrical Engineers, Dec., 1928, Vol. 48, No. 12.

24. Summers, C. M. *A theory of neon tube operation.* Electrical Engineering, Nov., 1932, Vol. 51, No. 11.

25. Lohman, R. W. *Neon tube characteristics.* Electrical Engineering, May, 1933, Vol. 52, No. 5.

26. Guntherschulze, A. *Electric Rectifiers and Valves.* John Wiley & Sons.

27. Jolley, L. B. W. *Alternating Current Rectification.* John Wiley & Sons.

28. Slepian, J., and Ludwig, L. R. *Backfires in mercury arc rectifiers.* Transactions of the American Institute of Electrical Engineers, March, 1932, Vol. 51.

29. Sepian, J., and Ludwig, L. R. *A new method of starting an arc.* Electrical Engineering, Sept., 1933, Vol. 52, No. 9.

30. Ludwig, L. R., Maxfield, F. A., and Toepfer, A. H. *An experimental ignitron rectifier.* Electrical Engineering, Jan., 1934, Vol. 53, No. 1.

31. Knowles, D. D. *The ignitron—a new controlled rectifier.* Electronics, June, 1933, Vol. 6, No. 6.

SUGGESTED ASSIGNMENTS

1. Referring to Fig. 4–11, explain why the two curves, one giving the characteristics of a high-vacuum diode, and the other for the gas diode, do not coincide below the point of intersection.

2. Determine the equation for the plate current of a diode, and compare with equation (4–1), page 80.

3. Determine the relative velocities of electrons and positive argon gas ions.

4. Referring to the data given on page 88, calculate the cathode heating power, the peak power loss within the tube, the average power loss within the tube, the total power handling capacity, and the efficiency of the tube.
5. Assume operating conditions for a typical x-ray tube and calculate the velocity of an electron when it strikes the target. Calculate the energy dissipated at the target during a one-minute operation period.
6. Referring to Fig. 4–11, explain why as the plate current of the *mercury vapor* tube is increased the voltage drop is found to rise to a maximum, drop slightly, and then again increase.

CHAPTER 5

THREE-ELECTRODE THERMIONIC VACUUM TUBES

Although the underlying principle of the thermionic vacuum tube was discovered by Edison in 1883, and the diode was used by Fleming in 1904 to detect high-frequency radio signals, the vacuum tube was a relatively unimportant device until De Forest, in 1906, introduced a control electrode, the **grid.** Since this very important contribution, the use of the vacuum tube has attained truly astonishing proportions.

In the preceding chapter, both high-vacuum and gas two-electrode tubes or diodes were considered. These tubes are used extensively as rectifiers of alternating power, and the diode principle is used for detection in radio-receiving sets. **Three-electrode tubes** or **triodes** [1] will be discussed in this chapter. These tubes contain an anode, a cathode, and a third electrode, the grid.[1]

Both high-vacuum and gas triodes will be included, the former in the first part of the chapter, and the latter in the last part. The discussion will be limited, however, largely to the theoretical features, leaving application information for later chapters. The presentation of the theory of high-vacuum triodes will follow closely the excellent method [2] used by Pidgeon.

35. The Grid.—The grid is an electrode in the form of a suitable mesh, screen, or spiral wires placed between the cathode and anode. It is often referred to as the **control grid,** but this distinction is only necessary in multi-electrode tubes containing more than one grid.

The current of electrons flowing from the cathode to the plate must pass through the grid. The grid is, therefore, in a strategic position, and can largely control this plate-current flow. A complete explanation of the action of the grid requires a thorough understanding of space-charge phenomena discussed on page 77, and a review of the subject is advisable.

Space Charge in Triodes.—In the triode (as in the diode) electrons are emitted by a hot cathode according to the laws given on page 55. The loss of these negative electrons leaves the cathode positively charged, and hence there are forces tending to draw them back. If the grid and the plate of a triode are connected *directly* to the hot cathode, a *few* of the emitted electrons will have initial energies sufficiently high to carry them across the space within the tube, to one of these electrodes, and on around the circuit and back to the cathode.   Most of the

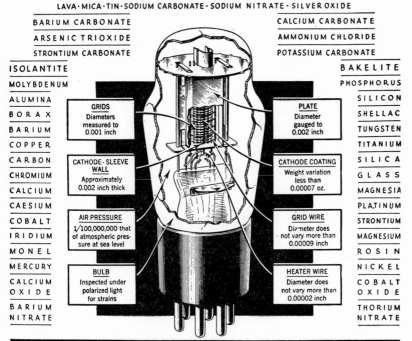

MISCH METAL · NIGROSINE · PORCELAIN · PETROLEUM JELLY · ZINC

CALCIUM ALUMINUM FLUORIDE · RESIN (SYNTHETIC) · ETHYL ALCOHOL

MATERIALS USED IN RCA RADIO TUBES

LEAD ACETATE · MALACHITE GREEN · GLYCERINE · ZINC CHLORIDE · IRON

MARBLE DUST · WOOD FIBER · STRONTIUM NITRATE · LEAD OXIDE · ZINC OXIDE

LAVA · MICA · TIN · SODIUM CARBONATE · SODIUM NITRATE · SILVER OXIDE

BARIUM CARBONATE	CALCIUM CARBONATE
ARSENIC TRIOXIDE	AMMONIUM CHLORIDE
STRONTIUM CARBONATE	POTASSIUM CARBONATE

ISOLANTITE   BAKELITE

MOLYBDENUM   PHOSPHORUS

ALUMINA   SILICON

BORAX   **GRIDS**   **PLATE**   SHELLAC

BARIUM   Diameters   Diameter   TUNGSTEN
                              measured to   gauged to
COPPER   0.001 inch   0.002 inch   TITANIUM

CARBON   SILICA

CHROMIUM   **CATHODE · SLEEVE**   **CATHODE COATING**   GLASS
                              WALL   Weight variation
CALCIUM   Approximately   less than   MAGNESIA
                              0.002 inch thick   0.00007 oz.
CAESIUM   PLATINUM

COBALT   **AIR PRESSURE**   **GRID WIRE**   STRONTIUM

IRIDIUM   1/100,000,000 that   Diameter does   MAGNESIUM
                              of atmospheric pres-   not vary more than
MONEL   sure at sea level   0.00009 inch   ROSIN

MERCURY   NICKEL

CALCIUM   **BULB**   **HEATER WIRE**   COBALT
OXIDE   Inspected under   Diameter does   OXIDE
                              polarized light   not vary more than
BARIUM   for strains   0.00002 inch   THORIUM

NITRATE   NITRATE

Gases Used in Manufacture

NEON — HYDROGEN — CARBON DIOXIDE — ILLUMINATING GAS
HELIUM — ARGON — NATURAL GAS — NITROGEN — OXYGEN

Elements Entering into the Manufacture

ARGON — ALUMINUM — BORON — BARIUM — CAESIUM — CALCIUM — COPPER — CARBON — CHROMIUM — CHLORINE
COBALT — HYDROGEN — HELIUM — IRIDIUM — IRON — LEAD — MAGNESIUM — MERCURY — MOLYBDENUM
NICKEL — NEON — NITROGEN — OXYGEN — POTASSIUM — PHOSPHORUS — PLATINUM — SODIUM — SILVER
SILICON — STRONTIUM — TUNGSTEN — THORIUM — TANTALUM — TITANIUM — TIN — ZINC — RARE EARTHS

(Courtesy RCA Manufacturing Co.)

electrons will remain in a *relatively thin region* or sheath around the cathode, charging this region negatively and thus forming a *negative space charge*.   They will then repel other electrons as they are emitted from the filament and a condition will soon be established where the electrons are repelled to the cathode at the same rate they are emitted (neglecting any high-velocity electrons which may reach the grid or plate).

If the grid is left *directly* connected to the cathode, and the plate is made *positive* with respect to the cathode, the positive electric field produced by the plate will partly neutralize the negative space charge, and will draw electrons from this region. The voltage distribution within the tube will now be approximately as shown in Fig. 4–5. If the plate is made *highly* positive, the negative electrons will be taken as fast as they are emitted, and *voltage saturation* will be reached as discussed on page 77. The space charge *sheath* will now be altered, and the electrons will be more uniformly distributed throughout the region between the electrodes (see page 78). For the conditions discussed, Figs. 4–3 and 4–4 apply to triodes.

It is very important to note that in most instances, for signal and speech purposes, *triodes are operated well below voltage saturation.* (They are, therefore, temperature saturated, page 76.) The space charge can be considered as a thin negative sheath close to the cathode, and the magnitude of this negative charge limits the flow of electrons for a given plate voltage.

The grid is placed between the cathode and the plate, and is closer to this space-charge sheath than is the plate. If the grid is made slightly *positive* with respect to the cathode, the positive electric field of the grid neutralizes partly the negative space charge field, thus permitting the positive electric field of the plate to draw over a *larger* electron current. If the grid is made slightly *negative*, then the negative electric field near the cathode is made stronger and the plate current becomes *smaller*. For most operations, the grid is made negative (page 130).

36. Static Characteristic Graphs.—The theoretical relations between grid voltage, plate voltage, and plate current considered in the preceding section can be shown by means of **char-**

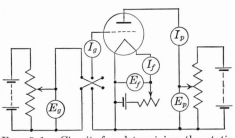

Fig. 5–1.   Circuit for determining the static characteristics of a triode.

acteristic graphs [1] or curves obtained with a circuit arranged as in Fig. 5–1. The negative filament terminal (or the cathode in an indirectly heated tube) is taken as the point of reference.[1] The magnitude of the grid voltage (often called **grid bias**[1]) is varied by the voltage divider and measured by the voltmeter E_g. The voltage impressed on the grid may be made either positive or negative. When the grid is *slightly* negative or is positive, a current measured by the milliammeter I_g will flow to it. The voltage impressed on the plate

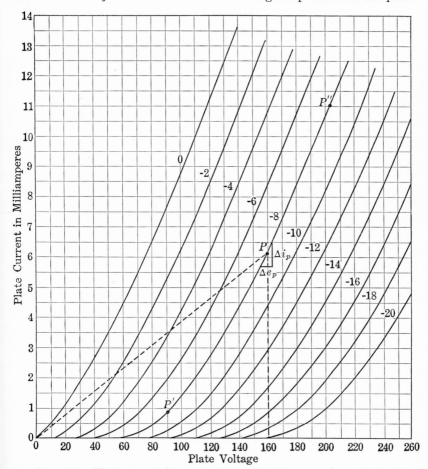

FIG. 5–2. Plate current-plate voltage characteristic curves for a triode determined by a circuit similar to Fig. 5–1. Grid voltage in volts shown on curves. (Adapted from vacuum-tube catalogue of Western Electric Co.)

may also be varied and measured by the voltmeter E_p, and the plate current measured by the milliammeter I_p.

For obtaining the characteristic curves of Fig. **5–2**, the filament current is held constant at the normal value, the *grid* voltage is held constant at the values indicated on the curves, and the *plate voltage is* *varied* giving the plate current values.   All the curves of this "family" have the same shape and are about equally spaced.   These follow approximately the three-halves power law (page 80).

For obtaining the curves of Fig. 5–3, the filament current is again held constant at the normal value, the *plate* voltage is held constant

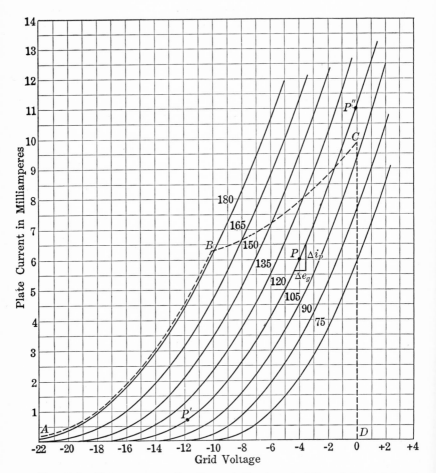

Fig. 5–3.   Plate current-grid voltage static characteristics of the triode of Fig. 5–2.   Operating region bounded by lines *ABCD*.   Plate voltage in volts shown on curves.   (Adapted from same source as Fig. 5–2.)

at the values indicated, and the *grid voltage is varied* giving the plate currents which are plotted as curves.   It will be noted that in this family each curve has the same shape, and for equal plate-voltage increments, the curves are equally spaced.   For each different plate voltage shown, the plate current can be reduced to zero by making the grid sufficiently negative.

The grid will attract electrons and conduct a current when it becomes positive. Grid current curves have not been plotted, but will be considered on page 123.

Curves taken in the above manner with direct voltages on the electrodes are known as **static characteristic curves** as distinguished from the **dynamic characteristic curves**, page 127.

In the curves of Fig. 5–2, the *grid voltage* is constant, and in those of Fig. 5–3, the *plate voltage* is constant; these are, therefore, constant grid-voltage and constant plate-voltage curves. Curves of constant plate current can also be plotted for a tube, and are sometimes useful in *design* work. Since they less clearly illustrate the operation of a tube from an *electronic* viewpoint, they have not been stressed, but are included in Fig. 5–4.

Amplification Factor.—Referring to Fig. 5–3, it is seen that with the plate 165 volts *positive*, no plate current flows if the grid is made 22 volts negative. Thus the grid, due to its greater influence on the space charge near the cathode, is 165/22 or *about* 7.5 times more effective than the plate.

The **amplification factor** is described [1] as a "measure of the effectiveness of the control-electrode voltage relative to that of the plate voltage upon the plate current." In the triode, the grid is the control electrode. The amplification factor is designated by μ. More exactly stated, [1] the amplification factor "is the ratio of the change in plate voltage to a change in control electrode voltage under the conditions that the plate current remains unchanged and that all other electrode voltages are maintained constant. The sense is usually taken as positive when the voltages are changed in opposite directions." As most precisely used, the term refers to infinitesimal changes as indicated by the defining equation,

$$\mu = - \left[\frac{\partial e_p}{\partial e_g} \right] i_p \text{ constant.} \qquad (5\text{–}1)$$

Partial derivatives are used because a third variable, i_p, the plate current in the tube, is held constant.

To be in exact accordance with the definition just given, infinitesimal changes must be used. Practically, however, the amplification factor can be approximately determined from Fig. 5–3 in the following manner. With 135 volts on the plate and − 6 volts bias on the grid the plate current is 5.5 milliamperes. With 120 volts on the plate and − 4.6 volts on the grid the plate current remains 5.5 milliamperes.

The approximate amplification factor is, therefore,

$$\mu = \frac{15}{1.4} = 11.7.$$

The amplification factor can also be determined from Fig. 5–2. Thus with a grid bias of $-$ 6 volts and a plate voltage of 134 volts,

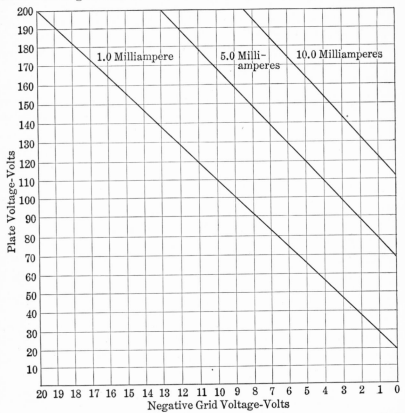

Fig. 5–4.   Constant plate-current curves plotted from data of Fig. 5–2. Such curves are also plotted with plate voltage on the X-axis and grid voltage on the Y-axis, and include both grid-current and plate-current curves.   (See page 68 of Reference 17.)

the plate current is 5.5 milliamperes.   With a grid bias of $-$ 4 volts and a plate voltage of 114 volts the plate current is also 5.5 milliamperes.   The approximate amplification factor is $\mu = 20/2 = 10.0$.

From the definition of amplification factor, it is apparent that if constant plate-current curves are plotted as in Fig. 5–4, this factor can be found.   Thus, $\mu = \partial e_p/\partial e_g$, which is the slope of the curve shown.

It is apparent that these **graphical methods** of determining the amplification factor give different results, largely due to errors in taking data, plotting curves, and reading the curves. They agree, however, fairly closely with the more exact method explained on page 116. These values also differ considerably from the calculations at cutoff in the first paragraph of this section. Although these first calculations illustrate the greater effectiveness of the grid, they are *not* made from data taken over the *same operating range* as the other calculations and the results are not comparable. The relative magnitude of the voltages applied to the electrodes affects the amplification factor (page 117).

The amplification factor for triodes varies from about 3 for power-output tubes to about 40 for tubes designed for voltage amplification (page 126).

Control-Grid—Plate Transconductance.—This is also called **mutual conductance,** and is derived from the general term **transconductance.** Transconductance from one electrode to another is defined [1] as "the quotient of the in-phase component of the alternating current of the second electrode by the alternating voltage of the first electrode, all other electrode voltages being maintained constant." As most precisely used, the term refers to infinitesimal amplitudes, as indicated by the defining equation

$$g_{jk} = \left[\frac{\partial i_j}{\partial e_k} \right] e \text{ constant.} \qquad (5\text{–}2)$$

Control-grid—plate transconductance, or mutual conductance as it is popularly called, is "the name for the plate current to control-grid voltage transconductance." The mathematical relations applying are, from equation (5–2),

$$g_{pg} \equiv g_m = \frac{\partial i_p}{\partial e_g}, \qquad (5\text{–}3)$$

where the control-grid—plate transconductance is represented by g_{pg} and by definition equals the mutual conductance g_m. Since there is only one grid in a triode, the term grid-plate transconductance, or merely transconductance, may be used without confusion.

The transconductance can be found graphically from the plate current-grid voltage curves. Suppose the tube is being operated with − 4 volts grid bias, and with 120 volts on the plate, giving the operation at point P on Fig. 5–3. If a *small* triangle is constructed as shown, the base of this triangle will be Δe_g and the height Δi_p. Then, from equation (5–3), the transconductance will be $g_m = \Delta i_p/\Delta e_g = 0.0009/0.8$

= 0.001125 mho, or 1125 micromhos, a value which checks closely with the data given in Fig. 5–8.

It is apparent that the transconductance or mutual conductance is the slope of the plate current-grid voltage curve *at the point of operation.* If the point is at P' or P'', instead of at P, the slopes of the curve are different at these two points and hence the transconductance values will be different.

Plate Resistance.—This term is derived from **plate conductance,** which is defined [1] as "the quotient of the in-phase component of the electrode alternating current by the electrode alternating voltage, all other electrode voltages being maintained constant." As most precisely used, the term refers to infinitesimal amplitudes, as indicated by the defining equation

$$g_{pp} = g_p = \frac{\partial i_p}{\partial e_p}. \tag{5–4}$$

Values of plate resistance are ordinarily used instead of plate conductance. Plate resistance is defined [1] as "the reciprocal of the plate conductance." Symbolically,

$$r_p = \frac{1}{g_p} = \frac{\partial e_p}{\partial i_p}. \tag{5–5}$$

Values of plate resistance can be determined graphically from the plate current-plate voltage curves of Fig. 5–2. Thus, suppose that the tube is being operated at point P with − 8 volts grid bias and 160 volts on the plate. If a small triangle is constructed as shown, then Δe_p will be 8 volts and Δi_p will be 0.0008 ampere. From equation 5–5 the plate resistance will be $r_p = 8/0.0008 = 10,000$ ohms, which agrees with the values of Fig. 5–10.

It is apparent that the value of the plate resistance is numerically equal to the reciprocal of the slope of the plate current-plate voltage curve *at the point of operation.* It is also apparent that if values are calculated at points P' or P'' they will differ from the value at point P.

Difference between Alternating and Direct Plate Resistance.—As will be explained in detail on page 123, under certain operating conditions both alternating and direct-current components flow in the plate circuit of a triode. If *no* alternating voltage is impressed on the tube, the direct plate-current component will be determined from point of operation P of Fig. 5–2. If an alternating voltage is impressed on the grid of the tube, then the plate current will vary above and below that value determined by point P, and an alternating plate-current component will exist.

The plate resistance r_p defined above is the *opposition* offered by the plate circuit to the flow of the *alternating-current component*. It is often called the **alternating-current plate resistance** or **a-c plate resistance**. The term "opposition" implies an impedance, and it is sometimes referred to as **plate impedance**. In most low-frequency work, it is sufficient to consider the opposition as a resistance, and this usage is largely accepted.

The opposition the tube offers at point P to the flow of the *direct-current component* can be determined from Fig. 5–2 from the triangle formed by the broken line from the origin to P. Thus the direct plate resistance is $R_p = 160/0.0061 = 26{,}300$ ohms, a value over 2.6 times the alternating plate resistance r_p calculated in the preceding section. As previously mentioned the alternating value, r_p, is the more useful term and *is the value listed in giving tube data.* When the term *plate* resistance is used, it almost universally means the *alternating-current* plate resistance represented by r_p.

Relation among the Coefficients.—The values of μ, g_m, and r_p are properly referred to [1] as **coefficients**. They are not constants, in the strict sense, because these values vary with the operating conditions. For a given set of conditions, however, a useful relation exists among these coefficients.

Thus, if equations (5–3) and (5–5) are multiplied together, the result is

$$g_m \cdot r_p = \frac{\partial i_p}{\partial e_g} \cdot \frac{\partial e_p}{\partial i_p} = \frac{\partial e_p}{\partial e_g} = \mu,$$

according to equation 5–1. The relations

$$\mu = g_m r_p, \qquad g_m = \frac{\mu}{r_p}, \qquad \text{and} \qquad r_p = \frac{\mu}{g_m} \qquad (5\text{–}6)$$

are often useful. Thus, from the data calculated in the preceding pages, $\mu = 10{,}000 \times 0.001125 = 11.25$, a value closely in agreement with the value of μ as determined on page 112.

37. Dynamic Measurements of Coefficients.—The graphical means previously outlined for determining triode coefficients from static curves are termed **static methods**. These are very useful for instructional work and for approximate calculations, but are not so accurate or so well suited to production testing as are the **direct measurements** by **dynamic methods** in which alternating-current bridge circuits are used.

In making these measurements by the methods to be explained, it is important that certain precautions, briefly summarized from

Reference 1, be observed. The value of the alternating voltage should be sufficiently small that the results are unaffected by a reduction of the impressed voltage. Care should be taken in arranging the bridge circuit that stray capacitive and inductive couplings do not cause errors or make balancing of the bridge difficult. Grounding and shielding of the circuits may be required. It is usually necessary to make allowances for direct-current voltage drops in the bridge network so that the correct direct voltage values are impressed on the electrodes of the tube.

A frequency of 1000 cycles per second is very satisfactory for these measurements. This frequency can be readily detected and the bridge balanced with a simple telephone receiver. It is sufficiently low so that stray couplings usually give little trouble. Furthermore, since the coefficients are unaffected by the value of the testing frequency, at least up to several million cycles per second, the coefficients determined at 1000 cycles are satisfactory for all but very high-frequency radio work.

Measurements of Amplification Factor.—One of the simplest circuits for measuring the amplification factor of a triode is shown in Fig. 5–5. As stated in these standards, the capacitance of the variable condenser C (which is not always necessary) balances the capacitances of the tube, and its value must be changed as R_2 is varied to obtain minimum tone in the receiver and balance of the bridge. When balance is obtained,

$$\mu = \frac{R_2}{R_1}. \tag{5-7}$$

In using this bridge, the plate current flows through R_2 and through the low-resistance choke coil shunting the receivers. Thus the direct voltage actually impressed *on the plate* of the tube is less by the IR drops in these elements. This can be compensated for by placing a low-resistance direct-current milliammeter in the plate circuit; measuring the current flowing and calculating the voltage drop; and then increasing the voltage applied until the voltage impressed on the plate is the correct value. If measurements are desired only at the normal operating value, the proper plate current (with all other values normal) indicates the correct voltage on the plate. Or, with curves such as Fig. 5–2 or 5–3 available, the current can be adjusted to the correct value assuring that the proper voltage is impressed *on the plate*. A transformer with a low-resistance primary may be used instead of the coil. A low-impedance unity-ratio transformer is very satisfactory for isolating the alternating-current source.

With a circuit such as Fig. 5–5, measurements of the amplification factor can be made at various grid and plate voltage values. By this means a complete set of curves such as Fig. 5–6 can be obtained. These and the curves of Fig. 5–11 show that the amplification factor of a conventional triode varies somewhat with operating conditions.

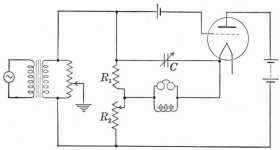

FIG. 5–5.   Circuit for measuring the amplification factor of a triode.

Measurements of Transconductance.—A circuit for the direct measurement of the grid-plate transconductance (mutual conductance) of a triode is shown in Fig. 5–7. When balance has been obtained by varying R_1, R_2, and M, then

$$g_{pg} = g_m = \frac{1}{R_2}. \tag{5–8}$$

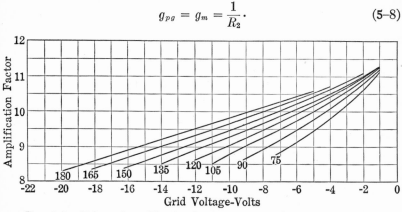

FIG. 5–6.   Values of amplification factor at various plate and grid voltages for the triode of Figs. 5–2 and 5–3.   Plate-voltage values shown on curves. (Adapted from vacuum-tube catalogue of Western Electric Co.)

If the direct-current resistances of the choke coil and of the coil M are low, no correction for the plate voltage is needed. It is well to place a low-resistance milliammeter in the plate circuit to be certain the tube is being operated correctly. If this is done, corrections for the voltage drops can be computed and applied. As in the previous circuit, a low-impedance unity-ratio transformer is very satisfactory for isolating the alternating-current source.

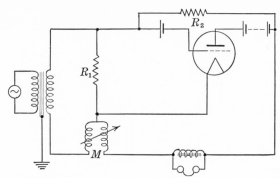

FIG. 5–7.   Circuit for measuring grid-plate transconductance or mutual conductance.

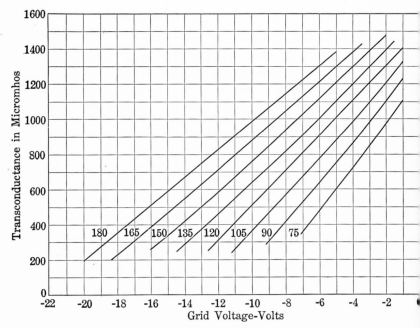

FIG. 5–8.   Values of grid-plate transconductance or mutual conductance at various plate and grid voltages for the triode of Figs. 5–2 and 5–3.   Plate voltages in volts shown on curves. (Adapted from vacuum-tube catalogue of Western Electric Co.)

The circuit of Fig. 5–7 is recommended for tubes having a low plate resistance such as is true for most triodes, and all power output triodes in particular.   This circuit requires a variable mutual inductance and this may not be available. Detailed information on tube measurements will be found in Reference 3.

Variations in transconductance with operating voltages for a typical triode are shown in Fig. **5–8**, and variations with plate current

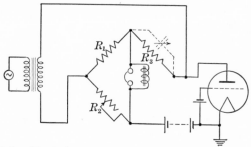

FIG. 5–9.   Circuit for measuring the plate resistance of a triode.

in Fig. **5–11**.   As is evident, the transconductance of the conventional triode varies widely with operating conditions.   The curves of Fig. **5–8** are known as **transfer characteristics,** defined as "a relation, usually shown by a graph, between the voltage of one electrode and the current to another electrode."

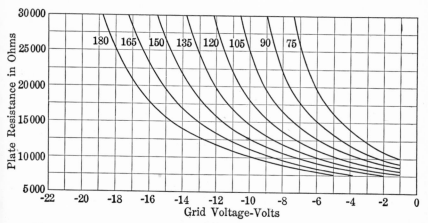

FIG. 5–10.   Values of the a–c plate resistance at various plate and grid voltages for the triode of Figs. 5–2 and 5–3.   Plate voltages in volts shown on curves. (Adapted from vacuum-tube catalogue of Western Electric Co.)

Measurements of Plate Resistance.—The *alternating-current* plate resistance r_p of the conventional triode can be measured by the simple bridge circuit of Fig. 5–9.   The variable condenser across R_3 balances the capacitance of the tube and may be necessary, but usually is not.

For the condition of balance,

$$r_p = \frac{R_2 R_3}{R_1}.$$ (5–9)

In making these measurements it is well to have a milliammeter in the plate circuit to measure the plate current and insure that the tube is being operated with the correct voltage *on the plate*. A transformer with a primary of low resistance may be used instead of the low-resistance choke coil across the receivers. As in the other circuits a low-impedance, unity-ratio transformer works well in the input circuit. With these precautions, very little plate current voltage drop occurs. Other circuits are included in References 1 and 3.

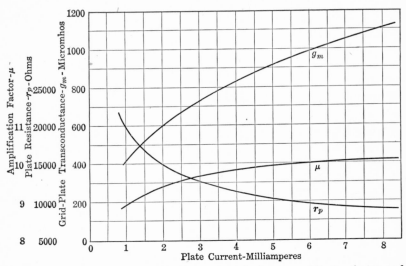

Fig. 5–11. Variations in grid-plate transconductance, amplification factor, and a–c plate resistance with plate current. Grid voltage held constant at − 8 volts, plate voltage varied.

Variations in the plate resistance with operating voltages for a typical triode are shown in Fig. 5–10, and variations with plate current in Fig. 5–11. As is evident, these values also vary widely with operating conditions.

38. Design of Triodes.—It is not the purpose of this section to go into this in detail and include actual design information, but it is advisable to consider this subject briefly. It should be recognized that in design work of this nature empirical equations based on experimental data are largely used.

Amplification Factor.—This may be calculated for certain types of triodes by equations due to King,[4] Miller,[5] and to Vogdes and Elder.[6]

Certain of these equations will be found in References **7** and **8**, and comprehensive treatment of the subject in Reference **9**.

The amplification factor is in reality the ratio of the *effectiveness* of the grid and plate voltages in producing electric fields near the surface of the cathode where the space charge is concentrated. It is the *resultant electric field* acting on the space charge which determines the plate current. This factor depends primarily on the type of grid structure, and will be increased by any modification causing the grid to *shield the cathode* more effectively from the effect of the *plate voltage*. Thus, for a given type tube, larger grid wires, closer spacing, or greater distance between grid and plate, all *increase* the amplification factor,[10] because all these reduce the effectiveness of the plate.

Plate Resistance.—This value can also be calculated for certain structures from an empirical equation listed in Reference 7, and by methods discussed in Reference 9.

The plate resistance becomes *less* if the area of the plate is increased. It is also made *less* by *increasing* the area of the cathode. *Decreasing* the distance between the anode and cathode also *decreases* the plate resistance, but this may not be advisable since it also lowers the amplification factor. Of course, the grid could be moved nearer the cathode to compensate for such a change in plate-cathode spacing, but because of the heating of the grid by the cathode, there is a practical limit to this.

Transconductance.—Since from equation (5–6), page 115, the transconductance or mutual conductance $g_m = \mu/r_p$, this factor need not be calculated, but can be found from the other coefficients. It will, of course, vary as either μ or r_p is changed.

39. Plate Current in a Triode.—As was shown on page 80 of the preceding chapter the plate current in a *diode* varies (over the central portion of the curve where the plate current is controlled by the space charge) according to a theoretical three-halves power law. In a *triode*, the plate current over the central portion of the curves of Fig. 5–2 is also determined by space charge; but, instead of being controlled (as in a diode) only by the plate voltage, the grid voltage must be considered as well. If the negative space charge is increased or decreased by the *fields* from the plate and grid, corresponding *decreases* or *increases* of the plate current will occur.

In a triode the electric field acting on the negative space charge close to the cathode consists of two parts: *first,* the field due to the grid; and *second,* the "stray" field due to the plate which is able to *reach through* the meshes of the grid to the space-charge region.[11] It is apparent that the more effective this shielding, the less will be the influence of the plate with respect to the grid, and the higher will be the amplification factor.

The resultant electric field in the space-charge region near the cathode is the *algebraic sum* of the field produced by the grid-bias voltage E_g and the "stray" field due to the *effective* plate voltage E_p/μ. Hence, the total field is proportional to $(E_g + E_p/\mu)$. This is sometimes called [8, 12] the **equivalent grid voltage.** Or, the total field at the cathode would be proportional to $(E_p + \mu E_g)$, called the **equivalent plate voltage.** Hence, the plate current is given by the theoretical three-halves power equations

$$I_p = K' \left(E_g + \frac{E_p}{\mu} \right)^{3/2}, \qquad (5\text{--}10)$$

or by
$$I_p = K(\mu E_g + E_p)^{3/2}. \qquad (5\text{--}11)$$

The values of K' and K are different and are determined by the geometrical construction of the tube.   It is apparent that in so far as the plate current is concerned, an *equivalent diode* can be designed for any triode.   For a complete discussion of this subject based on the original work of Van der Bijl, and for additional information on equations (5–10) and (5–11), Reference 3 should be consulted.

As in the case of the diode (page 81), various factors may cause the plate current to deviate from the three-halves power law.   That is, the exponent may be other than 3/2 or 1.5.   This exponent usually lies between the theoretical 1.5 and about 2.5, depending on the tube. Since the value 2.0 is somewhat of an average value, the mutual characteristic is sometimes said to follow a square law.   For additional information, and for methods of determining the value of this exponent for a particular tube by plotting the plate current values on logarithmic cross-section paper, consult Reference 12.

Variations in Plate Current.—With no alternating voltage impressed on the grid of a triode, a constant value of plate current flows. When an alternating voltage, such as the speech signals employed in voice-frequency communication, is impressed on the grid of a tube, the plate current is caused to vary in accordance with these signals. If the impressed alternating voltage follows a pure sine wave, the plate-current variations in a properly adjusted amplifier will also have a sinusoidal wave form.   These conditions are represented by Fig. 5–12.

The **quiescent value** [1] of the plate current is represented by I_p and is the direct current determined by equation (5–10) or (5–11).

For Fig. 5–12, I_p also represents the average value of the total current after an alternating voltage is impressed.   The **maximum value** of the *alternating current* component is I_m.   The **effective value** of the alternating current is $0.707 I_m$, and the **average value** is $0.637 I_m$.   The **instantaneous value** of the alternating current flowing is i_p.

Elaborate systems [1] of letter symbols have been developed for designating the plate currents, grid currents, and other quantities in vacuum tubes.   After careful consideration it seems unwise to follow these systems *in detail* as confusion may result.   In the following pages, therefore, the letter symbols used will be as simple and as descriptive as possible, and will follow closely the usages in the general field of electrical engineering.

Fig. 5–12.   Illustrating the current flow in the plate circuit of a tube before and after an alternating signal voltage is impressed on the grid.   The tube is being operated as a class *A* amplifier (page 209).

40. Grid Current in a Triode.—*Grid Negative.*—In the preceding discussions, no mention was made of the grid currents which flow in a high-vacuum triode.   It may be thought that when the grid is negative, no current will flow since it will *repel* the negative electrons.   This is true, but a *negative* grid will attract *positive* ions, and there are, accordingly, several reasons why a current will flow.

First, there is always some residual gas and hence positive ions present; these flow to the negative grid.   *Second,* the hot cathode gives off a few positive ions (page 10), and these also flow to the negative grid.   This effect is usually negligible.   *Third,* there is some leakage between the grid and cathode, and this allows some current to flow.   With the grid negative, these currents are *very low* giving a high equivalent resistance.   Also, these currents vary widely for different tubes, and with the age of the tube.   The manner in which the grid current varies for a *negative* grid is shown in Fig. 5–13.   Since curves for different tubes of even the same type vary so widely, numerical values are not shown.

Thus if a circuit such as Fig. 5–1 is studied, it will be found that with the plate at E_p volts and the grid at zero volts, an *electron* current flows to the grid because of the initial velocity of the electrons.   As the grid is made negative, *positive ions* will be attracted to the grid and the *electrons* will be repelled.   At some grid voltage the number of positive ions and electrons will be equal and the net grid current will be zero as Fig. 5–13 indicates.   As the grid is made more negative, the grid current reverses and increases to a maximum value and then *decreases* very slowly.

This peculiar shape of the grid current-grid voltage curve may be explained as follows: With the grid only *slightly* negative the positive ions and electrons neutralize as explained in the preceding paragraph. As the grid is made *more negative,* more positive ions are attracted to it. This cannot continue for long, however, because a more negative grid means *less plate current flow,* and the plate current determines the amount of ionization of the residual gas.   This causes the grid current to decrease slowly after passing through the maximum value. *Increasing* the plate voltage to a new value E_p' *increases* ionization by

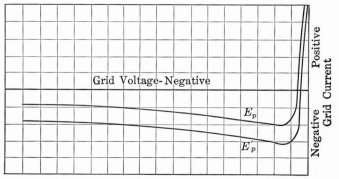

Fig. 5–13.   Approximate shapes of the grid-current curves for negative grid voltages.   Such currents are usually measured in microamperes.   The plate voltage E_p' exceeds E_p.

collision, thus providing more positive ions and a greater current flow as Fig. 5–13 indicates.   In actual operation as an amplifier, the grid is usually maintained negative (page 130).

Grid Positive.—The variations in the grid current for a *positive* grid (instead of negative as just considered) are shown in Fig. 5–14. The currents which flow to a positive grid are so *very much larger* than those flowing to a highly negative grid that Fig. 5–14 is plotted to a *much smaller scale* than is Fig. 5–13.

As the grid is made more positive, the current to it increases quite rapidly.   At some point, the electrons have velocities sufficient to produce secondary emission from the grid.   As the grid voltage is made more positive, these secondary electrons are released in large numbers and *are attracted to the plate.*   A study of Fig. 5–1 will show that this effect will cause the *net* grid current to decrease as in Fig. 5–14.

If the plate is made more positive to some potential E_p', the current flow to the grid will be less as indicated, because the more positive plate takes a greater percentage of the electrons withdrawn from the space charge region. Similarly, the secondary emission effects will be less pronounced.

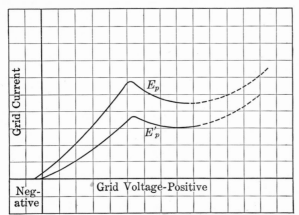

FIG. 5–14. Approximate shapes of the grid-current curves for positive grid voltages. These currents are usually measured in milliamperes. The plate voltage E_p' exceeds E_p.

Theoretically, as the grid is made more positive it should recapture the secondary electrons (page 44), and the grid current should again increase as shown by the dotted lines of Fig. 5–14. Actually, however, the tube might be ruined before this action was apparent. Care should be taken in operating a tube with a positive grid as it may be permanently damaged.

It is apparent that the resistance of the grid circuit varies from a very high value when the grid is negative to a low value of a few thousand ohms or less when it is positive.

41. Equivalent Circuit of a Triode.—For all practical purposes a triode may be considered as represented in Fig. 5–15. Although, as here applied, the discussion is for a linear or class A amplifier (page 209), it can be extended to cover other uses of the triode as well. The following discussion will be limited to the *alternating components*.

In operation, an alternating voltage E_g is impressed on the grid of the tube as indicated. From the discussion on page 111, this is equivalent to impressing a voltage of μE_g between the cathode and plate. This voltage acts in *series* with the plate resistance r_p and the load resistance R_L. The alternating current flowing in this simple series circuit is

$$I = \frac{\mu E_g}{(r_p + R_L)}, \tag{5–12}$$

and the voltage drop across the load resistor as indicated by the alternating-current voltmeter is

$$E_L = IR_L = \frac{\mu E_g R_L}{(r_p + R_L)}. \qquad (5\text{–}13)$$

This alternating voltage drop will vary as the impressed grid voltage E_g and with correct adjustments will be almost an exact replica of it. The weak alternating voltage impressed on the grid has been amplified, and the voltage E_L may be impressed on the grid of a second tube and further amplified if desired.

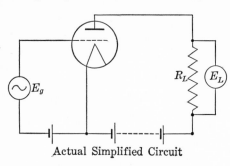

Actual Simplified Circuit

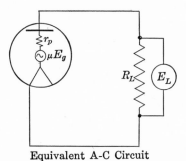

Equivalent A-C Circuit

FIG. 5–15. Actual and equivalent a-c circuit for a triode operating as a class A or linear amplifier.

If the **voltage amplification factor** A_v for the circuit of Fig. 5–15 is the ratio of the output alternating voltage to the input alternating voltage, then,

$$A_v = \frac{E_L}{E_g} = \frac{\mu E_g R_L}{E_g(r_p + R_L)}$$

$$= \frac{\mu R_L}{(r_p + R_L)}. \qquad (5\text{–}14)$$

Furthermore, the power output of the tube is

$$P = I^2 R_L = \frac{\mu^2 E_g^2 R_L}{(r_p + R_L)^2}. \qquad (5\text{–}15)$$

If it is desired, the resistor R_L can be replaced by an impedance Z_L and the equations generalized. Those desiring a mathematical proof for equation (5–12) should consult Reference 8.

42. Triode with Load.—The use of a triode as an amplifier was considered briefly in the preceding section. As was shown, a small alternating signal voltage produced a similar amplified voltage across the load resistor R_L as indicated by the reading of the alternating-current voltmeter E_L. It is apparent that a load must be connected in the output (or plate) circuit of a triode during normal operation so that the amplified voltage is available for impressing on the grid of the following tube, or for operating a loud speaker or other device (which may, itself, be the load).

The *static curves* of Fig. 5–3 were taken *without* a resistor or other load in the plate circuit. But, such a load affects the operation of a triode, and must be considered. Curves taken (or calculated) with a load resistance (or impedance) *in the plate circuit* are known as **dynamic characteristic curves.**

Dynamic characteristic curves can be obtained by slightly modifying the circuit of Fig. 5–1. With the apparatus *as shown*, there is zero resistance in the plate circuit, and the curves of Fig. 5–2 are static curves. For obtaining the *dynamic* curves, a resistor of several thousand ohms should be connected in the plate circuit. The voltage E_p should then be *increased* until the plate current at some grid bias (say − 6 volts) is the same as with *no* resistance in the plate circuit. The voltage *on the plate* (E_p') is now the same as with no resistance present. After this adjustment has been made, and with the supply voltage E_p *held constant*, the values of plate current I_p for various grid-bias voltages E_c will give the dynamic characteristic curves of Fig. 5–16.

When an impedance load instead of a pure resistance is used in the plate circuit, the simple method just outlined will not be satisfactory. The cathode-ray oscilloscope provides a very satisfactory means of obtaining the dynamic characteristic for such loads.[13]

For *calculating* the dynamic characteristic curves, the following method[2] is used. Assume that the tube having the static characteristics of Figs. 5–2 and 5–3 is being used and that the load resistance is 20,000 ohms. With no resistor in the plate circuit, the voltage E_p of Fig. 5–1 is impressed *on the plate*. With a resistor R_L in series, the voltage *on the plate* is

$$E_p' = E_p - I_p R_L, \tag{5–16}$$

since there is a drop in direct voltage across the load resistor (as well as the alternating drop previously considered).

Further assume that E_p is so increased that the voltage *on the plate* E_p' is 135 volts, that the grid bias is − 6 volts as indicated at the point P on Fig. 5–16, and that the value of E_p is then held constant. The plate current for this adjustment is 5.5 milliamperes. When the grid voltage is increased toward zero volts, the plate current will increase, but not along the 135-volt *static* curve because as the current tends to increase the voltage E_p' *on the plate* decreases according to equation (5–16).

Referring to Fig. 5–16, the dynamic curve for a 10,000-ohm load is found as follows: The dynamic curve will cross the 120-volt plate curve at a current value of 5.5 + [(135 − 120)/10,000] or 7.0 milliamperes.

Similarly, the corresponding point can be found for the 105-volt curve. Thus, the curve from P to P_1 is found.

If the grid voltage is now decreased, the current will decrease, but *not* along the 135-volt static curve. When the grid voltage decreases, the current tends to decrease, but this reduces the $I_p R_L$ drop, and since E_p is held constant, the actual voltage E_p' on the plate *rises*. The position of the curve $P - P_2$ is found as follows: The dynamic

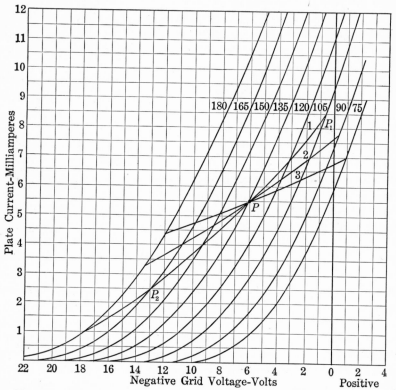

FIG. 5–16.　Static and dynamic curves for the triode of Figs. 5–2 and 5–3. Curves 1, 2, and 3 are for resistance loads in the plate circuit of 10,000, 20,000, and 40,000 ohms respectively.　Plate voltage in volts shown on curves.

curve will cross the 150-volt static curve at a current value of $5.5 - [(150 - 135)/10,000]$ or 4.0 milliamperes.　Similarly, points can be found for the other curves.

The dynamic curves calculated as just explained may be plotted as *load lines* on the curves of Fig. 5–2 (see problem 11, page 140).

Types of Amplifiers.—Amplification is one of the simplest and most important functions of a vacuum tube.　These amplifiers may be of two types: *first*, voltage amplifiers, and *second*, power amplifiers. These will be discussed in detail in Chapter 8, page 206 and Chapter 9, page 248, but it is important to distinguish between them at this time. To do this, consider a voice-frequency class A amplifier (page 211) for a sound system which uses a crystal microphone.

The crystal microphone generates a feeble voltage corresponding to the sound waves which strike it. These signal-voltage variations must be *amplified* until they are sufficiently strong to *drive a power output tube*. The problem is, therefore, one of *voltage amplification* until the last stage, containing the power output tube, is reached. This distinction must be made if the usual functions of vacuum tubes are to be clearly understood.

Distortion.—It is not the purpose of this section to consider distortion in detail, as this will be done in Chapter 8, page 209. The manner in which distortion occurs in the linear or class A amplifier of the preceding pages will be discussed, but briefly.

From the explanations given, it is apparent that in this amplifier the applied plate voltage (not the voltage on the plate) is held substantially constant and that the grid bias is held at a fixed value. The alternating voltage impressed on the grid adds to the bias on one half of the cycle and subtracts from the bias during the other half causing the plate current to follow the *dynamic* curve of Fig. 5–16.

If the load resistance is zero, then the dynamic and static curves coincide. As the load resistance is increased, however, they draw farther apart. The larger the resistance, the *longer* and *straighter* will be the dynamic curve. Thus, with a large load resistor, a greater signal can be impressed on the grid before distortion occurs.

Distortion occurs because the dynamic curve $P_2 - P - P_1$ is not a straight line over its entire length. If the maximum value of the alternating signal voltage is small, then the **grid swing** (variations in grid potential) about the point P are small and the distortion is low. Increasing the grid swing so that the tube operates on the curved part of the dynamic characteristic curve increases the distortion.

This distortion is further illustrated by Fig. 5–17. The alternating signal voltage impressed on the grid for amplification is represented by the pure sine wave of curve A. The grid is properly biased so that operation is on the "straight" portion of the characteristic. The output curve B is not a pure sine wave because the dynamic characteristic curve is not a straight line. The deviation from a sine wave and hence the amount of distortion is seen to depend on the magnitude of the alternating signal voltage or grid swing. As will be shown on page 251, this is largely a second harmonic distortion.

In most of the preceding discussions it was brought out that the grid is maintained negative for most operating conditions. There are many reasons for this, among which are the following: If the grid is permitted to swing positive, considerable grid current flows, and *power*

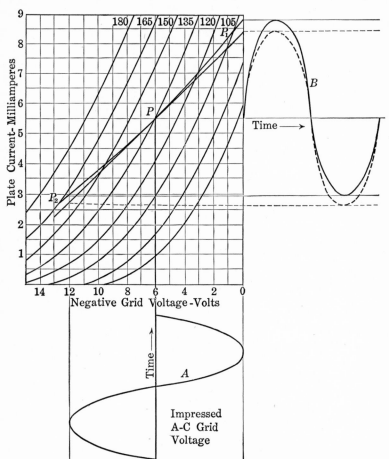

FIG. 5–17.   Showing how the curvature of the dynamic curve P_2, P, P_1 of Fig. 5–16 distorts the output signal wave, causing a large second harmonic. If the dynamic curve were straight, the output signal would follow the dotted curve resulting in negligible distortion.

is drawn from the source.   This is usually undesired, because if the source (such as an antenna or microphone) has not sufficient power-handling capacity and cannot supply this power at a fixed voltage, the voltage impressed on the grid drops and distortion of the signal results because the signal wave shape is changed.

Maximum Power Transfer.—It is advisable briefly to discuss at this time the transfer of power from a source to a load, because this is so important in vacuum-tube circuit design.   Thus in Fig. 5–18 is shown a generator, developing a *constant* open-circuit voltage E and having an *internal* resistance R_G, delivering power to a load resistor R_L.   The current flowing through the circuit is $I = E/(R_G + R_L)$, and the power delivered to the load is

$$P = I^2 R_L = \frac{E^2 R_L}{(R_G + R_L)^2}. \qquad (5\text{–}17)$$

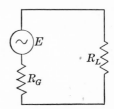

Fig. 5–18. The maximum power flows from a generator to a load when the resistance of the load equals the internal resistance of the generator.

Now let the effect of choosing different values of R_L be studied.   If $R_L = 0$, then the current will rise to a high value limited only by the internal resistance of the generator R_G, but since R_L is zero, no power will be delivered.   Now let R_L be very large, approaching an infinite value.   The current and the power delivered now approach zero.   At some value between these two limits **maximum power transfer** from the generator to the load occurs.

The point at which maximum power is transferred can be found [13] by differentiating equation (5–17) and equating the result to zero. It can also be obtained [14] by assuming values of R_L with respect to R_G (for example $R_L = 0.5R_G$, $R_L = 1.0R_G$, and $R_L = 1.5R_G$) and substituting these values in equation (5–17).   It will be found that the maximum power is transferred from a source to a load *when the resistance of the load equals the internal resistance of the source.*   This applies to alternating as well as direct power.

The efficiency of transfer is equal to the power delivered divided by the total power generated.   Thus, the efficiency equals

$$\text{Efficiency} = \frac{I^2 R_L}{(I^2 R_G + I^2 R_L)} = \frac{R_L}{(R_G + R_L)}. \qquad (5\text{–}18)$$

Thus, for the condition of maximum power transfer, when $R_G = R_L$, the efficiency becomes $R_L/2R_L = 0.5$ or *50 per cent.*

These relations are plotted in Fig. 5–19, and these principles should be carefully studied since they are the basis of much communication design.   Communication networks are not constant potential circuits as are power circuits.   Furthermore, in most communication work *maximum power output* rather than maximum efficiency is usually desired.   It should be noted, however, that the curve for power transfer is *quite flat*, indicating that from the standpoint of *power transfer alone*, rather wide deviations from the theoretical relation $R_G = R_L$ can be tolerated.   Such **mismatches** cannot be tolerated in some work; for example, in terminating long distance telephone lines, where the reflected energy would cause serious echo effects.[13, 14]

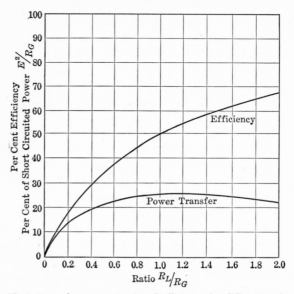

FIG. 5–19.   Variations of power output and efficiency for different values of R_L/R_G.

The relations were derived for maximum power transfer between circuits of pure resistance, but can be extended to cover impedances as well.   Thus, it easily can be proved that the maximum power will be delivered from one circuit to another when the circuits have *equal* resistances, but equal and opposite reactances (that is, **conjugate impedances**).[15]

Further, it can be shown [13] that when the *magnitude* of the load impedance, but not the angle, can be varied, the maximum power will be taken by the load when the *magnitude* of the load impedance equals the magnitude of the impedance of the source.   Transformers can be used for changing impedances,[14] and in this manner transformers are useful in **matching** loads to generators for maximum power output.   This will be considered further on page 226.

The application of these relations to the triode is as follows: As previously shown, the triode may be considered as a generator having a voltage of μE_g and an internal resistance of r_p.   It will, therefore, deliver *maximum power* when connected to a load having a resistance equal to the plate resistance r_p.   It has been found, however, that *maximum undistorted power* (without overloading the tube) is delivered when the relations are such that R_L equals approximately $2r_p$ for the triode (page 251).

43. Three-Electrode Gas Tubes.—High-vacuum tubes have been discussed in the preceding part of this chapter; gas-filled (or mercury vapor) three-electrode tubes will now be considered. These are often called by the trade names **Grid-Glow tubes** and **Thyratron tubes.** (See the footnote on page 75.)

In the high-vacuum tube, all traces of gas are removed to the extent that any remaining residual gas has no appreciable effect on the operation of the tube. In the high-vacuum triode, electrons are emitted by the hot cathode, and form a negative space charge about the cathode. Some of these electrons are drawn through the grid and over to the positive anode or plate, and the *plate current flow can be controlled by the grid potential.*

In the gas-filled (or mercury vapor) three-electrode tube (of the hot-cathode type) electrons are also given off by a hot cathode. This cathode is often of the heat-shielded type discussed previously (page 70). With *no* positive anode voltage applied, these electrons form a negative space charge about the cathode. When a positive anode voltage is applied, some of these electrons *may* be drawn over to the anode, and if the voltage is sufficient, they will cause ionization by collision with the residual gas atoms and thus produce positive ions.

The word *may* was used, because if the third electrode or *grid* in a gas tube is sufficiently negative (or not sufficiently positive in one type tube), then the negative grid *prevents* the electrons from passing to the anode and thus prevents ionization by collision. If, however, the grid is made *less* negative or the plate is made *more* positive, an anode current will flow, and ionization by collision will result.

A large grid-controlled gas-filled rectifier tube (Thyratron) with metal envelope. Rating as follows: Filament, 80 amperes at 5 volts; peak anode current, 600 amperes; peak inverse anode voltage, 1500 volts. Mercury vapor type. (Courtesy General Electric Co.)

As in the gas diode (page 83), these positive ions travel to the cathode, and there neutralize the negative space charge. This reduction in opposing space charge makes it easier for the electrons to flow to the anode. This means that *large* currents can flow from the cathode to the anode, and that *the voltage drop is low,* being only about 15 volts for the mercury-vapor tube. A low internal voltage drop means an efficient tube, because the internal I^2R losses are low.

There is an important distinction between the three-electrode high-vacuum tube and the gas (or vapor) tube. In the high-vacuum tube the grid maintains control of the plate current *at all times*. In the

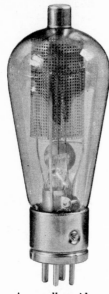

gas tube, the grid can control the instant at which current *starts* to flow from the cathode to the anode, but as soon as the current once starts, the *grid loses control* and (within operating limits) the *grid potential has no further effect* on the current to the anode.

Thus, in the high-vacuum tube, control by the grid makes possible the usual functions of amplification, oscillation, modulation, demodulation, and other uses. In the gas tube, the grid *loses* control and such functions *are not possible*, at least in the usual sense. Its greatest use is as a rectifier or as a controlling element such as a switch. The Grid-glow or Thyratron tube is often defined as a **grid-controlled rectifier.** It should be kept in mind, however, that the grid *loses control* as soon as current flows.

A small grid-controlled gas-filled rectifier tube (Thyratron) with glass envelope. Rating as follows: Filament, 5 amperes at 2.5 volts; peak anode current, 2 amperes; peak inverse anode voltage, 2500 volts. Mercury vapor type. (Courtesy General Electric Co.)

The reason the grid loses control when a current flows is as follows: After ionization the negatively charged grid is in a plasma or region of approximately equal numbers of positive and negative ions (page 16). The negative grid attracts to itself slowly-moving, massive, positive ions and repels the highly mobile negative electrons. By this action, the electrons are largely removed from the vicinity of the grid. A *positive-ion sheath* is therefore formed around this negative grid. The positive electric field from this sheath neutralizes the negative field of the grid, thus preventing the grid from further influencing the operation of the tube.[11, 16, 17]

The grid continues to be ineffective until the tube deionizes when the anode current ceases to flow; this can be caused either by opening the anode-circuit switch, or by reducing the anode voltage to a low value, when the positive and negative ions recombine and the tube is deionized. After this has occurred, the grid is again able to determine the value of the anode voltage at which the tube breaks down and conducts.

44. Types of Grid-Controlled Gas Tubes.—There are, commercially, two types of *grid-controlled* gas tubes.[16] These are *first*, the cold-cathode type, and *second*, the hot-cathode or thermionic type.

A third possible classification, as being a controlled rectifier tube, is the **Ignitron,** discussed on page 101. In this tube the electron emission is obtained from the cathode spot in a mercury-pool cathode. The starting of conduction is controlled by an "igniting" electrode, but not by the electric field from a grid, and thus the Ignitron was assumed to operate more like a diode, and was considered in the preceding chapter.

Cold-Cathode Tubes.—In this tube *initial* electron current is provided by the small amount of natural ionization (page 13) present in any gas. When the anode voltage is applied, the electrons produce ionization by collision, thus providing positive ions. These liberate electrons by positive ion bombardment of the cold cathode (page 43), thus providing the electrons for maintaining the discharge within the tube. A higher voltage drop and hence a larger power loss than in hot-cathode tubes is present. This limits the cold-cathode tube to low-power circuits.

The arrangement of the electrodes in a cold-cathode, grid-controlled gas tube is shown in Fig. 5–20. This tube actually contains a fourth electrode in the form of a shield about the anode. Since this shield is merely to secure a more definite tube failure at the end of its life, and to provide a greater uniformity

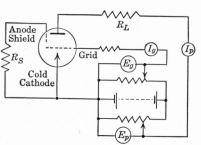

FIG. 5–20. Circuit for studying the characteristics of a cold-cathode grid-controlled gas tube. Actually, the anode shield screens the anode quite effectively.

and stability in its characteristic,[16] the device functions essentially as a three-electrode tube. This shield is at all times connected to the cathode through a resistor of *at least* 2 megohms, and higher values (up to 10 megohms) are usually desirable.[16]

The direct-current characteristics of a cold-cathode grid-controlled gas tube can be found using the simple circuit of Fig. 5–20. The resistor R_L is a load or protective resistor of about 10,000 ohms, R_g is a grid protective resistor of about 5 megohms, and R_s is a resistor in the shield electrode of 2 to 10 megohms. If the anode voltage is set on various positive values, the grid voltage varied, and the point of conduction observed by a deflection of the milliammeter in the anode circuit, a characteristic curve such as Fig. 5–21 is obtained.

It will be noted that the grid must be positive to permit ionization and hence conduction in this particular tube. If the grid were negative, the electrons could not pass through it and attain sufficient velocity to produce ionization by collision. Each time readings are taken it will be necessary to open the anode circuit to permit deionization.

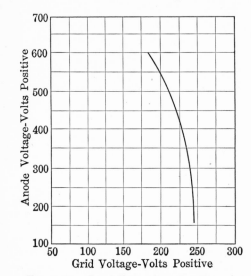

FIG. 5–21. Breakdown characteristics of a cold-cathode grid-controlled gas tube, taken with a grid resistor of 5 megohms. (From Reference 16.)

Hot-Cathode Tubes. — These are of two types, the **negative-grid** type, and the **positive-grid** type.[16, 17] The first of these was discussed on page 133. In this tube the conduction to the anode starts with a (comparatively) low value of *negative* grid potential. In the positive-grid type, the potential of the grid must be *positive* before discharge starts.

These differences are obtained largely by electrode construction. In the negative-grid tube the shielding of the cathode by the grid is not complete, and the positive electric field from the anode is able to *reach through* the grid and draw electrons from the cathode region against the negative potential of the grid. In the positive-grid type, the cathode is completely shielded by the grid from the effects of the anode voltage. The positive anode potential is unable, therefore, to influence, to any appreciable extent, the electrons emitted from the cathode and hence the operation of the tube. A positive grid is necessary before the tube conducts.

These tubes may be filled with any of the inert gases, neon or argon often being used. Or, they may be filled with mercury vapor. The gas or vapor employed depends on the use for which the tube is designed. Mercury vapor is slow to deionize, and hence such tubes cannot be used in alternating-current circuits of more than several hundred cycles per second. The inert gases may, however, be used at higher frequencies. On the other hand, the mercury-vapor tubes can carry higher currents and are more efficient.   Since the vapor pressure of the mercury tubes depends on the operating temperature, and since the

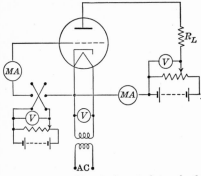

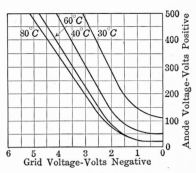

Fig. 5–22.   Circuit for studying both positive and negative grid-controlled hot-cathode gas tubes.   Mercury-vapor tubes should be immersed in a temperature-controlled oil bath.   The resistor R_L is to limit the maximum value of anode current.

Fig. 5–23.   Breakdown characteristics of a hot-cathode negative grid-controlled mercury-vapor rectifier. (From G. E. Review.)

operating characteristic depends to some extent on the vapor pressure, these tubes are less stable under certain conditions than the inert gas tubes.

Characteristics of Hot-Cathode Tubes.—These curves can be obtained by the circuit arrangement of Fig. 5–22.   The voltages at which ionization and conduction occur can be determined by the first deflection of

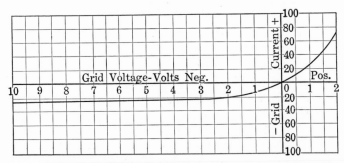

Fig. 5–24.   Grid current in milliamperes in the mercury-vapor tube of Fig. 5–23 after breakdown.   Positive values represent electron current to the grid.   Negative values represent positive ion current to the grid.   (Data from G. E. Review.)

the milliammeter in the anode circuit.   For the negative-grid tube the voltage on the grid should be negative, and for the positive-grid tube, it should be positive.

Curves for a negative-grid mercury-vapor tube are shown in Fig. 5–23. These curves show the positive anode voltage necessary (at the various temperatures) to cause the tube to conduct for different negative-grid voltages. The grid voltages are surprisingly small and the breakdown (or conducting) points quite definite. The relations between grid current and grid voltage after breakdown are shown in Fig. 5–24.

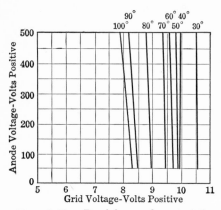

Fig. 5–25. Breakdown characteristics of a hot-cathode *positive* grid-controlled mercury-vapor tube. (Data from G. E. Review.)

Curves for a positive-grid mercury-vapor tube are shown in Fig. 5–25. As these curves indicate, the voltage on the anode has very little effect on the operation, the breakdown at the various temperatures being controlled almost entirely by the positive potential of the grid. As previously mentioned, this is because the grid almost com-

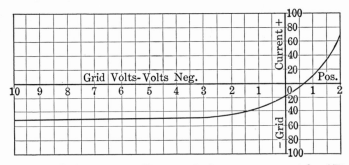

Fig. 5–26. Grid current in milliamperes in the mercury-vapor tube of Fig. 5–25 after breakdown. Positive values represent electron current to the grid. Negative values represent positive ion current to the grid. (Data from G. E. Review.)

pletely shields the cathode from the anode field. The relations between grid current and grid voltage after breakdown are shown in Fig. 5–26.

REFERENCES

1. Institute of Radio Engineers. *Reports of the Standards Committee.*
2. Pidgeon, H. A. *Simple theory of the three-electrode vacuum tube.* Journal of Society of Motion Picture Engineers, Feb., 1935, Vol. 24. Also Bell System Monograph B-852.

3. Chaffee, E. L. *Theory of Thermionic Vacuum Tubes.* McGraw-Hill Book Co.
4. King, R. W. *Calculation of the constants of the three-electrode vacuum tube.* Physical Review, April, 1920, Vol. 15, No. 4.
5. Miller, J. M. *The dependence of the amplification constant and the internal plate circuit resistance of three-electrode vacuum tubes upon the structural dimensions.* Proceedings of the Institute of Radio Engineers, Feb., 1920, Vol. 8.
6. Vogdes, F. B., and Elder, F. R. *Formulas for the amplification constant for three-electrode tubes in which the diameter of the grid wires is large compared to the spacing.* Physical Review, Dec., 1924, Vol. 24.
7. Henney, K. *The Radio Engineers' Handbook.* McGraw-Hill Book Co.
8. Glasgow, R. S. *Principles of Radio Engineering.* McGraw-Hill Book Co.
9. Kusunose, V. *Calculation of characteristics and the design of triodes.* Proceedings of the Institute of Radio Engineers, Oct., 1929, Vol. 17.
10. Terman, F. E. *Radio Engineering.* McGraw-Hill Book Co.
11. Koller, L. R. *Physics of Electron Tubes.* McGraw-Hill Book Co.
12. McIlwain, K., and Brainerd, J. G. *High-Frequency Alternating Currents.* John Wiley & Sons.
13. Everitt, W. L. *Communication Engineering.* McGraw-Hill Book Co.
14. Albert, A. L. *Electrical Communication.* John Wiley & Sons.
15. American Institute of Electrical Engineers. *Definitions of Electrical Terms.*
16. Westinghouse Electric and Manufacturing Co. *Industrial Electronic Tubes.* Course No. 25.
17. McArthur, E. D. *Electronics and Electron Tubes.* John Wiley and Sons. See also General Electric Review, March–Sept., Nov., Dec., 1933.

SUGGESTED ASSIGNMENTS

1. Enumerate the reasons triodes are operated below the voltage saturation region.
2. Derive equation (5–7).
3. Derive equation (5–8).
4. Derive equation (5–9).
5. Plot the characteristics of a triode and determine the equation for the plate current (refer to equations (5–10) and (5–11)) applying to this particular tube under given operating conditions.
6. A triode having an amplification factor $\mu = 3.5$ and a plate resistance $r_p = 2000$ ohms, is connected as a class A amplifier for maximum undistorted power output. If 30 volts effective value is impressed on the grid, calculate the amplified output voltage.
7. Calculate the power output for these conditions.
8. Calculate the power output for load resistances of 50 per cent, 75 per cent, 125 per cent, and 150 per cent of the value selected for maximum undistorted power output. What conclusions can be drawn from these figures?

9. A voltage of 0.5 volt effective value is impressed on the grid of a triode operated as a resistance-coupled voltage amplifier. The plate resistance $r_p = 11,000$ ohms, and the amplification factor $\mu = 9$. Calculate the output voltage available, and the voltage amplification.

10. Obtain the static characteristics of a triode and calculate dynamic curves for several load resistances.

11. Transfer the dynamic curves from Fig. 5–16 to Fig. 5–2 (from which the curves were omitted for clarity).

12. Referring to Fig. 5–15, draw vector diagrams for the currents and voltage in triode circuits when connected to (a) resistive loads, (b) inductive loads, and (c) capacitive loads. What special provisions must be made for part (c)?

CHAPTER 6

MULTI-ELECTRODE THERMIONIC VACUUM TUBES

The diodes and triodes discussed in the preceding chapters were used almost exclusively in the communication field for many years. In 1928, a four-electrode tube, the **screen-grid tube** or **tetrode**,[1] was introduced commercially, and about a year later a **five-electrode tube** or **pentode** [1] became available. These may be classified as **multi-electrode tubes** to distinguish them from the three-electrode tubes or triodes which preceded them.

The introduction of the screen-grid tube marked the beginning of a new era in the communication art. Until its appearance, the triode was the only tube used extensively for amplification. The screen-grid tube and the pentodes were closely followed by other special tubes, until today the communication engineer has available a vast array of thermionic devices, each serving best in certain capacities.

It will be recognized that it is inadvisable (and impossible) to discuss all these tubes individually. They are all based on certain fundamental electronic principles, and the important matter is thoroughly to understand these fundamentals. With this in mind, multi-electrode tubes may be divided into two classes.[2]

45. Classification of Multi-Electrode Tubes.—The *first* class includes tubes designed to perform some function *which cannot be performed* readily by a triode, or *which will perform some function better* than will a triode. The *second* class includes tubes having additional electrodes to permit them to *perform, simultaneously, more than one function,* or to permit them to *function in two or more ways.*

As an illustration of this classification, consider the screen-grid tube: It will more readily amplify radio-frequency voltages than will the triode because the screen grid shields the plate and prevents radio-frequency feedback. This tube, therefore, operates on a new basic principle, and belongs to the *first class.* Now consider the so-called duplex-diode high-mu triode (type 2A6). This tube contains two *diode* structures and a high-amplification *triode* structure in the same evacuated enclosure. Nothing new of a fundamental electronic nature is involved, so the tube belongs to the *second class.*

In other words, strictly speaking there are only a few basic electronic principles involved. Most of the new tubes are based on these few principles. Thus, it is only necessary to discuss the tubes of the first class—which introduce these new principles—and the operation of the tubes of the second class becomes apparent. This chapter will consider, therefore, only tubes of the first type. The treatment will follow very closely the excellent method [2] employed by Pidgeon.

In discussing multi-electrode tubes the introduction of new terms will be avoided whenever possible. The cathode will be treated as a single electrode although it may consist of a heater and an emitter as in the heater-type tube. The treatment will, in general, use the same terms as developed for the triode. The stress will be placed on the electronic principles rather than the applications. Since multi-electrode gas tubes are not in wide use, the chapter will be devoted largely to high-vacuum tubes.

46. Space Charge in Multi-Electrode Tubes.—In the three-electrode tube or triode discussed in the preceding chapter, it was shown that a cloud of electrons constituting a negative space charge existed (largely) in a thin sheath around the hot cathode. The current to the plate, and hence the performance of the tube, was seen to depend on the manner in which the electric fields from the positive plate and the (usually) negative grid acted upon this space charge.

In a multi-electrode high-vacuum tube, the negative space charge is also concentrated near the cathode. In explaining the operation of a multi-electrode tube, it is advisable to quote from the article [2] by Pidgeon.

"In multi-electrode tubes, as well as in triodes, the total space current drawn from the cathode is determined by the extent to which the resultant field, due to the electrodes, overcomes the opposing field produced by space charge. While space charge extends throughout the interelectrode space, it is relatively so much more dense in regions of very low electron velocity that, as a first approximation, its effect usually may be neglected in other regions. Except in space-charge-grid tubes and a few other special tubes, the only important space-charge region is confined to a relatively thin sheath near the cathode surface. Consequently, in such structures the total space current is determined largely by the extent to which the resultant positive field due to the electrodes neutralizes the negative field near the cathode surface produced by space charge. An appreciation of this fact is essential to a clear understanding of the characteristics of multi-electrode tubes."

Thus, it is seen that the theoretical considerations developed for the triode apply to multi-electrode tubes. It is only necessary to consider the influence of the additional electrodes in affecting the electron current to the plate.

47. Four-Electrode Tubes.—These tubes, called **tetrodes,** were studied [3] by Schottky as early as 1919. Two types of tetrodes have been developed. Each of these contains a cathode for emitting the electrons, *two* grids through which the electrons pass to reach the plate, and the positive anode or plate.

In the *first* type of tetrode, the grid *next to the cathode* is made positive with respect to the cathode, and the grid next to the plate is the control electrode. In the *second* type of tetrode the grid next to the cathode is the control grid, and the grid *next to the plate* is made *positive.* The first type is a **space-charge grid tetrode;** the second is the conventional **screen-grid tube** so widely used today.

Space-Charge Grid Tetrode.—This will be but briefly considered because it is relatively unimportant in this country although it was extensively used in Europe. An excellent summary of the performance of these tubes is included in Reference 3.

In this tube the electric field due to the positive grid next to the emitting cathode partially neutralizes the negative space charge.[3]

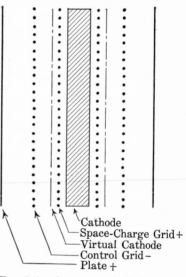

Cathode
Space-Charge Grid +
Virtual Cathode
Control Grid –
Plate +

Fig. 6–1. Arrangement of electrodes in a space-charge grid tetrode.

The effect of this is to produce a **virtual cathode** (page 165) or an apparent source of electrons (as far as the control grid and the plate are concerned), which is *outside* the positive or space-charge grid. The control grid and the plate then function much the same as in a three-electrode tube or triode.

The arrangement of the electrodes in a space-charge grid tetrode is shown in Fig. 6–1, and the operating characteristics in Fig. 6–2. This tube has a low amplification factor, a low plate resistance, and a high plate current. It is, therefore, essentially a power output tube (page 248). As is seen, the positive space-charge grid collects a large fraction of the total emitted current. This is one of the factors limiting the use of the tube.

The Screen-Grid Tetrode.—This is the second type of tube previously listed, and, as mentioned, is the conventional screen-grid tube so widely used. This tube is essentially a voltage-amplifier tube as distinguished from a power-output tube.   It was studied [4] extensively by Hull and Williams, and introduced commercially in this country about 1928.

The electrodes in a screen-grid tetrode are arranged as in Fig. 6–3. The tube is essentially a conventional triode with a fourth electrode, the positive screen grid, inserted between the plate and control grid (and also completely enclosing the plate) so that the plate is *electrically*

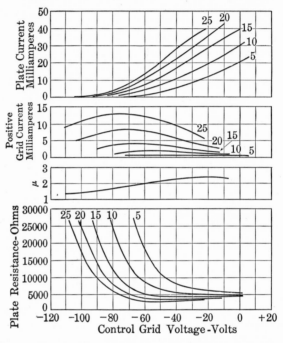

Fig. 6–2.   Characteristics of a space-charge grid tetrode.   Numbers on curves refer to positive voltage in volts impressed on space-charge grid.   (From Reference 3.)

shielded from the control grid.   This is of importance when amplifying radio-frequency signals because in triodes a signal voltage is fed back to the grid through the grid-plate capacitance, and thus oscillations may occur.   In the early days of triode amplification, special neutralizing circuits (page 238) were necessary to balance out this radio-frequency feedback.[5]   The development of the screen-grid tube with its effective shielding greatly simplified circuit design.

The shielding effect of the screen grid reduces feedback of radio-frequency signals as just discussed.   This grid is of a fine mesh, and therefore largely prevents the field due to the *direct* voltage applied to the plate from reaching into the cathode region.   As has been previously discussed (page 77), the negative space charge exists, effectively,

to close the cathode surface, and the *resultant* electric field in this region
controls the plate-current flow.   Thus, if the screen grid shields the
plate, then the electric field due to the voltage on the plate has little
influence on the current to the plate.

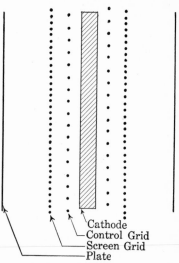

Hence, the presence of the screen
grid not only reduces feedback, but
also greatly affects the characteristics of the tube.   To overcome the
resulting reduction in plate current
the screen grid is usually held at a
positive direct voltage.   One effect
of this construction is to give it a
high amplification factor, apparent
from equation 5–1, page 111.

As will be discussed later (page
238), under usual operating conditions the potential of the electrodes
in a multi-electrode tube other than
that of the *control grid* and *plate* should
be maintained constant.   It will be
noted that this condition is specified
for the curves shown on the following
pages.   Thus, when a multi-electrode
tube, such as a screen-grid tube, is
amplifying alternating voltages, the

Cathode
Control Grid
Screen Grid
Plate

Fig. 6–3.   Arrangement of electrodes in a screen-grid tube.   The
screen grid is made of a very fine
wire mesh, and actually encloses the
entire plate, being placed on both
sides of it.

impedances to ground (for alternating currents) of these *auxiliary*
electrode circuits must be kept low, otherwise these electrodes would
vary in potential.[2]   To accomplish this, these electrodes are usually

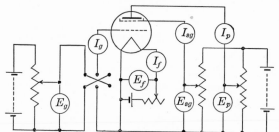

Fig. 6–4.   Circuit for determining the static characteristics of a screen-grid tetrode.

connected to ground through large condensers, thus effectively grounding them to the alternating components.

Static Characteristics of a Screen-Grid Tube.—These may be studied
with a circuit arranged as in Fig. 6–4.   For obtaining the curves of

Fig. **6–5**, the filament current and screen-grid voltage are held constant at the values indicated, and curves are taken at two different control-grid voltages. These curves show the way in which the plate and screen-grid current changes with plate-voltage variations.

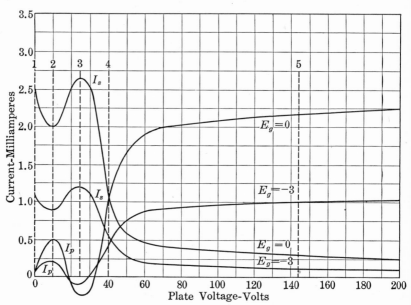

FIG. 6–5. Characteristics of a screen-grid tetrode. Filament current constant. Screen at + 45 volts. Control grid at voltages shown on curves. Plate voltage varied.

To explain these curves, assume the conditions of the preceding paragraph apply. Since the plate is so effectively shielded, the influence of its positive field in the space-charge region is negligible. Thus at all times the electron current *leaving* this region is determined largely by the voltages on the control and screen grids and *not* by the potential of the plate.

Thus, at point (1), where the plate voltage is *zero*, substantially the same total electron current flows from the cathode as when the plate is highly positive. At point (1), the positive screen grid collects the entire electron flow.

At point (2), the plate has been made slightly positive. Owing to the fact that the grid is a wire mesh, some of the rapidly-moving electrons pass through it, and many of these are pulled to the now positive plate. The resultant current to the screen grid therefore drops, so that the sum of the plate current and the screen-grid current equals (approximately) the current previously collected by the screen grid.

But, at point (2) a new phenomenon occurs.   Some of the electrons
attracted to the plate have reached sufficient velocity to cause *secondary
emission* (page 43) from the plate.   Now, the potential of the plate is
much lower than that of the screen grid, so many of these secondary

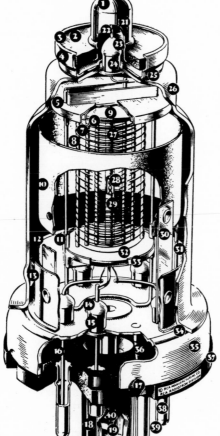

1 Solder	23 Glass Bead Seal
2 Cap Insulator	24 Eyelet
3 Rolled Lock	25 Brazed Weld
4 Cap Support	26 Vacuum-Tight Steel Shell
5 Grid Lead Shield	27 Cathode
6 Control Grid	28 Helical Heater
7 Screen	29 Cathode Coating
8 Suppressor	30 Plate Insulating Support
9 Insulating Spacer	31 Plate Lead Connection
10 Plate	32 Insulating Spacer
11 Mount Support	33 Spacer Shield
12 Support Collar	34 Shell-to-Header Seal Weld
13 Getter Tab	35 Header
14 Glass Bead Seal	36 Shell Connection
15 Eyelet	37 Octal Base
16 Lead Wire	38 Base Pin
17 Crimped Lock	39 Solder
18 Aligning Key	40 Exhaust Tube
19 Pinched Seal	
20 Aligning Plug	
21 Grid Cap	
22 Grid Lead Wire	

View of the construction details of a tube with a metal envelope.
(Courtesy RCA Manufacturing Co.)

electrons are pulled over to the grid.   If the number of secondary
electrons exceeds the primary electrons, the plate current may even
become negative as indicated.   Thus at point (3) there is a new source
of electrons due to secondary emission from the plate, in addition to
the electrons from the cathode space-charge region.   Thus, the screen-

grid current exceeds the (almost constant) value of electrons taken from the space-charge sheath.

As the plate voltage is increased beyond point (3), the plate potential approaches that of the screen grid. The plate is, accordingly, able to *recapture* the electrons released through secondary emission, and the plate current increases. Corresponding changes in the screen-grid current occur. When point (4) has been reached and the plate is highly positive, no further effect of secondary emission is observed (although it is taking place).

The screen-grid tube is usually operated (as an amplifier) over the portion of the curves marked (5). As is evident in this region the plate voltage has but little influence on the plate current. Also, the screen-grid current is very low and may be negative under certain conditions due to secondary emission *from the screen grid.*

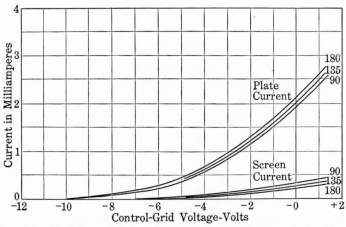

FIG. 6–6. Variations of plate and screen-grid current with control-grid voltage. Filament current constant. Screen grid at + 45 volts. Plate voltages shown on curves. (From vacuum-tube catalogue of Western Electric Co.)

Curves showing the effect of control-grid voltage on the plate and screen current are shown in Fig. 6–6. As is evident, the voltage on the control grid has a very *great* effect on the plate current. Thus, in the screen-grid tube the plate is so effectively shielded by the screen grid that the plate potential *does not* greatly affect the plate current, but the tube is so constructed that the control-grid voltage *does* affect the plate current, therefore the tube has a very high amplification factor.

For the screen-grid tetrode and similar voltage-amplifying tubes it is usually not necessary to plot dynamic curves as for triodes and power output tetrodes and pentodes.

Screen-Grid Tube Coefficients.—These coefficients can be determined approximately by graphical means from the curves of Figs. 6–5 and 6–6. The various coefficients developed in the preceding chapter for the triode apply, with but little change, to the screen-grid tetrode. Thus, the definition and the equation for amplification factor on page 111 apply without modification.

Referring to Fig. 6–5, if the plate voltage for the grid bias of − 3 volts is changed from 100 to 200 volts, the plate current only increases 0.07 milliampere. From Fig. 6–6, using the 135 volt curve, a change of grid bias from − 3 to − 2.8 volts produces a change in plate current of 0.07 milliampere. Thus, the amplification factor is approximately $(200 − 100)/(3 − 2.8) = 500$. Or, from Fig. 6–6, at a plate voltage of 180 volts and a grid bias of − 3 volts the plate current is the same as at a plate voltage of 90 volts and a grid bias of − 2.6 volts. The amplification factor is, from equation 5–1, page 111, $(180 − 135)/(3 − 2.6) = 225$. As is apparent, these graphical methods do not check, largely because of the errors involved in plotting curves and in obtaining data therefrom. The accepted methods of finding the coefficients will be discussed in the following pages.

The alternating-current plate resistance can be approximated from Fig. 6–5. Assuming the − 3 volt bias curve to be a straight line over the region from 140 to 160 volts, the corresponding current change is about 0.01 milliampere. This gives, from equation 5–5, page 114, a plate resistance of $20/0.00001 = 2,000,000$ ohms. As is apparent, plate resistance values taken in this manner will vary widely, and the measuring methods to be discussed are, therefore, recommended.

Grid-plate transconductance or mutual conductance values can be found from Fig. 6–6. Thus, on the 135-volt curve, at − 3 volts bias the plate current is 0.9 milliampere, and at − 2 volts it is 1.25 milliamperes. The mutual conductance is, therefore, $0.35/1 = 0.35$ mho or 350,000 micromhos, a value which is fairly accurate.

Coefficients by Dynamic Methods.—As explained in the preceding discussion, the graphic methods of obtaining the coefficients of a *screen-grid tube* are not entirely satisfactory, although if desired the curves can be plotted to a larger scale, thus giving more reliable values. Dynamic methods, similar to those outlined in the preceding chapter, are often used. In making these measurements, the precautions enumerated on page 115 should be observed.

For all vacuum tubes, the circuits and definitions of the coefficients given in the standards [1] are generalized. Those given in the preceding chapter were for the special case of triodes. The generalized circuits and definitions will now be introduced. It will be recognized that such

generalization is necessary for multi-electrode tubes.   In presenting
this material, the general terms will be introduced first, and the application to the screen-grid tube then considered.

   Measurements of Mu-Factor.—This is a general term from which
amplification factor is derived.   The mu-factor is defined [1] as "the ratio
of the change in one electrode voltage to the change in another electrode
voltage, under the conditions that a specified current remains unchanged and that all other electrode voltages are maintained constant.
It is a measure of the relative effect of the voltages on two electrodes
upon the current in the circuit of any specified electrode."   As most
precisely used, the term refers to infinitesimal changes as indicated by
the defining equation,

$$\mu_{jkl} = - \left[\frac{\partial e_j}{\partial e_k} \right] i_l \text{ constant.} \tag{6-1}$$

   A circuit for obtaining the mu-factor of *any* electrode is given in
Fig. 6–7, reproduced from Reference 1.   The electrode in which the

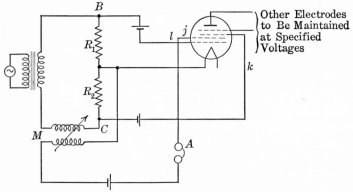

Fig. 6–7.   Generalized circuit for finding the mu-factor of any electrodes such as *jkl*.
(From Reference 1.)

current is to be held constant is connected to point A, and the other
two electrodes entering directly into the measurement are to be connected to points B and C.   When R_1, R_2, and M are adjusted for
minimum tone in the headphones,

$$\mu_{jkl} = \frac{R_2}{R_1}. \tag{6-2}$$

   The amplification factor is a special type of mu-factor measuring
the relative effectiveness of the plate and grid in a vacuum tube.   From
the definition given on page 111, it is apparent that this term applies
to a screen-grid tube as well as to a triode.

The circuit of Fig. 6–7 can be modified and applied to a screen-grid tube, or to a triode.[1] Or, the circuit of Fig. 5–5, page 117, can be used. If this latter circuit is employed, the tube is connected as shown with the screen grid (held at the correct potential by a series battery) connected directly to the cathode. Milliammeters may be used to ascertain if the tube is being operated correctly.

The variations in the amplification factor of the typical screen-grid tube of Figs. 6–5 and 6–6 are shown in Fig. 6–8. As is shown, the amplification factor is very high, largely because the screen so effectively shields the plate that the effect of plate-voltage change has but little influence on the plate current.

As indicated, the amplification factor of a typical screen-grid tube varies widely with operating voltages. It is also seen that the amplification factor *increases* with a more negative grid bias instead of decreasing as for the triode (Fig. 5–6, page 117).

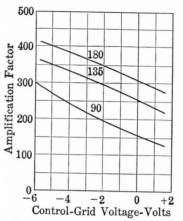

Fig. 6–8. Variations in the amplification factor for the screen-grid tetrode of Figs. 6–5 and 6–6. Plate voltages in volts on curves. Screen grid at + 45 volts. (Data from vacuum-tube catalogue of Western Electric Co.)

Measurements of Transconductance.—This coefficient was defined in the preceding chapter (page 113) in order to make clear the meaning of the special term, *mutual conductance*. As there stated, transconductance from one electrode to another "is the quotient of the in-phase component of the alternating *current* of the second electrode by the alternating *voltage* of the first electrode, all other electrode voltages being maintained constant."[1]

The circuit[1] of Fig. 6–9 can be used to find the transconductance for any of the electrodes in a multi-electrode vacuum tube. The values of R_2 and R_3 should be small so that their effects on the alternating currents in the electrode circuits will not be excessive.[1] Milliammeters in the electrode circuits will ascertain if the tube is being operated correctly, and will make possible adjustment of the direct voltages to compensate for drops in the resistors.

When balance has been obtained, the transconductance is given by the relation

$$g_{jk} = \frac{R_1}{(R_2 R_3)}.$$ (6–3)

The small condenser shown may be required to balance stray capacitance in the tube and apparatus.   The circuit of Fig. 5–7, page 118,

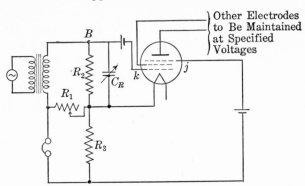

FIG. 6–9.   Circuit for finding the transconductance of any two electrodes such as jk.
(From Reference 1.)

may also be used, but as there mentioned, that particular circuit is best for power tubes having low values of plate resistance.

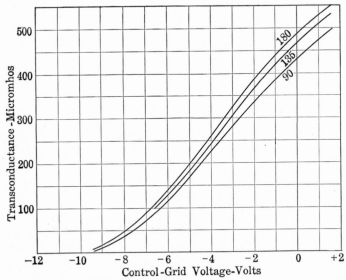

FIG. 6–10.   Variations in control grid-plate transconductance or mutual conductance for the screen-grid tetrode of Figs. 6–5 and 6–6.   Values on curves refer to plate voltages.   Screen grid at + 45 volts.   (Data from vacuum-tube catalogue of Western Electric Co.)

The manner in which values of the control grid-plate transconductance or mutual conductance vary with control-grid voltage is shown in Fig. 6–10. These agree closely in both magnitude of transconductance and in shape of the curves with those for the triode (Fig. 5–8, page 118).

This agreement is to be expected, because the grid voltage-plate current curves of the triode and screen-grid tube are similar (pages 110 and 148). This is because in both tubes the control grid is closest to the space-charge sheath, and thus the grid potential largely controls the plate current.

Measurements of Plate Resistance.—A circuit was given (Fig. 5–9, page 119) in the preceding chapter for finding the plate resistance of a triode. This circuit can be adapted to finding the plate resistance of a screen-grid tube. Such measurements are difficult, however, because the plate resistance is so high.

The circuit of Fig. 6–11 is recommended [1] for finding the plate-circuit resistance of multi-electrode tubes—such as screen-grid tubes—

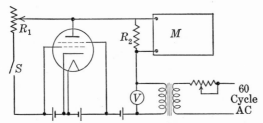

FIG. 6–11.   Circuit for measuring the plate-circuit resistance of multi-electrode tubes. (From Reference 1.)

which have high plate resistances. The operation of this circuit is as follows: [1] The tube is operated at normal voltages with switch S open. The value of R_2 is small compared with the plate resistance of the tube. The alternating voltage applied is adjusted until some convenient deflection is obtained on the high-impedance alternating voltmeter M. (This may be an amplifier and a vacuum-tube voltmeter.) The tube is then removed from the circuit, and the switch S closed. This action substitutes the rheostat R_1 for the plate resistance of the tube. The value of R_1 is varied until with the same applied alternating voltage the same deflection is obtained on the voltmeter. The value of R_1 is then the same as the plate resistance of the tube. The circuit can be made direct reading if desired.

As Fig. 6–12 indicates, the plate-resistance curves for a screen-grid tube are similar in form to those of the triode (page 119). The values are *very much higher*, however.

Plate resistance is (page 114) the reciprocal of plate conductance, and this is defined as the ratio of the in-phase component of the plate alternating current to the plate alternating voltage. Thus, if in a screen-grid tube the plate is so effectively shielded that changes in plate voltage do not appreciably influence the plate current, then from equation 5–5, page 114, the plate resistance will be very high, as is found for screen-grid tubes.

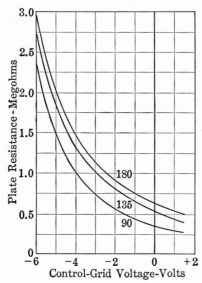

FIG. 6–12. Variations in the plate-circuit resistance of the screen-grid tetrode of Figs. 6–5 and 6–6. Plate voltages on curves; screen grid at + 45 volts. (Data from vacuum-tube catalogue of Western Electric Co.)

Equivalent Circuit of a Screen-Grid Tube.—In the preceding chapter it was shown that for amplification a triode could be represented as a generator producing a voltage of μE_g and having an internal resistance of r_p. When such a generator is connected to a load of resistance R_L, the current flowing and the other values desired are readily obtained.

This same reasoning applies equally well to multi-electrode tubes such as the screen-grid tube. Of course, it assumes that the tube is being operated as an amplifier over the straight portion of the output curve, and considers only the fundamental component, neglecting distortion. Thus, it follows that Fig. 5–15 also represents the equivalent circuit of a screen-grid tube, and that equations (5–12) to (5–15) inclusive apply.

Screen-grid tubes are usually operated as voltage amplifiers, and equations (5–13) and (5–14) indicate the amplification obtainable. Both the amplification factor and the plate resistance of screen-grid tubes are very high. The high plate resistance limits the amount of amplification obtainable. To secure a high voltage across the load resistor, a very large value of load resistance (compared to the plate resistance of the tube) must be used, or most of the generated voltage, μE_g, will be lost *inside* the tube.

There are, however, practical limits to the value of the load resistance. The direct component of the plate current must flow through this resistance, and hence an excessive direct voltage drop may occur. A few simple calculations will show that this is true even for the small plate currents in screen-grid tubes. This subject will be treated more in detail in the chapter on amplifiers, page 206.

The Power-Output Tetrode.—As has been mentioned, the usual screen-grid tube is a voltage amplifier. There is, however, at least one exception to this. A screen-grid tetrode has been developed which can be used as a power-output tube.

In this tube (type 48), an indirectly-heated cathode with a large emitting surface is used, and the control grid is provided with a heat radiator. The plate has a special rib structure fastened to its inner surface which serves to suppress the effects of secondary emission discussed on page 43. The secondary electrons emitted by the exposed surface of the plate are largely recaptured by the ribbed structure which is fastened to the plate and therefore is at the same positive potential. In this way the power output of the tube is not limited, as in conventional screen-grid tubes, and the characteristics of a power-output pentode (to be discussed in the following pages) are obtained.[6, 7]

Owing to its relative unimportance, this tube will not be considered further. Its characteristics can be obtained from tube manuals or experimentally.

48. Five-Electrode Tubes.—These tubes are often called **pentodes,** and were introduced commercially in this country in 1929. Two types, the **space-charge grid pentode** and the **suppressor-grid pentode,** have been manufactured commercially, but only the latter type has attained wide use. Although each of these tubes has five electrodes, they operate entirely differently.[8]

Screen-grid tetrode with very low plate to grid capacitance (0.14 micro-microfarads) for ultra-high frequency operation. (Courtesy Western Electric Co.)

The suppressor-grid pentodes were first designed for *audio-frequency power-output tubes,* but suppressor-grid pentode tubes are now extensively used for *radio-frequency amplification* as well.[7, 9]

Space-Charge Grid Pentode.—As inferred in the preceding section, this type tube is almost obsolete, but is, nevertheless, quite interesting. The arrangement of the electrodes in this tube is shown in Fig. 6–13. As is apparent, it differs from the screen-grid tetrode in having a *positive* space-charge grid next to the cathode. In fact, the tubes available were usually conventional screen-grid tetrode structures with the space-charge grid added.

The effect of the positive space-charge or **accelerator grid** is to reduce the space charge near the cathode and to produce a *virtual cathode* near the control grid (page 165). Since the accelerator grid further shields the plate and largely prevents the electric field of the plate from reaching the space-charge region, the amplification factor of the tube is very high, reaching a theoretical value of at least 1000 in a type once marketed. The space-charge or accelerator grid takes a rather large and constant current from the cathode.

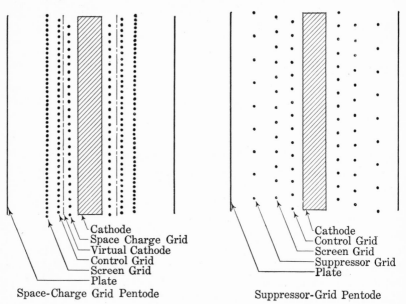

Cathode
Space Charge Grid
Virtual Cathode
Control Grid
Screen Grid
Plate

Space-Charge Grid Pentode

Cathode
Control Grid
Screen Grid
Suppressor Grid
Plate

Suppressor-Grid Pentode

FIG. 6–13. Arrangements of the electrodes in the space-charge or accelerator-grid pentode and in the suppressor-grid pentode. This latter tube as illustrated is of the power-output type with large spacings of the suppressor-grid wires. The suppressor grid is either internally or externally connected directly to the cathode. (From Reference 2.)

The effect of the *plate voltage* on the plate current and screen-grid current in a typical space-charge grid pentode is shown in Fig. 6–14. As would be expected, this tube exhibits the same phenomena of secondary emission as the conventional screen-grid tube. It is also seen that over the operating region of from 200 to 300 volts the plate voltage has little influence on the plate current.

Owing to its closeness to the virtual cathode, the *control-grid voltage* has a very great effect on the plate current and, as Fig. 6–15 indicates, causes cut-off at about − 3.5 volts.　The great influence of the control grid and the ineffectiveness of the plate cause the tube to have a very high amplification factor.　These curves also show that this tube

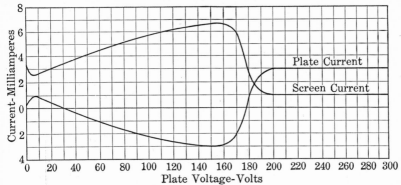

FIG. 6–14.　Plate and screen curves for a space-charge grid pentode with variations in plate potential.　Control grid at − 1.5 volts; space-charge grid at + 10 volts; and screen grid at + 180 volts.　Space-charge grid current approximately constant at about 5 milliamperes.

should have a very high plate resistance and grid-plate transconductance.　An extensive discussion of the space-charge grid pentode and complete curves are given in Reference 2.

Suppressor-Grid Pentode.—The arrangement of the electrodes in this tube also is shown in Fig. 6–13, page 156.　In some of these tubes the suppressor grid is *internally* connected directly to the cathode.　In others, all of the three grids are brought out to external terminals, and may be connected as desired outside the tube.　Such tubes are often termed **triple-grid tubes,** but these are usually connected as suppressor-grid tubes for operation.

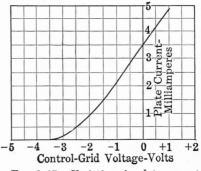

FIG. 6–15.　Variations in plate current with control-grid voltage for a space-charge grid pentode.　Operation substantially as for Fig. 6–14.

The purpose of the **suppressor grid** is to *suppress* the effects of secondary emission from the plate.　The suppressor grid is at the potential of the cathode.　The rapidly-moving electrons release secondary electrons from the plate, but the positive electric field from the *screen grid* is largely unable to reach through the suppressor grid and pull these secondary electrons away and they return to the plate. Thus, even though the plate voltage falls *below* that of the screen grid, the harmful *effects* of secondary emission are largely prevented. No "folds" occur in the plate voltage-plate current curves of Fig. 6–16 such as are caused in the curves of the screen-grid tube (page 146). Also, the plate may be operated at a direct voltage of the same value as that of the screen grid. This is in contrast with the screen-grid tube in which the plate voltage must be much higher than that of the screen.

The action of the suppressor grid is shown by Fig. 6–16. This curve was taken by using a triple-grid tube. The first set of curves (suppressor-grid voltage = 0) was taken with the third grid connected to the

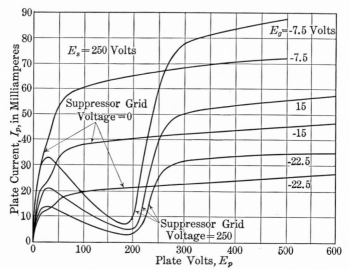

FIG. 6–16. These curves show the effect of the suppressor grid in a multi-electrode tube. (From Reference 2.)

cathode and therefore acting to suppress secondary emission. The second set of curves (suppressor-grid voltage = 250) was taken with the suppressor grid and the screen grid connected together and at the same potential, thus allowing the secondary electrons from the plate to flow to the grids, and therefore giving the tube the characteristics of the conventional screen-grid tetrode.

Suppressor-grid pentodes are used for two main purposes: *first,* as audio-frequency *power output tubes* (as distinguished from voltage amplifiers), and *second,* as audio-frequency and as radio-frequency *voltage amplifier tubes.* As a power-output tube, the pentode will deliver large amounts of power with a *small impressed signal voltage,* and with *low direct voltages* on the electrodes as compared to the con-

ventional power-output triode.   As a radio-frequency voltage amplifier
the suppressor-grid pentode will provide even greater radio-frequency
voltage amplification than can be obtained with a screen-grid tube.
This is largely due to the additional shielding provided by the suppressor grid.[7, 9]   As shown for the screen-grid tube (page 154), the suppressor-grid pentode also may be considered as a generator of voltage
μE_g and internal resistance r_p.

Characteristics of a Power Pentode.—The characteristics and theory
of a power pentode are excellently explained in Reference 2 from which

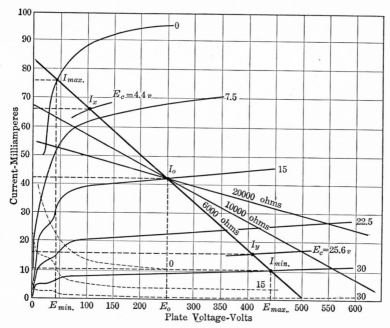

FIG. 6–17.   Characteristics of a power pentode.   Plate current curves shown
by full lines; broken curves represent screen-grid current.   Control-grid voltages in
negative volts shown at ends of curves.   (Data from Reference 2.)

the following discussion is largely summarized, and from which the
accompanying figures are reproduced.   The theory of the pentode,
with particular emphasis on the voltage distribution therein, is also
fully discussed in Reference 10.

A circuit for determining the static characteristics of a power pentode is essentially as shown in Fig. 6–4 for the screen-grid tube.   By
holding the cathode temperature and the screen-grid voltage constant,
and by varying the plate voltage, plate current and screen-grid current
curves as shown in Fig. 6–17 are obtained.   As indicated, the effects of

secondary emission are largely eliminated.   Load lines, to be discussed
later, are also shown.

The knees of the plate-current curves of Fig. 6–17 are quite rounded
and somewhat irregular.   This is due mainly to the effect of the zero-
potential suppressor-grid wires.[10]   Because of these wires the electric
field in the region of the suppressor grid is not uniform but is distorted;
hence, there is no definite value of plate voltage where the curves

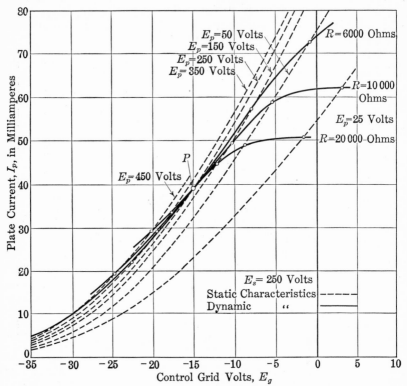

FIG. 6–18.   Plate current-grid voltage characteristics of a power pentode, with
dynamic characteristics for resistance loads of 6000, 10,000, and 20,000 ohms.   (From
Reference 2.)

flatten off.   Other factors influencing the roundness of the knees of the
curves are as follows: Shape and uniformity of the cathode; shapes and
pitches of the control and screen grids; relative distances between electrodes and grid side-rods; and the voltage applied to the electrodes.[10]
This peculiar shape of the plate-current curves is the cause of the high
distortion in power output pentodes.

The plate current curves are not so flat as for the screen-grid tube,
and at high values of plate voltage, they may turn up slightly.   This is

attributed [2] to the open character of the grids which permits the plate to have a slightly greater effect on the current than in the conventional screen-grid tube.   This slight turning up is not evident in the curves of Fig. 6–18.

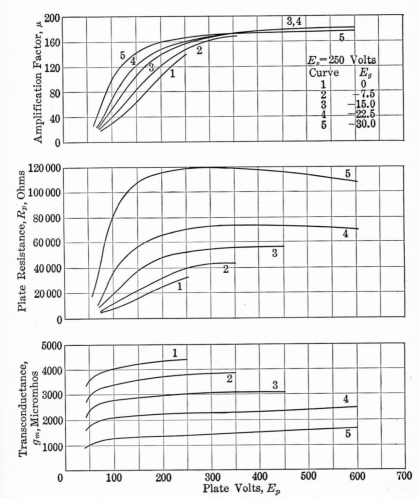

FIG. 6–19.   Amplification factor, plate resistance, and transconductance of a power pentode as functions of the plate voltage, with various values of control-grid voltage as parameters.   Screen grid at + 250 volts.   (From Reference 2.)

In the power pentode the screen grid is rather coarse because shielding is not of great importance.   Thus, although at *low* plate potentials, as Fig. 6–17 shows, the screen grid takes large currents as would be expected, when the plate potential becomes high, the current flow to the screen grid decreases to comparatively low values.

The way in which the plate current varies with control-grid voltage variations is shown in Fig. 6–18. For these curves, the cathode temperature and the screen-grid voltage are constant. As is evident, the static curves (dotted lines) are a parallel family of curves at the higher voltage values. As the voltage is decreased, however, these are no longer parallel, as the curves for $E_p = 50$ and $E_p = 25$ volts indicate. The dynamic curves shown will be discussed later (page 260).

Coefficients for Power Pentodes.—Coefficients for the power pentode can be obtained graphically from the curves of Figs. 6–18 and 6–19, or can be found by dynamic methods using circuits as discussed on pages 149 to 154.

Curves for the amplification factor, plate resistance, and grid-plate transconductance are shown in Fig. 6–19. These correspond in general form to the curves for the screen-grid tube (Reference 2). The maximum points on some plate-resistance curves are attributed [2] to the points of inflection on the plate-current curves.

Dynamic Curves for Power Pentode.—These are shown in Fig. 6–18 for three load resistance values. Such curves may be calculated as explained on page 127. A comparison of these curves with those of the triode (page 128) is very interesting.

For the *triode*, the greater the load resistance, the straighter the dynamic curves, and the *less the distortion*. The *opposite* is true for the power pentode, however. The greater the load resistance, the more curved the dynamic curves become. Thus, with the power pentode the greater the load resistance, the *greater the distortion* for a given magnitude of alternating input signal voltage applied to the grid (usually called a given grid "swing").

These relations are further illustrated by the upper curves of Fig. 6–20. For low input voltages, the *power output increases* as the load resistance is increased. This is in accordance with the theory on pages 131 and 132, that maximum power output should occur when the load resistance and the plate resistance were equal. Of course, this assumes that the characteristics of the tube remain constant. The decrease in power output with increasing load resistance and at higher inputs is due to the decrease of the characteristics as shown in Fig. 6–18.

Thus, although the output of the power pentode follows the simple theory of matched resistances at low values of resistance and input, this theory cannot be applied throughout the operating range. As Fig. 6–18 indicates, it is necessary to use low values of load resistance (compared to the plate resistance) to minimize distortion. For the power pentode here considered, a load resistance of about 6000 ohms would probably be used, sacrificing output to some extent, but obtain-

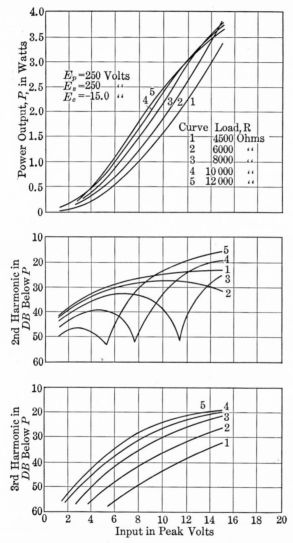

FIG. 6–20. Characteristics of a power pentode. Sinusoidal voltage applied to control grid, peak values as indicated. (From Reference 2.)

ing higher quality as the lower sets of curves show. Further information on distortion in power pentodes will be found on page 261, where their use in amplifiers is considered.

49. Beam Power Tube.—This tube, which is a *tetrode* or four-electrode tube, should logically be considered following the screen-grid power-output tube on page 155. This so-called **beam power tube** is so important and its theory so well follows that of the power-output pentode, however, that it will be considered at this time.

The popular name, *beam power tube,* is somewhat misleading in that the term electron beam has for years been used to describe a ray or beam of electrons in such a device as the cathode-ray tube (Chap. 14). The term *beam* has, through usage, been associated with deflector plates, or coils, and targets. The so-called beam power tube (6L6) does *not* operate on this principle.

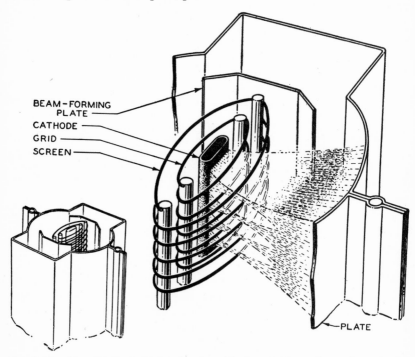

BEAM–FORMING PLATE

CATHODE

GRID

SCREEN

PLATE

Fig. 6–21.   Showing the formation by the grid wires of electron beam sheets in the beam power tube.   (Courtesy RCA Manufacturing Co.)

As mentioned, this tube is a tetrode, or four-electrode tube having, therefore, a cathode, a control grid, a screen grid, and a plate. It *does not* have the characteristics of the conventional screen-grid tube (Fig. 6–19), but because of special construction its characteristics are similar to, and even better than, those of the power pentode. This special construction suppresses secondary emission *without* the use of a suppressor grid as in the pentode. By eliminating this grid, the distortion caused by its presence in the power pentode is prevented. The knees of the plate-current curves are quite sharp as will be shown.

Theory.—The special construction of this tube is shown by Fig. 6–21. The cathode is large, is indirectly heated, and has the shape indicated. The wires of the screen grid are *exactly the same* size *and exactly behind* the wires of the control grid. The screen-grid wires may be mentally pictured as being in the "shadow" of the control grid. The beam-forming plate is at zero potential, being connected to the cathode.

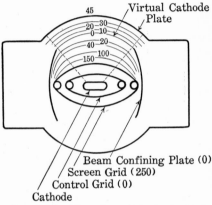

Owing to the fact that the highly-positive screen grid is quite effectively enclosed by the beam-forming or zero potential deflecting plates, a region of zero potential exists [10, 11] somewhat as shown in Fig. 6–22. Secondary electrons emitted from the plate are not drawn back to the highly-positive screen grid. At such a region of zero potential a **virtual cathode** [10] (region of zero potential gradient and zero absolute potential) exists. In this connection it should be remembered, however, that at all times the *control grid* is actually determining the electron flow to the plate.

Fig. 6–22. Top view of electrodes in the so-called beam power tube showing potentials in the beam. (Courtesy RCA Manufacturing Co.)

Thus, the screen-grid wires are immediately behind those of the control grid and the initial repulsion given the electrons by the negative control-grid wires prevents the electrons from striking the positive screen-grid wires as Fig. 6–21 illustrates. The current taken by the screen grid is, therefore, very small except at low plate potentials. Furthermore, little secondary emission can occur from the screen grid because few electrons hit it. And as previously mentioned, the zero potential gradient (virtual cathode or space charge if desired) prevents secondary emission from the plate from causing distortion.

Characteristics.—The relation between the plate voltage and plate and screen-grid currents is shown in Fig. 6–23. A load line for a 2500-ohm load is also indicated. This has been corrected for the rectification occurring with large signals.[10] For these curves the cathode temperature was held constant and the screen-grid voltage

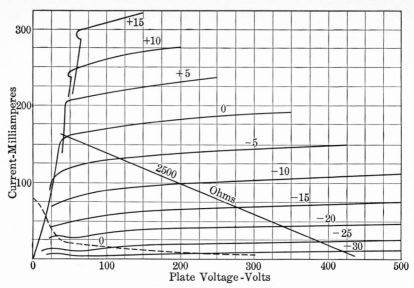

FIG. 6–23. Plate-current characteristics (solid lines) of the beam power output tube. Control-grid voltages shown on curves. Screen-grid current when control-grid voltage is zero shown by broken line. Screen-grid at + 250 volts. (From Reference 10.)

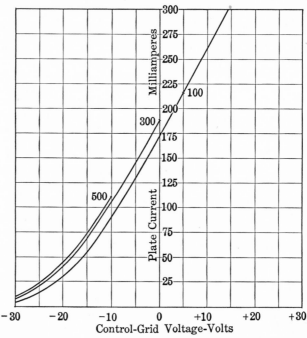

FIG. 6–24. Variations in plate current with changes in control-grid voltage for a beam power output tube. Plate voltages shown on curves. (Data from Fig. 6–23.)

fixed at 250 volts positive. The curves were taken at various control-grid values. The manner in which the plate current changes with control-grid variation is shown in Fig. 6–24. As previously mentioned, the knees of these curves are *quite definite* and occur only at *low values of plate voltage.* This makes it possible for the tube to handle large amounts of power with low distortion and with low plate voltage.

Although relatively new, a variety of applications have already been developed for this tube. As a linear or class *A* amplifier (page 209) the operation characteristics are shown in Figs. 6–25 and 6–26. This new tube has high efficiency, large power output, high sensitivity, and low distortion.

50. Co-Planar Grid Tubes.—In the multi-electrode tubes previously considered, the electrodes are arranged one within the other. One of the important effects of this is so effectively to shield the plate that, *first,* the amplification factor is high; but *second,* the plate resistance is also high. This is well illustrated by the power-output pentode.

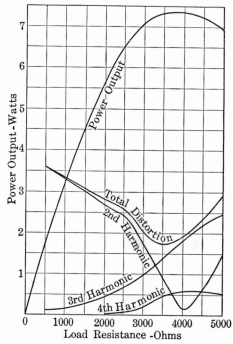

Fig. 6–25. Variations in power output and distortion with load resistance in a beam power tube. (From Reference 10.)

In the co-planar grid tube, which is a tetrode or four-electrode tube, the two grids are arranged as in Fig. 6–27, so that they are *in the same plane.* This tube has been discussed in Reference 3 and as a supplement to Reference 2 published in Reference 12. A co-planar grid tube, called the Wunderlich tube, has been developed and used for demodulation or detection in radio receivers.[13] Only the co-planar grid tube as a *power-output tube* will be discussed at this time.

As a power-output tube, the action of the two grids is explained in the following summary.[2] As Fig. 6–27 shows, one grid (sometimes called a *net* and often represented by *n*) is held at a fixed positive potential and the other is the control grid. The positive grid *tends to* act as a space-charge reducing or accelerator grid, being held at about + 65 volts in certain tubes.   At high values of *negative control-grid* voltage, the effect of the field from the positive space-charge grid is largely neutralized; as the *control-grid* voltage approaches zero, however, the positive grid becomes very effective in drawing electrons out of the space-charge region.   The non-symmetrical arrangement of the grid, illustrated by the drawing at the left of Fig. 6–27, makes this combined action of the two grids more effective.

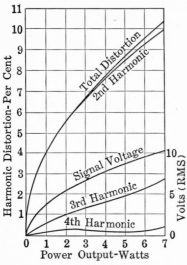

Fig. 6–26.   Relation between distortion and power output of a beam power tube.   (From Reference 10.)

The effect of this action on the plate current is as follows: The control grid can be driven highly negative by the applied signal voltage before cut-off of plate current occurs, because the control grid must overcome the electric field of the positive space-charge grid.   Also, when the control-grid voltage approaches zero, the positive grid assists the plate in drawing a plate current.   Furthermore, this assistance is rendered at the instant it is needed most, because, when the plate is drawing the *maximum* current (as it does when the control-grid voltage approaches zero), the voltage *on the plate* is minimum since the $I_p R_L$ drop of the plate current in the load resistor is greatest *at that instant* and this drop is subtracted from the plate-supply voltage.

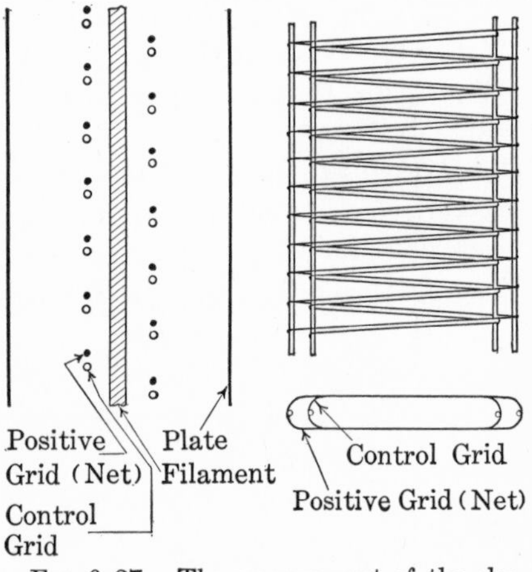

Characteristics.—Curves for this tube showing the variations in plate current with control-grid and positive grid

Positive Grid (Net)   Plate Filament   Control Grid

Control Grid   Positive Grid (Net)

Fig. 6–27.   The arrangement of the electrodes in a co-planar grid tube.   (From Reference 2.)

(net) voltages are shown in Fig. 6–28.   These curves illustrate the shifting of the plate current-grid voltage curves by the positive voltage applied to the net. As is evident, with larger values of positive net voltages, larger control-grid voltage input values may be applied before the grid becomes positive.

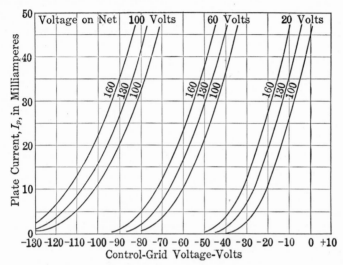

FIG. 6–28.   Effect of the positive-grid (or net) voltage on the characteristics of a co-planar grid tube.   Net voltages at tops of curves; plate voltages along curves. (From Reference 2.)

A more extended family of curves is shown in Fig. 6–29. A dynamic characteristic curve is drawn on these for a load resistance of 3400 ohms. This is the plate resistance at point P as noted by "operating conditions" on the lower figure. Thus it is seen that for power output service the co-planar grid tube has a higher amplification factor than comparable triodes, and a much lower plate resistance than pentodes. This low plate resistance is due to the effect of the positive net, and to the construction of the tube. The fact that the grids are in the same plane, rather than one *within* the other, makes a decreased distance between the cathode and plate possible.

It will be noted that the dynamic curves of the co-planar grid tube are very similar to those of the power pentode of Fig. 6–18, page 160. A pronounced decrease occurs at the lower values of plate voltages. This is due to the fact that at low values of plate voltage the positive grid or net takes an increasing percentage of the total space current from the space-charge region as the lower set of curves of Fig. 6–29 indicates.

It should be expected, therefore, that the power output curves and the distortion curves for the co-planar tube and the power pentode will be similar.   That this is true is illustrated by Fig. 6–30.   The co-planar grid tube has never been widely used as a power-output tube.   Although its characteristics are satisfactory, the low amplification factor,

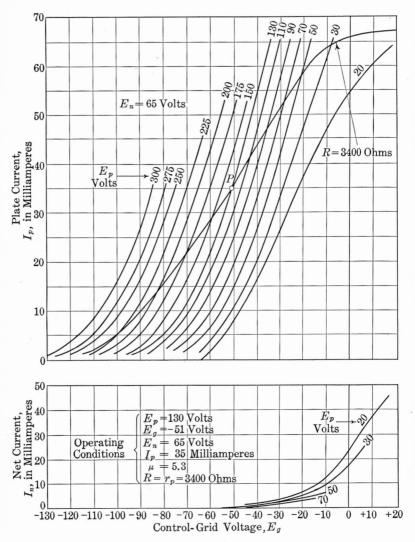

FIG. 6–29.   Plate current-grid voltage and net current-grid voltage characteristics of a co-planar grid tube.   The net (positive grid) potential is maintained constant at 65 volts.   The dynamic characteristic, P, shown is for a resistance load of 3400 ohms. E_p is the plate voltage, E_g is the control-grid voltage, and E_n is the net voltage, all in volts.   Data on operating conditions are for use as a linear amplifier. (From Reference 2.)

compared to the power pentode, makes a larger input signal voltage necessary.

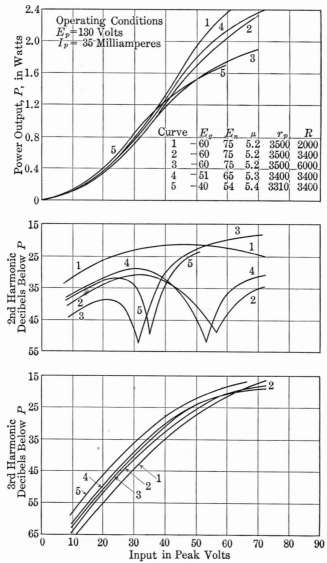

Fig. 6–30.   Power output and distortion of a co-planar grid tube.   For meaning of E_p, E_g, and E_n, refer to Fig. 6–29.   (From Reference 2.)

51. Variable-Mu or Super-Control Tubes.—For many purposes a tube with a *variable* amplification factor is very desirable.   Such a tube

was developed [14] and is called a **variable-mu** or **super-control tube.**
Both screen-grid tubes or tetrodes and suppressor-grid pentodes are
made in this form. They are voltage-amplifying, as distinguished
from power-output, tubes.

The characteristics of a tube of this type are shown in Fig. 6–31
compared with a screen-grid tube. As is indicated, a large negative
control-grid voltage is required to cause cut-off in the super-control
tube. This means that when the tube is operated as an amplifier the
bias may be so adjusted that various values of amplification are possible.
Thus if the tube is biased to − 5 volts, operation is on the steep portion
of the characteristic and a large
plate current change is produced by a small alternating signal voltage impressed on the grid.
If the tube is biased to − 30
volts, however, the same alternating grid voltage will produce
a small plate current change.

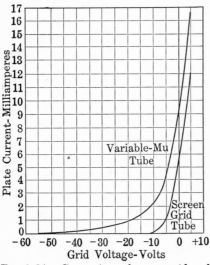

FIG. 6–31.   Comparison of screen-grid and
variable-mu or super-control tubes.

Of course this is also true
with the screen-grid tube and
with triodes, but there is a difference in the magnitude of the
signal voltage which may be
impressed. With the super-
control tube, *relatively large* alternating signal voltages may be
impressed at the point selected
for operation without the curvature causing excessive distortion.

Various combinations [14] of non-uniformly wound and spaced control and screen grids will give the remote cut-off characteristics of
Fig. 6–31. In one widely-used super-control tube the control grid is
uniformly wound at the ends, but the turns at the center are omitted.

The super-control tubes are extensively used in automatic volume-
control circuits (page 342) of radio-receiving sets. When a strong
signal is being received, the tube is biased so that operation is on the
lower part of the curve where the amplification is low. When the
transmission path changes and a weak signal is received, the bias automatically is reduced, and the tube is operated on the portion of the
curve where the amplification is high. Manual operation of the bias to
vary the amplification may also be used.

52. Multi-Electrode Gas Tubes.—As mentioned in the opening pages of this chapter, multi-electrode *gas* tubes are not in wide use compared with vacuum types.   There are, however, several multi-electrode gas tubes of special interest, and these will now be considered.

Amplifier Tubes.—Much experimental work [15, 16] has been done, especially abroad, on gas-filled amplifier tubes.   In this country, such work has led to the development of a gas tube [16] which is very satisfactory for use as an amplifier, and for other purposes as well.   One such tube (RK-100) is illustrated in Fig. 6–32.

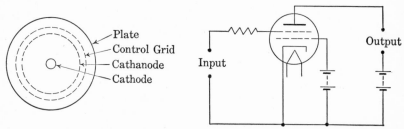

Fig. 6–32.   Electrode arrangements and a typical test circuit for a multi-electrode gas amplifier tube.

This tube contains mercury vapor, but the inert gases may be used if complete absence of temperature effects is desired (page 133).   A hot cathode supplies electrons.   These electrons are drawn over to an electrode, 8 to 13 volts positive, termed the **cathanode.**   Ionization by collision occurs within the tube.   Thus far, this tube is similar to the grid-controlled rectifier described on page 133.

As Fig. 6–32 shows, the cathanode and the control grid are placed *very near* the plate.   Also the grid openings are very small.   The short electron paths between the control grid and plate, the small grid openings, and the low gas pressure combine to prevent *cumulative* ionization (page 12) from occurring *between the control grid and the plate.*[16]   Of course, some positive ions are formed in this region, but only enough to *reduce* space-charge effects.

As a result of this special construction, the tube operates somewhat as follows: Between the cathode and the positive cathanode cumulative ionization by collision occurs.   As in other gas tubes (page 86) the positive ions thus formed neutralize the negative space charge, permitting large electron currents to flow.   Many of these electrons pass through the meshes of the cathanode and into the region beyond.   The negative space charge outside the cathanode is reduced by the relatively few positive ions formed as previously mentioned.   The electrons in this region are attracted to the positive plate, but the negative control grid is able to control the flow, thus making amplification and other applications [16] possible.

As is evident, the tube is similar in amplifying action to a simple triode. The region near the cathanode acts as a source of electrons, or as a *virtual cathode* (page 165). The electron flow to the plate is regulated by the control grid. Since the first grid acts as an anode to the portion of the tube within it, and as a cathode to that without, the term *cathanode* is quite descriptive of its action. Because there are insufficient positive ions present, no sheath is formed around the negative control grid; thus, it is *not* rendered ineffective as in the grid-controlled rectifier tubes.

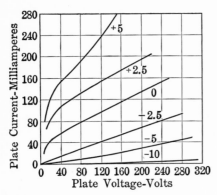

FIG. 6–33. Characteristic curves for a typical multi-electrode gas amplifier tube. Control-grid voltages shown on curves. Cathanode voltage about + 10 volts. (Data from Reference 15.)

The plate voltage-plate current curves for a tube of this type (RK-100) are shown in Fig. 6–33. The tube has low impedance (plate resistance), high mutual conductance, and high cathode efficiency.[16]

Rectifier Tubes.—The grid-controlled gas rectifier tubes (also called Grid-Glow tubes and Thyratrons) discussed on page 133 contain a cathode, grid, and anode sealed in an enclosure containing an inert gas or mercury vapor at low pressure. In these tubes, the potential of the grid determines the anode voltage at which the tube becomes conducting and passes current. After conduction occurs, however, the grid loses control, and will not again regain control until the tube deionizes on the negative half cycle if alternating voltage is used on the anode, or until the circuit is opened for an instant if a direct voltage is impressed on the anode.

Although the three-electrode tube just described has been very satisfactory, the addition of a fourth electrode, in the form of a shield around the grid, improves operation [17] as follows: *First*, less grid current is passed with the shielded-grid construction both before and after breakdown. The grid current before breakdown is very important, because in high-impedance control circuits, the drop in voltage caused by the grid-current flow decreases the voltage (from a control device such as a phototube) impressed on the grid. *Second*, the shield isolates the discharge from electric charges which accumulate on the walls of the tube. *Third,* the "control" grid is shielded from material sputtered and evaporated from the cathode. *Fourth,* this grid is heat shielded and lower grid emission occurs. There are other advantages of the shield-grid construction, but these are among the most important. Curves showing the advantages of the shield grid, and also other characteristics, are included in Reference 17.

REFERENCES

1. Institute of Radio Engineers. *Reports of the Standards Committee.*
2. Pidgeon, H. A. *Theory of multi-electrode vacuum tubes.* Electrical Engineering, Nov., 1934, Vol. 53.
3. Pidgeon, H. A., and McNally, J. O. *The output power from vacuum tubes of different types.* Proceedings of the Institute of Radio Engineers, Feb., 1930, Vol. 18.
4. Hull, A. W., and Williams, N. H. *Characteristics of shielded-grid pliotrons.* Physical Review, April, 1926, Vol. 27, No. 4.
5. Terman, F. E. *Radio Engineering.* McGraw-Hill Book Co.
6. RCA Radiotron Co. *Tube Manual.* Technical Series, RC-13.
7. Henney, K. *The Radio Engineering Handbook.* McGraw-Hill Book Co.
8. Henney, K. *Two kinds of pentodes.* Electronics, April, 1930.
9. Pender, H., and McIlwain, K. *Electrical Engineers' Handbook.* Vol. V, Electric Communication and Electronics. John Wiley & Sons.
10. RCA Manufacturing Co. *Application note on the operation of the 6L6.* Application Note No. 60, June 10, 1936.
11. Dreyer, J. F. *The beam power tube.* Electronics, April, 1936, Vol. 9, No. 4.
12. Pidgeon, H. A. *Theory of multi-electrode vacuum tubes.* (Containing supplement to Reference 2.) Bell System Technical Journal, Jan., 1935, Vol. 14, No. 1.
13. Terman, F. E. *The Wunderlich Tube.* Arcturus Radio Tube Co., Newark, N. J.
14. Ballantine, S., and Snow, H. A. *Reduction of distortion and crosstalk in radio receivers by means of variable-mu tetrodes.* Proc. I. R. E., Dec., 1930, Vol. 18, No. 12.
15. *Tubes with cold cathodes.* Electronics, Jan., 1933, Vol. 6, No. 1.
16. Le Van, J. D., and Weeks, P. T. *A new type of gas-filled amplifier tube.* Proceedings of the Institute of Radio Engineers, Feb., 1936, Vol. 24, No. 2.
17. Maser, H. T., and Livingston, O. W. *Shield grid thyratrons.* Electronics, April, 1934, Vol. 7, No. 4.

SUGGESTED ASSIGNMENTS

1. Referring to the statement at the close of the section on page 148, why is it usually not necessary to plot dynamic curves for the conventional screen-grid and suppressor-grid voltage-amplifying tubes?

2. On page 154 it is stated that the screen-grid tube can be considered as a hypothetical generator of voltage μE_g and internal resistance r_p. From a tube manual obtain typical operating values for such a tube and determine the voltage amplification when operated as a resistance-coupled amplifier.

3. Repeat the above for a suppressor-grid pentode.

4. Calculate the direct voltage drop in the load resistor in the plate circuit of each of the above tubes.

5. Explain why a control grid arranged as explained on page 172 should give the desired remote cut-off characteristics.

CHAPTER 7

RECTIFIERS

A rectifier is defined [1] as "a device which converts alternating current into uni-directional current by virtue of a characteristic permitting appreciable flow of current in one direction only." The rectifying action depends on its ability to offer very low resistance to current flow in one direction, but to offer very high or practically infinite resistance to flow of current in the opposite direction.

Rectifiers of many types have been devised. All these may be broadly classified under two headings: First, **mechanical rectifiers;** and second, **electrical rectifiers.** The commutator on an ordinary direct-current machine is an example of a mechanical rectifier. Only *electrical rectifiers* will be considered in this chapter.

The **rectifier unit** includes the rectifier with its essential auxiliaries and the rectifier transformer equipment. Accordingly, in the discussions which follow, the term *rectifier* will designate the device which *distorts* the wave due to its asymmetrical (or non-symmetrical) conducting properties. Also, the term *rectifier unit* will usually be employed to designate the entire device including the rectifier itself and all of the associated circuits. Since this distinction is not generally employed in practice, its *complete* adoption at this time is difficult.

An *ideal* rectifier is a device which offers *zero* resistance to current flow in one direction, and *infinite* resistance to current flow in the opposite direction. Thus, the ideal rectifier merely is a "switch" which opens and closes the circuit as the voltage impressed on the circuit changes. Various natural and artificial crystals are used as rectifiers (page 339). Also, oxide layers, and layers of gas (electrolytic rectifiers) will produce rectification. Of all these devices, the vacuum tube is the most widely used. The term *vacuum tube* is used in its widest sense, covering a variety of types including the vacuum, gas, and vapor tubes discussed in Chapter 4.

53. Analysis of Rectified Waves.—*A rectifier is in reality a distorter.* This statement is justified by the following facts: Distortion is defined [1] as "a change in wave form." When a *pure sine wave* voltage is impressed on a rectifier, then the output current which flows *is not a pure sine wave.* The wave shape has been *changed*, and *distortion* has resulted.

177

If the rectified or output currents or voltages of Figs. 7–1 and 7–2 are examined, it will be apparent that these values are uni-directional, and that they contain a direct component. What is not so apparent, however, is the fact that they contain sinusoidal *alternating components* produced by the *process of distortion* referred to as rectification.

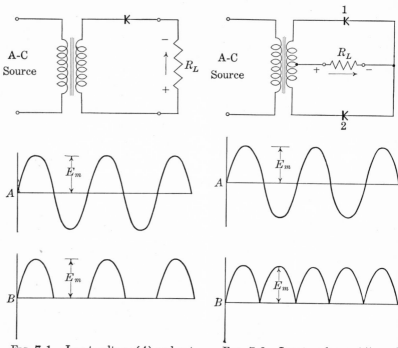

FIG. 7–1. Input voltage (*A*) and output current and voltage (*B*) for a half-wave rectifier with resistance load.

FIG. 7–2. Input voltage (*A*) and output current and voltage (*B*) for the full-wave rectifier with resistance load.

Thus, if a *perfect* rectifier is used in the half-wave rectifier circuit of Fig. 7–1 to rectify the *pure sine-wave voltage* of maximum value E_m and frequency f, the rectified voltage will be as indicated by *B*, and can be represented [3] by the following series:

$$e = \frac{E_m}{\pi} + \frac{E_m}{2} \sin \omega t - \frac{2E_m}{3\pi} \cos 2\omega t - \frac{2E_m}{15\pi} \cos 4\omega t \cdots. \quad (7\text{–}1)$$

The first of these terms is the direct component since it contains *no* frequency term ($\omega = 2\pi f$). The other terms represent the sinusoidal alternating components. For the half-wave rectifier the first of these alternating terms would be the *same frequency as the alternating voltage being rectified;* the second would be twice the frequency; and the third would be four times the frequency. The first term of equation (7–1) would be the voltage indicated by a direct-current *voltmeter* connected across R_L of Fig. 7–1, and the second, third, and fourth terms would be as measured by a *wave analyzer* when set on these various frequencies. The proof of this can be demonstrated in the laboratory quite easily if a wave analyzer (page 275) is available.

Similarly, if *perfect* rectifiers are used in the full-wave rectifier circuit of Fig. 7–2, and if the *pure sine-wave voltage* shown by curve *A* is impressed, the rectified voltage will be as shown by *B*, and can be represented by the following series:

$$ e = \frac{2E_m}{\pi} - \frac{4E_m}{3\pi}\cos 2\omega t - \frac{4E_m}{15\pi}\cos 4\omega t - \frac{4E_m}{35\pi}\cos 6\omega t \cdots. \quad (7\text{–}2) $$

The first term is the direct component which would be measured by a direct-current *voltmeter* connected across R_L of Fig. 7–2. The other terms are the alternating components which would be measured by a *wave analyzer* connected across R_L. Since these statements can be readily verified experimentally they justify the viewpoint that *rectification is a process of distortion*.

54. Rectifier Units.—A simple rectifier unit is shown in Fig. 7–1. The transformer increases or decreases (as desired) the alternating voltage impressed on the rectifier. This is connected to a load resistor R_L, although a battery to be charged could be connected in its place. Current passes through the rectifier *only* in the direction of the arrow.* That is, the resistance is assumed to be *zero* for current in the direction of the arrow, and *infinite* in the opposite direction. Thus, if the alternating voltage of curve *A* is induced in the secondary of the transformer (assumed to be perfect), then the *current* through the load R_L and the *voltage* across R_L will be as shown by *B*. This rectifier unit is known as a **half-wave rectifier.**[1]

A simple rectifier unit employing *two* rectifiers is shown in Fig. 7–2. When the upper end of the input transformer secondary is *negative* so that current *passes* through rectifier 1, the lower end of the transformer will be *positive* and *no current* will pass through rectifier 2. On the next half cycle of the impressed alternating voltage, the *lower* end of the transformer will be negative and rectifier 2 instead of rectifier 1 will conduct. In this manner, *both* halves of the impressed alternating

---

* This statement refers to the *conventional* direction of current flow as distinguished from the direction of *electron* current flow. Care must be taken to prevent confusing the *symbol* of a rectifier such as shown in Fig. 7–1 with the *symbol* for a rectifier tube as shown in Fig. 7–14. In Fig. 7–1 *conventional* current flows in the direction of the arrow; in Fig. 7–14, conventional current flows from the *plate to the filament*. The possibility for confusion arises because the symbol of Fig. 7–1 may be mistaken for a plate and a filament of a vacuum tube.

impulses will be rectified. With an alternating voltage A induced in
the secondary of the transformer, the current through the resistor R_L
and the voltage across the resistor R_L will be as shown by B of Fig. 7–2.
This device is a **full-wave rectifier**,[1] and is extensively used for converting from alternating to direct power. The circuit of Fig. 7–2 is
sometimes called a **transformer bridge circuit**.

The circuit of another rectifier unit is shown in Fig. 7–3; this is
called a **Graetz bridge** or just a **bridge circuit**. Four rectifiers are
used in a balanced bridge arrangement. When the *upper* bridge
terminal is made positive by the applied alternating voltage, current
will flow down through rectifier 1, across through R_L, and down through
rectifier 2. Theoretically no current will flow through rectifiers 3
and 4. When the applied alternating voltage reverses direction on the
next half cycle, and the *lower* end is positive, current will flow up
through rectifier 3, across through
R_L, and up through rectifier 4.
Hence, current flows through R_L
in the same direction for *each half
cycle* of the applied voltage giving
a *full-wave* rectifier unit and a
rectified current such as B of
Fig. 7–2. The circuit of Fig. 7–3
is extensively used in measuring

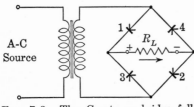

Fig. 7–3. The Graetz or bridge full-
wave rectifier circuit.

instruments [2] and in modulators and demodulators (page 328).

The *rectifier unit* is composed of the several elements illustrated by
Fig. 7–4. For some purposes a voltage divider (tapped resistor)
would be connected across the output terminals so that various direct
voltages can be taken off as desired.

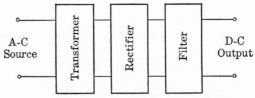

Fig. 7–4.   The elements of a rectifier unit.

The transformer increases or decreases the supply voltage depending on whether direct current at high voltage or at low voltage is
desired. The transformer may be omitted if a direct connection to
the power source is permissible. The purpose of the filter is to
suppress the alternating components of the rectified wave as listed in
equations (7–1) and (7–2). For battery-charging uses, often no filter

is required; for most voltage supply purposes, such as to vacuum tubes, very complete filtering is necessary.

55. Theory of Wave Filters.*—The operation of the entire rectifier unit is so closely related to the characteristics of the filter that this device will be considered in some detail. The discussion will be limited to low-pass filters since these will pass the direct current and attenuate the harmonics of the distorted or rectified wave produced by the rectifier.

It is assumed that the inductance and capacitance units composing the filter have *no losses;* that is, they are without *effective resistance.*

With this assumption, low-pass T and π sections are shown in Fig. 7–5. These are often called **choke input** and **condenser input** filters.

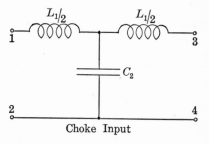

Choke Input

Such filters have two very important characteristics. The *first* of these is the **cut-off frequency,** and the *second* is the input or **iterative impedance** (often incorrectly called characteristic impedance).[4] To explain the first of these characteristics, suppose that the filter is properly terminated with a load equal to its iterative impedance[4, 5, 6] and that equal voltages *of various frequencies* are impressed across the input terminals 1–2. For the low frequencies, currents will flow; after the cut-off frequency is reached, essentially no current flows to the

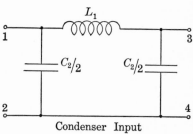

Condenser Input

Fig. 7–5.　Low-pass filters.

load connected across points 3–4. If this cut-off frequency is well below the lowest alternating components of equations (7–1) and (7–2), then the output of the rectifier tubes will be filtered and *only direct current will flow to the load.* For both the T and the π sections, this cut-off frequency is [4]

$$f_c = \frac{1}{(\pi\sqrt{L_1 C_2})}. \qquad (7\text{–}3)$$

The iterative impedance of a filter section equals the input impedance between terminals 1–2 when the output terminals 3–4 are

---

* It is recognized that this elementary theory of filters is not necessary at this time. It is included because certain of the more advanced students will undoubtedly be interested in the relation between such theory and the approximate methods used in rectifier filter design.

terminated by a load equal to the iterative impedance of the filter section. The iterative impedance Z_K is the impedance of an infinite number of sections connected in tandem, one to the other. For the simple sections of Fig. 7–5, the iterative impedance at *zero frequency* is

$$Z_K = \sqrt{\frac{L_1}{C_2}}. \qquad (7\text{--}4)$$

Although the iterative impedance varies with frequency, it is customary to terminate the sections of Fig. 7–5 with the impedance calculated by equation (7–4). This statement is made with respect to its use as a transmission element in communication circuits (such as voice-frequency telephony) where alternating currents *must be passed*. It does not apply to the voltage dividers or bleeders used to terminate filter rectifiers for direct-current supply purposes. In these *no transfer* of alternating components is desired.

The *input impedance* of a properly-terminated *ideal* filter is *pure resistance* over the band passed, and *pure reactance* over the band suppressed. Over the band passed, the filter must take maximum power from the source and pass it on to the load. To do this, the input impedance of the filter must be pure resistance. Since the filter elements are pure reactances, no power is dissipated in the filter and it is all passed to the load. Over the band suppressed (which is of interest in rectifier-circuits), the input impedance *must be pure reactance*. Then, no alternating-current power is taken from the source, and none is passed on to the load.

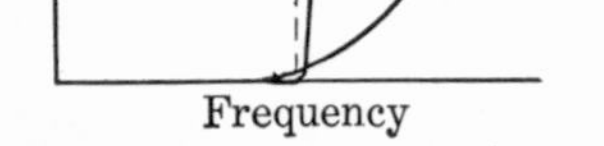

FIG. 7–6. A composite filter composed of constant k sections with m-derived terminating half sections gives a much sharper cut-off (m) than for the constant k sections (k) alone.

In terms of the iterative impedance and cut-off frequency, the design equations [4] for the T and π sections are as follows:

$$L_1 = \frac{Z_k}{(\pi f_c)} \quad \text{and} \quad C_2 = \frac{1}{(\pi f_c Z_k)}, \quad (7\text{--}5)$$

where L_1 is in henrys and C_2 is in farads. These are for designing what is called **constant-k filters** [4] which are the type usually employed in rectifier circuits.

The attenuation characteristics of a properly-terminated low-pass filter section, such as Fig. 7–5, are as shown by curve k of Fig. 7–6. This attenuation curve does not rise to a high value immediately following cut-off. The letter k was used because these simple networks are constant-k filters. If constant-k sections *are combined* with **m-derived** terminating sections, then the resulting attenuation curve will be quite sharp as indicated by m of Fig. 7–6.

A diagram of a constant-k filter with a terminating m-derived half section is shown in Fig. 7–7. This half section places a series resonant circuit across the rectifier causing the sharp cut-off. The constant-k

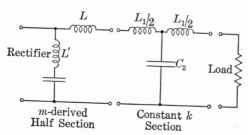

FIG. **7–7.** Illustrating the design of a composite or "tuned input" filter. In constructing such a filter, L, $L_1/2$, and possibly L' would be combined into one unit.

section gives the required attenuation considerably beyond **cut-off.** These filters when used with rectifiers are often called **tuned-input filters.** They are usually designed by approximations. Their exact design by conventional filter theory is not difficult. Such filters are treated in great detail in Reference 7, and are also discussed in References 4, 5, and 6. Although these special tuned-input filters may offer some additional filtering for a particular alternating component, they are *not* generally necessary; they are required only in special installations.

As previously mentioned, the iterative impedance of filter sections must be resistive over the band passed and reactive over the band suppressed. The manner in which this impedance varies (with frequency) over the band passed is relatively unimportant in rectifiers because the band passed (that is, the cut-off point) must be made considerably *below* the first alternating component of equations (7–1) and (7–2). The impedance offered to the various frequencies *above cut-off* is important, however. The ideal filter for rectifier use should, of course, offer zero resistance to direct current, but infinite impedance to the alternating components.

56. Theoretical Considerations of Rectifier Operation.—Contrary to popular opinion, it is not difficult to explain the operation of a rectifier and its associated filter circuit. If *certain assumptions* are made, then the operation can be explained on the basis of usual filter theory. Such an explanation will now be given; the limitations will be made clear by the following paragraphs.

In Fig. 7–8 is shown a circuit representing, for example, the full-wave rectifier of Fig. 7–2. The voltage output of the generator is shown by curve B of Fig. 7–2, and is represented mathematically by equation (7–2).

The direct current which will flow through the load R_L should equal the direct voltage component of equation (7–2) divided by the total series resistance of the cir-

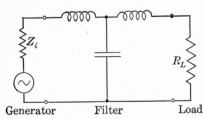

Generator   Filter   Load

Fig. 7–8. Equivalent circuit for a rectifier unit. An additional condenser is often connected directly across R_L.

cuit. Similarly, the magnitude of each alternating-current component should equal the *voltage value* of that component *which will exist across* R_L divided by the resistance (or impedance) of R_L. In other words, ordinary series-parallel circuit theory may be applied. Also, it is possible to calculate the current at each frequency by the application of advanced filter theory [7] in which the loss in decibels caused by the filter *at each frequency* is correctly applied to the impressed voltage at that frequency.

Straightforward as these methods appear, they have not been widely used in rectifier filter design. Among the many reasons for this are the following: *First*, the true nature of rectifier action, in which the rectifier produces a distorted wave containing a direct and alternating components, is often not fully understood; *second*, in applying these methods many assumptions must be made, and some of these do not seem to be justified, as the following sections will indicate; *third*, it is far easier and usually entirely satisfactory to "design" rectifiers and their associated circuits by approximate methods; that is, make "brute force" filters, as they are often called. If the inductance and capacitance units are made very large, the filter *must* attenuate the alternating components and hence produce sufficient "smoothing action."

An excellent analysis of rectifier filter circuits and their operation was made by Stout and reported in Reference 8. This study was devoted largely to rectification with thermionic *vacuum tubes*. An excellent analysis of *copper-oxide rectifier* circuits was made by Huss and reported in Reference 9. These two articles explain the operation of rectifier circuits in a most satisfactory manner, and they are recommended to those desiring an *exact understanding* of the problem.

The subject is so involved, if handled in a meaningful way, that space permits of only a brief summary of the operation of rectifier filter circuits. This summary and the illustrations are based largely on the two references just given. Before considering a rectifier and an actual filter circuit, such as used in practice, a rectifier with *three* different types of load will be studied.

Rectifier with Resistive Load.— Suppose that the rectifier of Fig. 7–9 is connected to a pure resistive load as indicated. If the internal impedance to the left of terminals 1–2 is neglected, then the voltage across these terminals will be as shown by curve *B*, and represented by equation (7–2). The corresponding current flowing through the

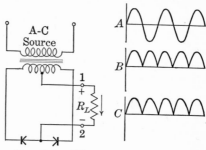

FIG. 7–9. When a sinusoidal voltage (*A*) is impressed on the full-wave rectifier circuit with a *resistance* load, the voltage across the load and the current through the load will be as shown by curves (*B*) and (*C*).

resistor R_L will be as shown by curve *C*. Each term in the equation for the current can be found by dividing the corresponding term of the voltage equation by the resistance.

Rectifier with Inductive Load.—The rectifier of Fig. 7–10 is connected to a load consisting of inductance in series with the resistance load R_L. If the impressed voltage is as shown in *A*, the rectified voltage will be represented by *B*, and the current flow by *C*. As is evident, the current wave has been considerably "smoothed" by the action of the inductor.

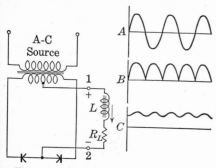

FIG. 7–10. When a sinusoidal voltage (*A*) is impressed on the full-wave rectifier with an inductive load, the voltage across the load and the current through the load will be as shown by curves (*B*) and (*C*).

An explanation for this smoothing action is as follows: The rectified voltage is given by equation (7–2) and shown by curve *B* of Fig. 7–10. The *direct* component of the current of curve *C* is equal to the first term divided by the total *direct-current resistance*. Each *alternating* component of the current *C* is equal to the voltage for that frequency component divided by *the impedance at that frequency*. The impedance increases, therefore, for the higher-frequency terms of equation (7–2). The phase angle of each component is determined by the frequency,

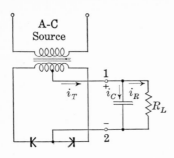

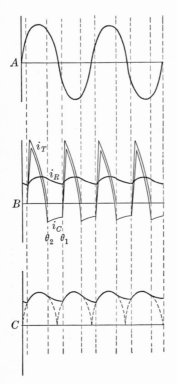

the resistance, and the reactance. The instantaneous sum of these components gives the current wave C. Thus, the magnitudes of the various components are reduced and the phases so changed that a "smoothed current" flows. It should be noted that the peak instantaneous current *does not* rise to a high value, and that rectified current flows *from the rectifiers at all times.*

Rectifier with Capacitive Load.—This circuit is given in Fig. 7–11, and consists of capacitance C connected across the resistance load R_L. This is a very important part of the general problem of rectifier design, and should be carefully studied. Furthermore, Reference 8 should be consulted.

Briefly, the operation of the circuit is as follows: Suppose that the shape of the voltage wave *to be rectified* is as shown by curve A of Fig. 7–11. The *rectified* voltage would be impressed on the condenser C and the load resistor R_L in parallel. The condenser would draw a *high peak charging current* as indicated by i_C of curve B. (In this case it is assumed that the condenser was partially charged as would be true after the rectifier had been in operation a few cycles.) Current i_R will also flow to the resistor as indicated.

When the rectified voltage reaches its peak value and starts to decrease, the current through the condenser must pass through zero, reverse in direction, and the condenser will discharge as indicated by i_C of curve B. The current i_R to the resistor R_L is now composed of that flowing from the rectifier, and that supplied by the dis-

Fig. 7–11. When the sinusoidal voltage (A) is impressed on the full-wave rectifier with a capacitive and resistive load, the instantaneous currents flowing will be as in (B), and the voltage across the load as in (C). This statement applies to any filter load in which cut-out occurs.

charging condenser. This current i_R must be maximum when that through the condenser is zero, because this is the instant of maximum rectified impressed voltage.

The condenser can discharge only through R_L, because *the rectifier prevents reversed current flow.* Thus as indicated by i_T, the total or rectifier current drops to zero at an angle θ_2. The condenser then discharges until θ_1 is reached at which time the rectified voltage again starts to charge the condenser. The current flowing through the rectifier must be the instantaneous sum of i_C and i_R as given by i_T. This current is even more peaked than the condenser charging current alone. A high peak anode or plate current flows through the rectifier. Note in particular that the rectifier current is zero for a large part of the cycle.

The product of the instantaneous current i_R and the load resistance R_L is equal to the voltage across input terminals 1–2. Since the load resistance is constant, then this voltage must have the same shape as the current i_R. This is indicated in Fig. 7–11, C. Since the shape of the actual wave as shown by the *heavy* line is *not* the same as that of the dotted wave but includes a greater area under it (since it never reaches zero) equations (7–1) and (7–2) *do not apply* to the voltage wave for condenser input. It is readily seen that the *direct voltage component* is higher in the rectifier of Fig. 7–11 with a condenser input than in either of the other circuits considered. This is the well-known phenomenon of condenser-input filter circuits, but its cause usually is not clearly understood. Furthermore, the equations do not apply because the frequency components will be different. There are certain limitations [8] as to the value of the condenser which will cause the action described.

The angle θ_2 at which the rectifier *ceases* to conduct is referred to by Stout as the **cut-out point.** Similarly, the angle θ_1, at which the tube *starts* to conduct, is called the **cut-in point.** The calculation of these points depends on the circuit constants and can be made as explained in Reference 8.

Comparison of Rectifier Circuits.—Suppose that the two filter circuits of Fig. 7–12 are considered. These are often called "choke" input and "condenser" input in practice. It has been indicated (page 181) that both these are low-pass filters. With the usual values of inductance and capacitance the cut-off frequencies of the filters are far below the lowest components of equations (7–1) and (7–2).

In the preceding sections it was shown that two fundamental types of rectifier circuits existed; *first,* those in which current flowed continuously from the rectifiers, and *second,* those in which cut-out occurred. The second type circuit was found to give a higher rectified voltage, but was also shown to draw a *high peak or maximum instantaneous current*, a serious objection with gas rectifier tubes.

From the similarity of the filters of Fig. 7–12 with the circuits of Figs. 7–10 and 7–11, it might be inferred that cut-out *never* occurred for the *choke* input filter, and *always* occurred for the condenser input filter of Fig. 7–12. This is not true, however. As Stout shows,[8]

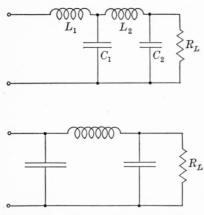

cut-out of the rectified current is due to energy storage of a condenser somewhere in the circuit; it is *not necessary* that the condenser be directly across the input terminals. He also shows that a condenser input does not always produce cut-out of the rectified current, and furthermore, that the condenser across the input terminals produces *no* filtering or "smoothing" effect *unless* its capacitance is *sufficiently large to produce cut-out*. It is apparent that if cut-out is not caused the condenser will be ineffective

FIG. 7–12. Choke and condenser input rectifier filters with resistance loads.

in changing the shape of the voltage wave impressed across the filter as in Fig. 7–11 *C*.

The high inductance in the choke-input filter maintains the peak value of the rectified current low (see page 186). Thus, for the same peak currents, higher alternating voltages (for rectification) can be impressed on the plates of rectifiers with choke-input filters than for rectifiers with condenser inputs. For *equal* alternating voltages, the advantage of the condenser-input filter in maintaining a higher *direct* voltage at the filter input terminals (and hence across the load) is evident from Fig. 7–13.

Filters with *choke input* are almost universally used with gas or vapor thermionic vacuum tubes because the input choke prevents the flow of high instantaneous peak currents which will damage these tubes. Filters with *condenser input* are extensively used with high-vacuum tubes where a high instantaneous current is permissible. For comparable conditions, there is little difference in the power efficiencies of the two systems.

57. Design of Filter Systems.—As has been mentioned, filter systems are usually "designed" by approximate methods based on

experimental data.   In other words, the condenser and coils are made
large enough so that the power hum is not objectionable, and the secondary voltage of the transformer is made large enough so that sufficient

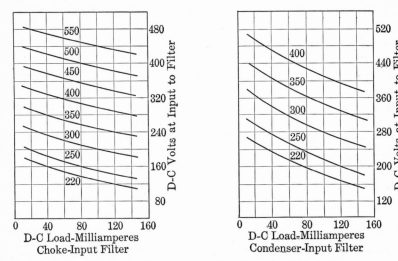

Choke-Input Filter   Condenser-Input Filter

FIG. 7–13.   Illustrating the increased d-c voltage available with the condenser
input filter in which cut-out is produced giving the voltage wave shape of Fig. 7–11 C.
Numbers on curves are the RMS values of the voltage impressed *on the plates* of the
rectifier tubes.   (Data from Reference 22, for a type 80 high-vacuum tube.)

voltage is obtained.   Probably the most logical procedure is to start
with the direct current and voltage requirements at the load and then
proceed to design the filter and the transformer.   Extensive data and
instructions for these calculations will be found in Reference 10.

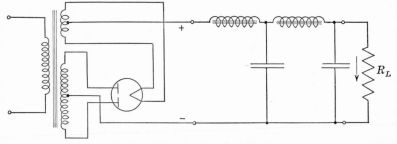

FIG. 7–14.   A typical full-wave rectifier unit with the inductance in the *positive* lead.

Much valuable information will also be found in References 6, 11, 12, and
13.   Only a few general statements regarding design will be included.
    It has been shown [14] that for filters of the types shown in Fig. 7–14
the inductance coils should be placed in the *positive lead* as indicated;

that is, in the connection from the load to the cathode and not in the lead between the anode transformer and load. If this is not done, residual hum will result due to current which flows through the distributed capacitance between the secondary winding and ground, and back to the cathode without passing through, and being impeded by, the chokes.

As has been mentioned, a choke-input filter ordinarily is used with gas or vapor tubes. This first coil is sometimes called the **input choke,** and is often of the "swinging" variety; that is, its inductance varies with the amount of current being carried. Inductance values of 10 henrys at 100 milliamperes and 15 henrys at zero current are typical.

The second inductor is often called a **smoothing choke.** The ratings on these have, in the past, been very misleading. Since the inductance of interest is the *incremental* inductance (page 235) the value of direct current assumed should always be specified. A value of 20 henrys at 120 milliamperes is typical. The terms *input* choke and *smoothing* choke are somewhat misleading, because a critical analysis of filter action will show that the first (or input) choke contributes greatly to the filtering.

One of the requirements of a rectifier and associated filter for certain purposes is that its regulation be good; that is, that the voltage does not rise greatly when the load is decreased or entirely removed. As has been mentioned, following the analysis of Stout [8] it is apparent that the voltage rises on a circuit when cut-out occurs, and this *can occur with choke input as well as condenser input filters.*

Filters with choke inputs which prevent cut-out and resulting high peak currents are usually used with gas tubes, especially in the larger sizes. The inductance of the input choke must be sufficiently great if cut-out is to be avoided. An equation, apparently based on the experimental work [13] reported by Dellenbaugh and Quimby, is extensively used for filter design. This equation is

$$L_1 = \frac{R}{1000}, \tag{7-6}$$

and is used as follows: If R is the resistance of the load, then the *minimum* inductance of the input choke L_1 must be as given by equation (7-6) or cut-out will occur, a high peak current will flow, the voltage will rise, and the regulation will be poor. Thus, if R is 10,000 ohms, L_1 must be 10 henrys for good regulation. This equation can be derived on a theoretical basis,* using the cut-out method of analysis.

* This was done in 1937 by W. F. Goetter while a student at Oregon State College. The results have not been published to date. The theoretical derivation gives an equation $L_1 = R/1140$ (approximately).

Much misconception exists regarding the purpose of the "swinging" choke. When a *large* direct current is being drawn, a *low* value of inductance in the input choke can be used and cut-out will not occur. But when the direct current is *low*, cut-out, high peak currents, and resulting poor regulation may occur with this low inductance. Thus, the swinging choke merely is a choke which is designed with sufficient inductance to prevent cut-out at low current values. No attempt is made to maintain the incremental inductance constant as the core approaches magnetic saturation at large direct-current values where such a large value of inductance is not needed to prevent cut-out.

Referring to the *choke input filter* of Fig. 7–12, approximate design equations are easily derived. For this figure, the ratio of the *alternating* voltage across the load resistor R_L to the *alternating* voltage (such as the components of equation (7–2)) impressed across the filter input terminals is

$$\text{voltage ratio} = \frac{1}{(\omega^4 L_1 L_2 C_1 C_2)}. \tag{7–7}$$

If L_2 and C_2 are omitted from the filter giving a simpler type composed only of an input choke L_1 and a condenser C_1 shunted across the load R_L, the corresponding equation is

$$\text{voltage ratio} = \frac{1}{(\omega^2 L_1 C_1)}. \tag{7–8}$$

In deriving these equations it is assumed that the inductive reactances are very large at the frequency ($\omega = 2\pi f$) under consideration, and that the capacitive reactances are quite small and for certain purposes negligible. It is also assumed that the load resistance R_L is large and that the resistance of the choke is negligible.

As mentioned, these equations give the ratio of the alternating voltage across the load, at each frequency component, to that existing at the same frequency in the impressed rectified voltage wave. They do *not* give the *per cent ripple* at the load. This is computed as the ratio of the effective value of the alternating component of the voltage (or current) at the load to the direct voltage (or current) value at the load. These equations can be derived using the same assumptions as for equations (7–7) and (7–8). In all these equations the results must be multiplied by 100 to convert to per cent, and the inductances and capacitances are expressed in henrys and farads respectively.

As was mentioned on page 183, filters with *tuned inputs* have been used. There are certain advantages and various objections to these.

An advantage is that the tuned input can be used to increase greatly the attenuation which the filter offers to a given alternating component of the rectified wave. Disadvantages are added cost, complexity, bulkiness, and the fact that although the attenuation may be high for one alternating component, others may cause trouble. Furthermore, the inductance and the tuning may vary with the direct-current load. The use of such filters was never extensive and is decreasing. With large condensers and inductors (chokes) such special filters are seldom of an advantage.

As is indicated on page 276 and discussed on page 259, the final or power-amplifying tubes often do not need their plate supply so well filtered as is required by the preceding voltage-amplifying tubes operating at low signal level. This is especially true for a push-pull power output stage. Thus, plate supply voltages are often tapped off ahead of the last choke (Fig. 9–22). Such connections, which are *very* commonly made, further complicate the exact design of rectifier filter systems.

The filter condensers used are of two general types: paper condensers and electrolytic condensers. As the name implies, the dielectric of the first is paper, which may be dry, or may be impregnated with paraffin, oil, or other substance. The dielectric of the second type is a layer of gas. Two precautions are necessary when using the latter: *First*, a polarizing voltage must be used on the electrolytic type to form the layer of gas. This means that they cannot be used in alternating-current circuits in their *usual* form although types for alternating-current circuits have been developed. The *second* precaution is that electrolytic condensers should not be operated in series unless a high resistor is connected in parallel with each to equalize the voltage across them. Otherwise they will divide the voltage unequally, and will be damaged if the voltage is sufficiently high.

In many rectifier units **voltage dividers**[1] are connected across the output terminals of the rectifier. These are usually resistors, often of about 25,000 ohms. Fixed or adjustable taps are available so that the desired voltages can be obtained.[10] In addition to serving in this manner, the divider tends to prevent the terminal voltage from increasing when the load is removed, thus improving the regulation. In many instances it is necessary to connect large condensers across the divider elements [10] to reduce feedback due to common impedances (page 203).

58. Polyphase Rectifiers.—In the preceding discussions, only *single-phase* half-wave and full-wave rectifiers have been considered. For rectifying large amounts of power, above about one kilowatt for instance, **polyphase rectifiers** are often used, especially for plate-supply voltages for radio transmitters.[15] Two of these polyphase rectifiers are shown in Fig. 7–15.

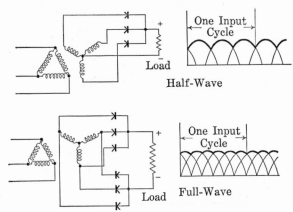

FIG. 7–15. Two types of three-phase rectifiers.

The first of these is a three-phase half-wave rectifier. Owing to the fact that the phase voltages are 120 degrees out of phase, the rectified currents combine as indicated, giving a relatively smooth resultant rectified output current and voltage for the load. The second diagram is for a three-phase full-wave rectifier. The rectified output current and voltage are even more smooth for this arrangement. The load for these two rectifiers is pure resistance as indicated. Filters are employed to reduce the harmonic content, and these may be less elaborate than with single-phase rectification, because, as the rectified waves indicate, less filtering is required. Another advantage of the polyphase rectifiers is that they give a higher output voltage in pro-portion to the peak alternating voltage applied than do the single-phase types. Polyphase rectifiers utilizing as high as *twelve* phases have been developed.[16]

59. Voltage-Doubling Rectifiers.—A voltage-doubling circuit, such as is employed in certain small radio-receiving sets, is shown in Fig. 7–16. A simplified diagram is also included. The manner in which this simplified circuit operates to produce a *direct* voltage approximately twice the maximum value of the impressed *alternating* voltage is essentially as follows: During the part of the alternating cycle that generator terminal 1 is positive and 2 is negative, *conventional* current will pass through the upper rectifier and charge the upper condenser. On the negative half cycle, when terminal 1 is negative and 2 is positive, the lower rectifier will conduct, and the corresponding condenser will be charged. Thus, when no direct-current power is taken, the voltage across the output terminals will be approximately $2E_{max.}$ as indicated, where $E_{max.}$ is the *maximum* value of the applied alternating voltage.

If a resistor is connected across the output terminals, a rectified or direct current will flow. The shape of this current will be as indicated

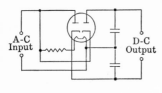

Actual Circuit

in Fig. 7–16; it is seen to be comparatively smooth. Some filtering must be accomplished, however, before this voltage can be applied to the plates of receiver tubes. The manner in which the output voltage varies for given load currents is shown in Fig. 7–17. The advantage of large condensers is apparent. As previously mentioned, voltage

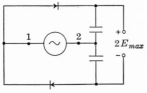

Equivalent Circuit

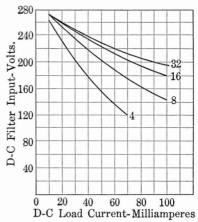

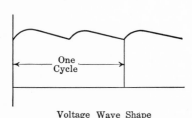

Voltage Wave Shape
for Resistance Load

Fig. 7–16. The voltage-doubling rectifier.

Fig. 7–17. Variations in d-c voltage input to filter for a voltage doubler. Numbers on curves refer to capacitance in microfarads of each condenser of Fig. 7–16. (Data from Reference 22.)

doublers are used in small radio receivers; other uses are in x-ray sets, and in high-voltage, cathode-ray oscillographs. The first cost of voltage doublers is, comparatively, very low.

60. Rectifier Tubes.—The type of tube to be used for a given rectifier will, of course, be determined by the use for which the rectifier is designed. Both high-vacuum and gas (or vapor) thermionic tubes are extensively used. These were discussed in Chapter 4, page 74.

High-vacuum rectifier tubes are usually employed in radio receivers and in many small sound-system amplifiers, because the power involved is small, and efficiency is of little importance.　Furthermore, gas (or vapor) tubes cause radio interference and require special shielding and filtering precautions in radio-receiving sets.　Gas tubes are often used in sound-system amplifiers, and are widely used in plate-supply rectifiers for radio transmitters.　High-vacuum tubes also are used for this purpose.

An interesting cold-cathode glow rectifier tube (page 93) containing helium gas at a low pressure has also been used to a limited extent as a rectifier for radio-receiving sets.　A discussion of this tube (Raytheon), and the circuit used will be found in Reference 10.

As mentioned on page 74, the peak current and the peak inverse plate voltage are factors limiting the life and hence the rating of tubes. The peak current is especially important in gas (or vapor) tubes, because if a certain value is exceeded, then the safe internal voltage drop will be too large and the tube will be damaged (page 87).　If the safe peak inverse plate voltage is exceeded, the tube may arc back.

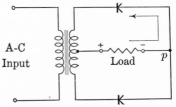

It is of interest to examine the voltages between electrodes during the normal operation of a tube. This is illustrated, for the full-wave

Fig. 7–18.　Substantially the entire secondary voltage appears as an inverse voltage across the rectifier which at the instant is not conducting.

rectifier, by Fig. 7–18, in which the tube is replaced by a generalized rectifier unit.

When the upper end of the transformer is negative, a conventional current will flow as indicated by the arrow, but *no current* will flow through the *lower* unit.　When the upper unit conducts, the resistance of this unit, and the voltage drop across it, become very low.　Hence, point p assumes a potential approaching as a limit that of the upper end of the transformer winding.　Now at the same instant the upper end of the transformer secondary is negative, the lower end is positive. Thus, substantially the *entire* secondary voltage appears as an *inverse voltage* across the lower rectifier unit which is not conducting at the instant under consideration.　This inverse voltage tries to force a current through, and break down, the lower unit.　On the next half cycle the action is reversed.

61. Copper-Oxide Rectifiers.—The theory of these rectifiers has been discussed (page 48) and will not be repeated.　This section will consider the use of these devices in actual rectifier circuits. The theory has been fully treated in an article [9] by Huss, from which the following is summarized.

A copper-oxide rectifier offers *low* resistance to current flow when the *current* (not electron) is from the oxide to the copper, and offers

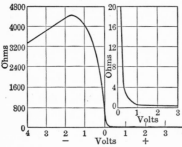

high resistance when the current flow is in the opposite direction. These relations are shown in Fig. 7–19. It will be noted that the resistance in the non-conducting direction is far from the infinite value of an *ideal* rectifier. These rectifiers are used in the conven-

FIG. 7–19. Characteristics of a copper-oxide rectifier unit. Negative sign means oxide negative and copper positive. Positive sign means oxide positive and copper negative. (From Reference 14, page 52.)

tional circuits of Fig. 7–20, called (a) the transformer bridge, and (b) the Graetz bridge. When an alternating voltage is impressed across a copper-oxide rectifier, an appreciable current will flow through the capacitance of the unit. Thus, the term *impedance* should be employed in connection with alternating-current circuits, especially at the higher audio frequencies and above.

As previously mentioned, the resistance of this rectifier is *finite* for both the conducting and "non-conducting" directions. Furthermore, from Fig. 7–19 it is evident the rectifier could be replaced (for an

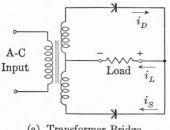
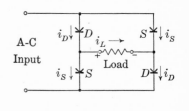

(a) Transformer Bridge   (b) Graetz Bridge

FIG. 7–20. Current relations in copper-oxide rectifier circuits. Some current flows on the negative half cycle because the rectifier is imperfect as Fig. 7–19 indicates. (From Reference 9.)

approximate analysis) by a *small* fixed resistor for the conducting direction and a *large* fixed resistor for the non-conducting direction. Thus, for an approximate analysis, the letter D is used to represent the resistance for the *conducting* direction, and S for the inverse or "non-conducting" direction.

With these assumptions the current relations in the circuits of Fig. 7–20 can be represented, at a given instant, as indicated. By theoretical considerations [9] the voltage produced across the resistance load can be calculated. For the circuits of Fig. 7–20, these would be full-wave voltages similar to curve A of Fig. 7–2, page 178, and containing a direct and alternating components *somewhat* as given by equation (7–2). If a rectified and *filtered* current were desired, the filters would be connected between the load and the rectifier. An analysis of copper-oxide rectifiers with associated filters is also given in Reference 9.

62. Controlled Rectifiers.—There are some instances, such as for certain electric welding operations, where a closely controlled rectified current is required. Another need is for dimmers for large lighting installations such as in theatres. Many methods, such as adding a rheostat in series, *could* be used to give close control, but such methods would be wasteful of power. The hot-cathode grid-controlled gas (or vapor) rectifier tubes (often called Thyratrons) discussed on page 133, and the igniter-type mercury pool tubes (often called Ignitrons) discussed on page 102, largely have solved these and similar problems.

The technical literature has contained much material on the theory and uses of these tubes; this material largely has been summarized in References 6, 17, and 18, which list the various articles on the subject. A brief discussion of the uses of these two tubes will now be given.

Grid-Controlled Rectifier Applications.—The characteristics of the *negative* type of hot-cathode grid-controlled gas tubes or Thyratrons were given on page 137. There are two *common* methods for controlling the rectified current flowing in the plate or anode circuit and hence through the load resistance. The first is **amplitude control** and the second is **phase shift control.**[18]

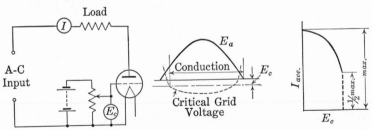

Fig. 7–21. With this type amplitude control, current flows whenever the grid bias E_c exceeds the critical grid voltage. The average anode current I is controllable from maximum to $\frac{1}{2}$ maximum value as indicated. (Adapted from Reference 18.)

A simple circuit for amplitude control is shown in Fig. 7–21. The operation of this is based on Fig. 5–23, page 137. The tube will conduct for the various values of *critical grid voltage* indicated. Referring now to Fig. 7–21, if the grid-bias voltage E_c is less than the dotted line marked *critical grid voltage*, the tube will break down and conduct; once conduction occurs, it will continue until the anode voltage falls to zero. An analysis will show that by this means the *average* rectified current can be controlled between the values of maximum and one-half maximum.

The method of phase-shift control is also based on Fig. 5–23, page 137. The theory underlying it is illustrated by Fig. 7–22 in which the dotted line indicates the critical grid voltage values. If the grid voltage is more positive than this critical value at any time, the tube will start to conduct and will continue to do so until the plate voltage falls to zero and deionization occurs. Thus, when the grid voltage and plate voltage are almost 180 degrees out of phase, only a small amount of current will flow, and this will be as indicated by the peaked shaded area of curve A. When the grid voltage and plate voltage are more nearly in phase, the current will flow as shown by the shaded area of B, and when they are in phase, the current flows for the entire cycle and the magnitude is limited by the resistance in the anode circuit.

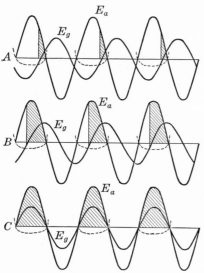

Fig. 7–22. Illustrating the theory of phase shift control of the rectified anode current. Current starts only when the anode voltage E_a is positive, and when the voltage on the grid is less negative than the critical grid voltage shown by the broken lines. The shaded portions indicate the shapes of the current impulses.

Several methods [17, 18] are available for shifting the phase of the grid voltage and hence giving the desired control. One method is as shown in Fig. 7–23. Varying the value of R changes the phase relation of the grid voltage so that the average rectified current can be controlled from a maximum value (limited by the load resistance) to zero value.

Controlled Pool Rectifiers.—In these tubes, an electrode immersed in a mercury pool "ignites" or "fires" the tube (causing an arc to be established and the tube to conduct) at the desired part of the cycle. The amount of power required by the igniting electrode is small.

The reason for the descriptive name Ignitron is apparent.   The characteristics of this device were discussed on page 101.

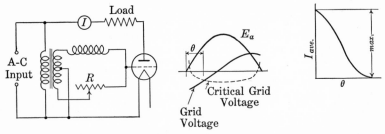

FIG. 7–23.   Phase shift control.   The angle between the grid voltage and anode
voltage E_a is varied by shifting R.   The angle θ at which current flows is thus controlled.   The average rectified current flowing through the load can be regulated
from a maximum value to zero as indicated.   (Adapted from Reference 18.)

Many uses [16, 17] have been developed for these igniter tubes.
Among these is the circuit shown in Fig. 7–24 in which the tubes are
used to control the welding current.   The firing of the tubes is determined by the grid-controlled tubes which are in turn regulated by
any suitable means such as those discussed in the preceding paragraphs.

An extensive list of articles
giving applications of these
tubes is included in Reference 17.

Inverters.—These are devices employing *gas* or *vapor*
tubes for converting direct-
current power into alternating-current power.   When
this is done with *high-vacuum tubes*, the devices are
called oscillators.   The in-

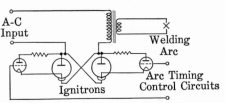

FIG. 7–24.   Illustrating the use of Ignitrons
or pool rectifier tubes for welding current
control.   The firing of the pool tubes is controlled by the grid-controlled rectifiers and
their associated circuits.   (Adapted from
Reference 18.)

verters use grid-controlled gas tubes or Thyratrons.   The efficiency
of an inverter is high compared with an oscillator because of the low
internal loss in gas tubes.   Inverters are, therefore, used where large
amounts of power are to be converted.

Many types of inverters [17, 18] have been developed.   Some of
these employ two tubes, especially where large amounts of power are
involved, but single-tube inverters such as those shown in Fig. 7–25 also
are used.   The operation of this circuit [17, 18] essentially is as follows:
At the instant the switch closes, the voltage between the anode and
cathode is zero.   As the condenser C charges through R, the voltage

across the condenser increases; and thus the voltage between anode and cathode of the tube also increases. When this voltage is sufficient, the tube breaks down and passes current through the inductance L.

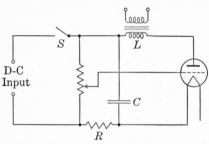

FIG. 7–25. Simplified circuit of an inverter which uses a gas triode for converting from direct to alternating-current power.

When this occurs, the voltage across the condenser cannot exceed that of the arc-drop across the tube which is about 15 volts. The condenser therefore discharges through L.

When the voltage of the condenser reaches that of the arc, the current flow is maintained by the energy stored in the coil L. This charges the condenser in the opposite direction, and permits the anode to be driven negative so that deionization occurs. When the arc ceases, the charge across the condenser builds up as before, and the operation is repeated. Since the current through L starts from zero, increases to a maximum, and then decreases to zero, an alternating voltage will be induced in the secondary coil magnetically coupled to it.

63. Direct-Current Transmission.—As is well known there are objections and limitations (such as instability) to the transmission of power by alternating-current systems, and there are many factors in favor of (and also against as summarized [17] by Henney) the transmission of power over high-voltage direct-current systems. The possibilities of generating alternating power, rectifying it with gas tubes, transmitting it as direct current, and then changing the transmitted power back to alternating current for distribution have been investigated.[19, 20] Inverters are used to convert to alternating-current power.

The details of this system are very interesting but can be best obtained fom the original articles listed. The summary [17] made by Henney is also very helpful.

One important phase of the use of gas or vapor thermionic tubes in rectifiers and inverters is often overlooked; this is **inductive interference.** The mercury-vapor tube was tried in radio receivers, and then abandoned. At least one reason for this was the excessive interference caused. The mercury-arc rectifier has caused much interference both with radio reception and with telephone systems. Thus, in the design of rectifiers and inverters for handling large amounts of power, especial care must be exercised to prevent inductive interference with neighboring communication systems,[4, 5] and with radio reception. Such interference will tend to be especially troublesome where such power devices feed into open-wire lines and trolley systems. Trouble can be largely prevented by the use of filters and care in the design of the power equipment. It is a point to which attention should be directed; many of the electronic devices now theoretically possible will produce severe interference if installed for commercial operation.

64. Power Supplies for Amplifiers.—One extensive use of the diode rectifier is in direct-current power supplies for audio-frequency amplifiers and radio-receiving sets which operate from alternating-current sources of power. Such an amplifier is shown in Fig. 9–22. This circuit was chosen because of its simplicity. A brief analysis of the power-supply features of this amplifier will now be given.

A dotted line has been drawn dividing the first two stages of the amplifier into two parts. Of course, direct voltages and direct components of current must be impressed on, and flow through the tubes. These will have alternating audio components superimposed on them, and these *should be kept above the dividing line* shown on Fig. 9–22. Furthermore, since the resistance to direct current of the transformer primary windings is quite low, it is not misleading to regard all parts above the line as an alternating-current circuit, and all parts below the line as a direct-current circuit.

As noted on this figure, resistors R-3 and R-4 are both connected to the $+$ "B" or positive high-voltage terminal of the power-supply filter. Also, the resistors R-2 and R-3 are connected to ground, to which the negative terminal of the power-supply filter is also connected. With these connections, the plate *direct current* of the first tube must flow through R-3 (25,000 ohms) and that of the second tube through R-4 (15,000 ohms). These resistors will, accordingly, have I_pR drops across them, and will reduce the $+$ "B" voltage to the correct amounts for impressing *on the plates* of the respective tubes.

The direct current (electrons) flowing to the plate must return *to the cathode* and these plate currents flow through the resistors R-2 of 2500 ohms each. An I_pR drop will occur across each of these, and this direct voltage will bias the grid of the tube *negatively*. The reasons for the condensers C-1 and C-2 will now be considered.

When the amplifier is in operation with an alternating audio-frequency signal impressed on the input circuit, a low-impedance path for the alternating-current components must be supplied. This low-impedance path is provided by the condensers C-1 and C-2 of 4 microfarads and 2 microfarads respectively. Thus, the reason for drawing the dotted dividing line on Fig. 9–22 is apparent. The condensers aid in separating the alternating-current and the direct-current components.

Methods of Obtaining Self-Bias.—In the early speech amplifiers and radio-receiving sets the direct bias voltage for the grids of the tubes was usually supplied by "C" batteries. After the adoption of tubes with separate heaters, self-biasing methods, such as those considered in the preceding paragraph, were employed. A small and compact source of direct voltage called a "biasing cell" has been placed on the market. The extent to which it will be used is not now apparent.

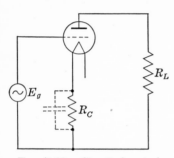

The circuit of Fig. 7–26 can be used for studying the effect of the self-biasing or cathode resistor R_c on the characteristics of a resistance-coupled amplifier. When connected as indicated *without the by-pass condenser*, the alternating component of the plate current which flows through the load resistance R_L will also flow through the load

FIG. 7–26. Circuit for studying the effect of a self-biasing resistor.

resistor R_c. There will be an IR_c drop due to this alternating component, and this will *subtract* from the impressed grid voltage because the plate-current changes are 180 degrees out of phase with the grid-voltage variations. It can therefore be shown that

$$i_p = \frac{\mu e_s}{[r_p + R_c(\mu + 1) + R_L]}. \tag{7-9}$$

Thus, *without the by-pass condenser*, and for a *resistance* load, the biasing resistor causes a very great loss acting as a resistor $R_c(\mu + 1)$ in reducing the output current. For the pure resistance load this decrease in output will be independent of the frequency, but for an inductive load the effect will be greater at the high frequencies. This *reduction* of output is called a **reversed feedback** effect or **degeneration,** and has been used to advantage in one type of feedback amplifier (page 278).

If a large condenser is connected across the resistor as indicated by the dotted lines of Fig. 7–26, then a negligible alternating voltage drop will result, and this reversed feedback effect and the resulting loss of output is largely prevented. For the lowest frequencies to be amplified, the reactance of the condenser must be small compared to the resistance of the biasing resistor R_c. When a low-impedance path for the alternating component is provided by a condenser as by C-2 of

Fig. 9–22, page 276, then the alternating current need not flow through the R-2, C-1 circuit and this also reduces degeneration.

Special methods,[21] different from the biasing resistor and condenser connection of Fig. 7–26, have been employed particularly when low-capacitance paper condensers were used. The availability of reliable electrolytic condensers of low voltage and high capacitance ratings (such as 25 volts, 25 microfarads) has caused the wide adoption of the method shown in Fig. 7–26. In this connection it should be noted that in a more modern amplifier than Fig. 9–22, page 276, C-1 and C-2 would probably be of this larger-capacitance electrolytic type.

Common Impedances.—Again referring to Fig. 9–22, the preceding discussion has shown the desirability of keeping the alternating-current components above the dotted line. Thus, considering the

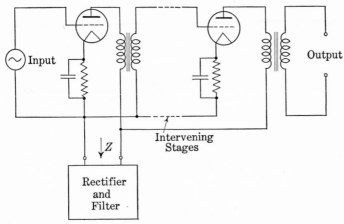

Fig. 7–27.   Circuit for illustrating the effect of common impedances.

first tube, for the *ideal* situation the alternating plate-current component should flow only through the primary of the transformer, the condenser C-2, and from the cathode to the plate. Similarly, the alternating-current component of the plate current of the second tube should be confined to the plate circuit of this tube. *It is very important that the alternating-current components do not flow through circuits or impedances which are common to both.*

To illustrate this point, consider the circuit of Fig. 7–27. If a *"B"* battery having *zero* internal impedance were used, then the circuit should operate satisfactorily. But, in practice the rectifier and filter will have a certain internal impedance Z. Since the by-passing condensers are omitted, the plate currents flowing through the rectifier and filter will contain *both* direct and alternating components.

Thus, the greatly-amplified alternating component of the plate current of the output tube will flow through the internal impedance of the rectifier and filter. This will cause the voltage between the output terminals of the filter to change in accordance with the output-current variations. These plate-voltage changes will cause the plate current of the first tube to vary accordingly, and thus the output of the amplifier is *coupled back to the input* through the common impedance. The phase relations of this feedback may be such as to cause an increase or a decrease in the amplification at a given frequency. This feedback may cause the amplifier to oscillate at a certain frequency. In resistance-coupled amplifiers these oscillations are of a very low frequency (because of the lack of a resonant circuit) and the amplifier is said to be **motor-boating.** It should be mentioned that this may occur with "*B*" battery plate supply under some conditions.

Although the prevention of oscillations and motor-boating is simple in theory, it is sometimes difficult to achieve in practice. To prevent such action all common impedances should be avoided. This can be done by *first* confining all alternating-current components to their individual circuits, as previously discussed, and *second* by connecting very large condensers across any impedance which is common to the two circuits. This last possibility is quite effective at radio frequencies. For additional information, References **11, 21,** and **22** are suggested.

REFERENCES

1. American Institute of Electrical Engineers. *Definitions of Electrical Terms.*
2. Sahagen, J. *The use of the copper oxide rectifier for instrument purposes.* Proc. I. R. E., Feb., 1931, Vol. 19, No. 2.
3. Jolley, L. B. W. *Alternating Current Rectification.* John Wiley & Sons.
4. Albert, A. L. *Electrical Communication.* John Wiley & Sons.
5. Everitt, W. L. *Communication Engineering.* McGraw-Hill Book Co.
6. Pender, H., and McIlwain, K. *Electrical Engineers' Handbook.* Vol. 5, Electric Communication and Electronics. John Wiley & Sons.
7. Shea, T. E. *Transmission Networks and Wave Filters.* D. Van Nostrand Co.
8. Stout, M. B. *Analysis of rectifier filter circuits.* Electrical Engineering, Sept., 1935, Vol. 54, No. 9.
9. Huss, P. O. *An analysis of copper-oxide rectifier circuits.* Electrical Engineering, March, 1937, Vol. 56, No. 3.
10. Henney, K. *Radio Engineering Handbook.* McGraw-Hill Book Co.
11. Terman, F. E. *Radio Engineering.* McGraw-Hill Book Co.
12. American Radio Relay League. *The Radio Amateur's Handbook.*
13. Dellenbaugh, Jr., F. S., and Quimby, R. S. *A series of articles on rectifier design.* Q. S. T., Feb., March, April, 1932.

14. Terman, F. E., and Pickles, S. B. *Note on a cause of residual hum in rectifier-filter systems.* Proc. I. R. E., Aug., 1934, Vol. 22, No. 8.
15. Armstrong, R. W. *Polyphase rectification special connections.* Proc. I. R. E., Jan., 1931, Vol. 19, No. 1.
16. Westinghouse Electric and Manufacturing Co. *Industrial Electronic Tubes.* Course 25.
17. Henney, K. *Electron Tubes in Industry.* McGraw-Hill Book Co.
18. McArthur, E. D. *Electronics and Electron Tubes.* John Wiley & Sons.
19. Willis, C. H., Bedford, B. D., and Elder, F. R. *Constant current d. c. transmission.* Electrical Engineering, Jan., 1935, Vol. 54, No. 1.
20. Bedford, B. D., Elder, F. R., and Willis, C. H. *Power transmission by direct current.* Gen. Elec. Rev., May, 1936, Vol. 39, No. 5.
21. Glasgow, R. S. *Principles of Radio Engineering.* McGraw-Hill Book Co.
22. R.C.A. Manufacturing Co. *Receiving Tube Manual.*

SUGGESTED ASSIGNMENTS

1. Calculate the cut-off frequency and the iterative impedance of a choke input and a condenser input filter of the type shown in Fig. **7–5** which could be used in a rectifier for the power supply of an audio-frequency sound-system amplifier.
2. Referring to Fig. **7–8**, and to the discussion on page 184, assume that the generator has negligible internal impedance and that it impresses a voltage wave such as B of Fig. **7–2** on the filter. Assume values of this voltage, of the filter elements, and of the load, and calculate the magnitudes of the various alternating-current components which flow through the load.
3. Referring to the method outlined by Stout in Reference 8, assume the necessary data and calculate the magnitudes and phase angles for the alternating components of the current through a circuit such as Fig. **7–10**.
4. Derive equations (**7–7**) and (**7–8**) on page 191.
5. Following the discussion on page 191, derive equations corresponding to (**7–7**) and (**7–8**), but giving the per cent ripple. Discuss the factors which would cause these equations to be only approximate. Will they apply in filters in which cut-out occurs?
6. Obtain data for typical filters from a tube manual or a radio parts catalogue. Use equations (**7–7**) and (**7–8**) and the equations derived in assignment 5 to calculate the filtering effectiveness in per cent.
7. Enumerate the advantages and disadvantages of high-voltage alternating current and of high-voltage direct current transmission systems.
8. Fully explain why less filtering is required for a push-pull stage of amplification than for a single-tube stage.

CHAPTER 8

VACUUM-TUBE VOLTAGE AMPLIFIERS

As is well known, the thermionic vacuum tube is very extensively used as an **amplifier** [1] in audio- and radio-frequency circuits. Probably the first extensive commercial use of the tube for this purpose was in 1914 as an audio-frequency amplifier or "repeater" in the long-distance transcontinental telephone lines of the Bell System. Previous to this, it was necessary to use mechanical devices for this purpose; these were not entirely satisfactory.

In considering amplifiers, it is of importance clearly to understand the problem involved. Thus, suppose that an audio amplifier is to be designed to amplify the output of a microphone and drive several loud speakers. The speech sound waves actuate the microphone causing it to develop a very small audio-frequency voltage across the input terminals of the amplifier. The vacuum tubes in the first several stages are operated as **voltage amplifiers.** These increase the weak input voltage until it is sufficient to drive a **power amplifier** tube (or tubes).

This distinction between *voltage* amplifiers and *power* amplifiers is very important. The design of the tubes and the associated circuits for these two uses is not the same. The first stages act merely to *increase the voltage* until this voltage is sufficiently large to *control the output* of the power tube which actually supplies the power to the loud speakers or other load. In addition to their use for amplifying voltage and power, amplifiers may be used to amplify currents.

65. The Decibel.—This unit is widely used in rating and discussing amplifiers, and should, therefore, be considered before proceeding with the theory of amplifiers. The **decibel** is based on the **bel,** defined [1] as follows: "The bel is the fundamental division of a logarithmic scale for expressing the ratio of two amounts of power, the number of bels denoting such a ratio being the logarithm to the base 10 of this ratio." Thus, the number of bels is given by the equation,

$$N = \log_{10}\left(\frac{P_1}{P_2}\right), \tag{8-1}$$

where P_1 and P_2 represent two amounts of power.

The decibel (abbreviated db) is defined [1] as "one tenth of a bel, the number of decibels denoting the ratio of two amounts of power being 10 times the logarithm to the base 10 of this ratio." The number of decibels is given by the equation

$$n = 10 \log_{10}\left(\frac{P_1}{P_2}\right), \tag{8–2}$$

and it follows that

$$\frac{P_1}{P_2} = 10^{0.1 \times n}, \tag{8–3}$$

where P_1 and P_2 represent two amounts of power.

It is usually difficult to measure directly values of power in communication circuits, because no generally satisfactory wattmeter has been developed which will operate at the low power levels and the high frequencies of such circuits. Since power is equal to $EI \cos \theta$ or to I^2R it is possible to expand equations (8–1) and (8–2) so that voltage or current measurements may be used and the power need not be directly measured. Expanding equation (8–2)

$$n = 10 \log_{10}\left(\frac{P_1}{P_2}\right) = 10 \log_{10}\frac{E_1 I_1 \cos \theta_1}{E_2 I_2 \cos \theta_2} = 10 \log_{10}\frac{E_1^2 Z_2 \cos \theta_1}{E_2^2 Z_1 \cos \theta_2}$$

$$= 20 \log_{10}\frac{E_1}{E_2} + 10 \log_{10}\frac{Z_2}{Z_1} + 10 \log_{10}\frac{\cos \theta_1}{\cos \theta_2}. \tag{8–4}$$

In terms of current values,

$$n = 10 \log_{10}\left(\frac{P_1}{P_2}\right) = 10 \log_{10}\left(\frac{I_1^2 R_1}{I_2^2 R_2}\right)$$

$$= 20 \log_{10}\left(\frac{I_1}{I_2}\right) + 10 \log_{10}\left(\frac{R_1}{R_2}\right). \tag{8–5}$$

From equations (8–4) and (8–5) it is seen that the number of decibels can be found *under special conditions* from the voltage relation

$$n = 20 \log_{10}\left(\frac{E_1}{E_2}\right), \tag{8–6}$$

and that

$$\frac{E_1}{E_2} = 10^{0.05 \times n}. \tag{8–7}$$

Also, the number of decibels can be found *under special conditions* from the relation

$$n = 20 \log_{10}\left(\frac{I_1}{I_2}\right), \tag{8–8}$$

and that

$$\frac{I_1}{I_2} = 10^{0.05 \times n}. \tag{8–9}$$

As previously mentioned, equations (8–6) and (8–8) hold only under certain special conditions, which are that the *magnitude* and the angle of the impedances of the output circuit under test and the terminating load are equal.

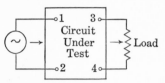

FIG. 8–1.   Circuit for explaining the decibel.

The above theory is illustrated by Fig. 8–1. If a voltmeter is connected across the terminals 1–2 and another is connected across the terminals 3–4, then equation (8–6) can be used to give the *power loss* or *gain* of this circuit only when the impedance measured into the circuit at terminals 1–2 with the driving oscillator disconnected is equal in magnitude and angle to the load impedance.   If this is not true, equations (8–6) and (8–8) do not give the *power* loss or gain in decibels in a circuit as defined by equation (8–2).

Ratings of Tubes and Amplifiers.—The input power to a tube operated with the grid always negative, is negligible and often assumed zero. Thus, the power input to many amplifiers is negligible and they may be considered as voltage-operated devices.   Therefore, when the term *decibel* is used in connection with the ratings of tubes and amplifiers, it often does not have the meaning given by the definition on page 206. As used in many fields, particularly radio and sound amplification, the decibel usually specifies voltage ratios and *not power ratios*.   This is a loose usage of the term and if it is so used, a statement to that effect should be included.

Thus, if E_1 volts are impressed across *any* circuit and E_2 volts appear across the output of that circuit, then equation (8–6) can be used to express the *voltage* ratio in decibels.   Similarly, equation (8–8) can be used for expressing *current* ratios.   The decibel is so used for expressing the *voltage gain* of an amplifier, but this is *not a power calculation* in accordance with equation (8–2).

Furthermore, the output circuits of many amplifiers contain step-down transformers to match the impedances and supply the large voice currents for the low-impedance dynamic loud speakers so widely used. Thus, the voltage *output* may not be greatly different from the voltage input, and yet a large amount of power amplification has resulted.

The decibel is also used for specifying **power levels.**   Thus, if an arbitrary zero level is selected, the power at any other point may be so many decibels above (positive) or so many decibels below (negative) this arbitrary level as given by equation (8–2).   Many arbitrary zero levels have been advocated and used.   For example, 0.001 watt, 0.006 watt, 0.01 watt, etc.   The standards [1] of the American Institute of

Electrical Engineers and of the Institute of Radio Engineers [2] do not recognize any arbitrary value as a zero reference level at present.

From the preceding discussion it is apparent that the *decibel* is used in many ways, and that if its use is to be exact, the *conditions* such as assumed zero level and other necessary data *should be specified*.

66. Distortion.—This is defined [1] as a "change in wave form." Unfortunately, in general the output wave form of an amplifier is not an exact replica of the input signal and hence distortion has occurred. The various types of distortion will be defined at this time so that the distortion caused by amplifiers may be understood. The quotations included are from the Standards of the American Institute of Electrical Engineers, Reference 1.

Frequency Distortion.—In this type of distortion, "the change is in the relative magnitude of the different frequency components of a wave, provided that change is not caused by non-linear distortion." For example, if an amplifier has a gain of 80 db at 100 cycles, and 90 db at 6000 cycles, frequency distortion would result.

Non-Linear Distortion.—This is a form of distortion "which occurs when the ratio of voltage to current, using root-mean-square values (or analogous quantities in other fields), is a function of the magnitude of either." Thus, if the impedance of a circuit or device varies with the magnitude of the impressed current or voltage, the shape of the output waves will not be the same as that of the input, and will contain harmonics. These harmonics of the impressed fundamental are due to distortion. A non-linear device may have many useful applications such as for modulators and demodulators (page 310). This has been called harmonic distortion.

Delay Distortion.—This is defined as "that form of distortion which occurs when the velocity of propagation of a wave varies with frequency." Thus, if impulses of different frequencies pass through a device at different speeds, they will not arrive at the output terminals in their original phase relations, and the signal is distorted. Although considerable delay distortion can be tolerated for speech and music, such distortion is very objectional in the transmission of pictures and images as in telephoto systems and in television. This form of distortion is also called velocity and phase distortion.

Of course where exact wave form must be reproduced (as in television) any reactive element introduces a change in wave form, and so distortion. Unless compensated it may cause blurring of the picture.

67. Classification of Amplifiers.—The distinction between voltage amplifiers and power amplifiers was explained on page 206. Amplifiers may be further classified as to the *method of operation* of the tubes.

They may also be classified on the basis of the *method of coupling* between stages. Thus, a voltage amplifier may consist of resistance-coupled, linear, or class *A* stages; or, it may contain transformer-coupled class *A* stages.

The classification into class *A*, *B*, or *C* amplifier stages is of extreme importance because this classification is based on the principle of operation *as a circuit element*. In discussing these classifications the Standards of the Institute of Radio Engineers [2] will be quoted so that the statements will be exact.

"The operating point on the grid-plate characteristic determined by the grid bias and the amplitude of the exciting grid voltage varies over a wide range in amplifiers designed for different fields of application. The plate efficiency of the amplifying tube and the degree to which the alternating component of the plate current is a reproduction of the alternating grid voltage depend upon the operating point on the grid-plate characteristic as determined by the grid bias and upon the magnitude of the exciting grid voltage.

"Amplifiers are grouped into three general classes (*A*, *B*, and *C*) according to the region of the grid-plate characteristic in which the operating point, as determined by the grid bias, is located, and the magnitude of the exciting grid voltage. There is nothing fundamental in this classification. It is a recognition of current practices in amplifier design and offers a convenient terminology for the description of amplifiers. It is understood that this classification refers only to single-stage amplifiers; a multi-stage amplifier may consist of two or more classes.

Class A Amplifier.—"A class *A* amplifier is an amplifier in which the grid bias and alternating grid voltages are such that plate current in a specific tube flows at all times.

" The ideal class *A* amplifier is one in which the alternating component of the plate current is an exact reproduction of the form of the alternating grid voltage, and the plate current flows 360 electrical degrees.

"The characteristics of a class *A* amplifier are low efficiency and output.

Class B Amplifier.—"A class *B* amplifier is an amplifier in which the grid bias is approximately equal to the cut-off value so that the plate current is approximately zero when no exciting grid voltage is applied, and so that plate current in a specific tube flows for approximately one-half of each cycle when an alternating grid voltage is applied.

" The ideal class *B* amplifier is one in which the alternating component of plate current is an exact replica of the alternating grid voltage for the half cycle when the grid is positive with respect to the bias voltage, and the plate current flows 180 electrical degrees.

"The characteristics of a class B amplifier are medium efficiency and output.

Class C Amplifier.—"A class C amplifier is an amplifier in which the grid bias is appreciably greater than the cut-off value so that the plate current in each tube is zero when no alternating grid voltage is applied, and so that plate current flows in a specific tube for appreciably less than one-half of each cycle when an alternating grid voltage is applied.

"Class C amplifiers find application where high plate circuit efficiency is a paramount requirement and where departures from linearity between input and output are permissible.

"The characteristics of a class C amplifier are high plate circuit efficiency and high power output."

Additional classifications are sometimes used.[3]   Thus, in the *class AB* (or A prime) amplifier the bias adjustment and the magnitude of the alternating signal voltage impressed on the grid are such that plate current flows for appreciably more than half but less than the entire electrical cycle.   The efficiency and output are intermediate to those of the class A and class B amplifiers.   In the class BC amplifier, adjustments are such that plate current flows for less than one-half cycle, but is not suppressed to the extent common in class C operation.   Its characteristics are between the class B and class C amplifiers.   The class BC amplifier is of relatively little importance.

Amplifiers may be further classified as to frequency range, into **audio-frequency** (a-f) or **radio-frequency** (r-f) amplifiers.   This chapter will discuss both audio-frequency and radio-frequency *voltage* amplifiers.   The succeeding chapter will be devoted to *power* amplifiers.

In audio-frequency amplifiers, and in radio-frequency amplifiers for reception, the voltage-amplifying stages are class A.   The audio-frequency power-output stages are class A, AB, or B.   Radio-frequency power output amplifiers are usually class B or C.

68. Class A Voltage Amplification.—*Triode.*—For *audio-frequency* voltage amplification, the triode gives excellent results.   The theory was considered on page 126, and need only be briefly reviewed here.

The tube is operated with the grid *at all times negative*, and hence requires negligible driving power.   The alternating signal voltage impressed on the grid causes the plate current to vary.   Since the dynamic curve of the tube is essentially a straight line as Fig. 5–16 indicates, the plate-current variations are almost exact replicas of the grid voltage. An impedance is placed in the plate circuit, and the current changes cause an IZ voltage drop.   Thus, an amplified voltage appears across this load impedance.   This voltage may be further amplified in successive stages if desired.

The load impedance may be a pure resistance, an inductance, or the primary of a transformer, depending on the type of coupling (page 215) desired.   For analytical purposes, it is convenient to consider the load impedance to be pure resistance as in Fig. 5–16.   The equivalent alternating-current circuit is very simple,[4] the tube then acting as a generator with an open-circuit voltage of μE_g volts, and internal resistance r_p, connected to a load of resistance R_L.   From page 126, the amplified alternating voltage across the load will be

$$E_L = \frac{\mu E_g R_L}{(r_p + R_L)}, \tag{8–10}$$

where E_L is the effective value in volts when μ is the amplification factor of the tube, E_g is the effective value of the alternating signal voltage impressed on the grid of the tube, and r_p and R_L are the plate and load resistances in ohms.   Also, from page 126, the voltage amplification will be

$$A_v = \frac{E_L}{E_g} = \frac{\mu R_L}{(r_p + R_L)}, \tag{8–11}$$

Triodes for voltage amplification should have a high amplification factor.   They have been commercially available with amplification factors as high as 40.   Some of the newer multi-electrode pentode tubes can be *connected as triodes* by connecting the screen and suppressor grid to the plate, and certain of these have amplification factors higher than the conventional triode.

Tetrode.—For *audio-frequency* voltage amplification the screen-grid tube or tetrode is operated with resistance in the plate circuit, and with the grid negative.   The equivalent circuit of Fig. 5–15b and the accompanying theory apply to the screen-grid tube.[5]   Thus, equations (8–10) and (8–11) can be used to compute the approximate voltage across the load resistor and the voltage amplification.

The plate resistance of the screen-grid tube is very high, of the order of 1.0 megohm.   Since the direct component of the plate current must flow through the load resistance causing a considerable voltage drop (thus necessitating a high value of plate-supply voltage), and since resistors of very high values are often noisy and unstable, it is impracticable to use extremely high resistors in the plate circuit.   Thus, although the amplification factor of a screen-grid tube may be 400 or more, it cannot be fully utilized.

Load resistors of from 0.1 to 0.25 megohm are commonly used in the plate circuits of screen-grid tubes operated as audio-frequency voltage amplifiers.[3] Assuming $\mu = 500$, $r_p = 1.0$ megohm, and $R_L = 0.25$ megohm, the amplification as given by equation (8–11) would be

$$A_v = \frac{500 \times 250,000}{(1,000,000 + 250,000)} = 100.$$

In discussing the screen-grid tetrode as an amplifier, dynamic curves, such as used for the triode, need not be considered.   The plate current which flows is largely independent of the plate voltage over the operating range, which is the flat portion of the curve of Fig. 6–5, page 146. Furthermore, the load resistance is small compared with the plate resistance of the tube.   Thus, the static and dynamic curves are the same.

As mentioned on page 158, the potential of the plate (plate-supply voltage minus the drop in the load) must at all times be considerably above that of the screen grid, so that the tube will be operated on the flat portion referred to in the preceding paragraph.   If the potential of the plate approaches that of the screen-grid, distortion will result as the plate current-plate voltage curve shows.

Pentode.—As an *audio-frequency* voltage amplifier the suppressor-grid pentode tube is operated with resistance in the plate circuit, and with the control grid negative.   The equivalent circuit of Fig. 5–15, page 126, and the accompanying theory applies.   Equations (8–10) and (8–11) can be used to compute the approximate voltage across the load resistor and the voltage amplification.

It should be remembered that there are two types of suppressor-grid pentodes.   One is designed for *voltage* amplification and the other for *power* amplification; voltage amplifiers are now being considered. These usually have all connections brought out to the base so that they may be connected in various ways.   As a suppressor-grid pentode the plate resistance is about 1.5 megohms, the amplification factor about 1500, and the control grid-plate transconductance about 1225.

Just as for the screen-grid tubes discussed above, the plate current is small and largely independent of plate voltage over the usual operating range; also, the load resistance is a low value compared to the plate resistance.   The dynamic and static plate current-grid voltage curves may therefore be considered the same.   The permissible grid swing (that is, the magnitude of the alternating signal voltage which may be impressed on the grid without excessive distortion) can be determined from the grid voltage-plate current curves, or from the plate voltage-plate current curves.

For a typical voltage-amplifiying, suppressor-grid pentode the load resistor should be about 0.25 megohm.   Knowing the impressed alternating grid voltage, the approximate output voltage across the load resistor in the plate circuit can be calculated from equation (8–10), page 212. The approximate voltage amplification is, according to equation (8–11), $A_v = 1500 \times 250,000/(1,500,000 + 250,000) = 215$.

As Barton brings out in discussing vacuum-tube amplifiers,[6] the values of the amplification factor and plate resistance as previously given for the voltage-amplifying, suppressor-grid pentode are somewhat uncertain values, but the transconductance is more reliable and definite. Using this coefficient, and *neglecting* the resistance of the load, the alternating plate current flowing when a signal of E_g volts is impressed on the grid will be $I = E_g g_m$, and the voltage drop across the load resistor will be $E_L = IR_L = E_g g_m R_L$. Then, the *voltage amplification* $A_v = E_L/E_g = g_m R_L$. Using the data for the pentode previously given, the voltage amplification $A_v = 1225 \times 10^{-6} \times 250,000 = 281$. This value is too high due to neglecting the resistance of the load as mentioned above.

Gain per Stage.—As discussed in the preceding paragraphs, the audio-frequency voltage gain per stage can be computed from equation (8–11), page 212; also, as discussed on page 208, it is convenient to express voltage ratios in decibels. Thus, suppose that a triode is connected as in Fig. 8–2, and that the gain in decibels is desired. If $\mu = 10$, $r_p = 10,000$ ohms, and $R_L = 30,000$ ohms, the voltage gain will be, from equation (8–11), page 212, $A_v = 10 \times 30,000/(10,000 + 30,000) = 7.5$ From equation (8–6) the gain in decibels will equal $n = 20 \log_{10} 7.5 = 17.5$ decibels.

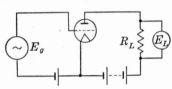

FIG. 8–2.   Circuit for calculating the gain per stage of a triode.

The *power gain* in decibels can also be computed if an input resistance to the tube is *assumed*, or if a resistor is connected from grid to cathode when the tube is tested to determine its gain. Thus, one manufacturer [4] measures the gain with 600,000 ohms connected from grid to cathode.

With an input resistor R_E so connected, the power dissipated in the grid circuit will be (assuming the grid itself takes negligible power) E_g^2/R_E, and from equation (5–15) the power output is $\mu^2 E_g^2 R_L/(r_p + R_L)^2$. The **power amplification** will be the ratio of these two expressions, **or**

$$A_p = \frac{\mu^2 R_L R_E}{(r_p + R_L)^2} . \tag{8–12}$$

For the triode of Fig. 8–2 (which is primarily a voltage-amplifying tube, but handles power as well), the power amplification will be

$A_p = 10^2 \times 30{,}000 \times 600{,}000/(10{,}000 + 30{,}000)^2 = 1125$.   From equation (8–2) the corresponding power amplification will equal $n = 10 \log_{10} 1125 = 30.5$ decibels.

Multi-Stage Amplifiers.—The voltage or power gain per stage can be calculated as shown in the preceding paragraphs.   Often, one stage of amplification is insufficient to give the gain desired, and two or more stages are connected in **tandem** or **cascade** to secure greater amplification.   Such multi-stage audio amplifiers often consist of several stages of voltage amplification driving a final stage of *power* amplification to furnish the power for a loud speaker or other device. In audio-frequency amplifiers, the voltage amplifying stages are class A, and the power-output stage is either class A, AB, or B.

The various stages usually are connected together in one of three ways: *First*, by **resistance-capacitance coupling**, often called **resistance coupling**; *second*, by **impedance-capacitance coupling**; and *third*, by **transformer coupling**.

69. Input Impedance of Vacuum Tubes.—Before discussing the methods of connecting amplifying stages just enumerated, it is advisable to consider the total equivalent input impedance a tube offers between the grid and cathode under *actual operating conditions*.   An exact analysis of this subject requires a generalized treatment and then a study under the three special conditions of resistance, capacitance, and inductance in the load circuits.   Such treatments will be found in References 7, 8, and 9 which should be consulted for additional information.   In the following paragraphs, such a generalized treatment will not be given, a brief summary only being included.   Such a treatment is sufficient for most purposes.

An actual and an equivalent circuit for a triode with a *resistance load* in the plate circuit is shown in Fig. 8–3.   The capacitance C_{pf} between the plate and filament has a negligible effect in

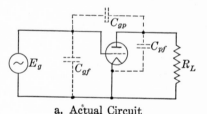

a. Actual Circuit

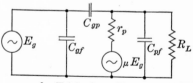

b. Equivalent Circuit

Fig. 8–3.   Circuits for a triode with negative grid.

determining the input capacitance of the grid circuit and may be neglected.   The input capacitance is, therefore, determined by the sum of the *capacitive effects* of the capacitances C_{gf} and C_{gp}.   The grid-filament capacitance is fixed in value and the circuit may be further simplified as in Fig. 8–4.

The words *capacitive effects* were *italicized* in the preceding paragraph because the voltage amplification of the tube and its associated circuit affect the input capacitance. Although it appears that the impressed alternating signal voltage E_g and the equivalent voltage μE_g are in opposition, this is not the case. As has been shown before, when the grid goes less negative during the positive half cycle, the plate current increases, and the voltage on the plate decreases due to the drop in the load. Also, when the grid goes more negative the plate current decreases and the voltage on the plate increases.

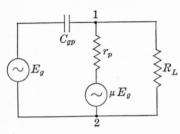

Fig. 8–4.   Simplified circuit for studying the input capacitance of a triode.

Thus, E_g and μE_g are effectively in series and are added insofar as the grid-plate capacitance C_{gp} is concerned. This is not exactly true, because the voltage μE_g is not all available across points 1–2. This voltage depends also on the load resistance R_L. If R_L is infinite, then the voltage μE_g is all effective between points 1–2; if R_L is zero, then no voltage can exist across points 1–2.

The effective charging current through C_{gp} is thus proportional to $E_g + A_v E_g$ or to $E_g(1 + A_v)$, where A_v is the voltage amplification of the *tube* and *load*. The total charging current flowing from the source of voltage is the sum of that flowing into the grid-filament capacitance C_{gf} and the charging current through the grid-plate capacitance C_{gp}. Thus, the total equivalent input capacitance of a triode is approximately equal to

$$C_g = C_{gf} + C_{gp}(1 + A_v). \qquad (8\text{–}13)$$

From this discussion it is apparent that nature of the load impedance influences the input impedance of a tube. For *audio-frequency* amplifiers it is usually sufficient to consider the input impedance equal to pure capacitance. In many instances this may be entirely neglected, but in others the effect of this input capacitance is of importance, especially at the higher audio frequencies.

In the preceding paragraphs it was shown that the grid input impedance of a triode was substantially pure *capacitance* when the load was *resistive*. In the references listed in the first paragraph of this section it is shown that for a capacitive load the input impedance is composed of resistance and capacitive reactance and that the resistance is positive as under usual circuit conditions. For an *inductive* load, although the input grid impedance is still resistance and capacitance, the *resistance is sometimes negative,* a condition which may cause feed back as will be studied on page 239.

It should be mentioned that triodes are seldom employed in radio-frequency voltage amplifiers in *receiving* sets, multi-electrode tubes being used. For the screen-grid tetrode and the pentode the plate is so effectively shielded that the feedback to the grid is negligible as com-pared with a triode.

70. A–F Resistance-Capacitance-Coupled Amplifiers.—In this type amplifier (also called a resistance-coupled amplifier) a resistance-capaci-tance network serves to couple the various stages of a multi-stage class *A* voltage amplifier. Two stages of a typical circuit using triodes are shown in Fig. 8–5. This circuit and the discussion is largely for *audio frequencies.*

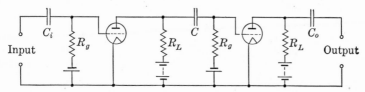

FIG. 8–5.   Two stage resistance-capacitance-coupled voltage amplifier using triodes.

Starting at the input terminals, the various elements function as follows: The input condenser C_i is to prevent direct voltages which may be present in the device connected to the input terminals from changing the direct grid potential of the input tube and thus affecting its operation. The resistance R_g, often called a "grid leak," impresses the negative grid-bias potential E_c on the grid of the tube. Negligible direct current flows in the grid cir-cuit, and hence no appreciable direct voltage drop occurs across R_g.

The equivalent alternating-cur-rent circuit for the two amplifying tubes and the coupling network be-tween them is shown in Fig. 8–6. The alternating signal voltage E_g impressed *on the grid* of the first tube is amplified to μE_g as indicated. The plate resistance of the tube is represented by r_p. The load resistor R_L (often called a **coupling resistor**) is, for triodes, usually equal to from 2 to 5 times the plate resistance of the tube. The value of the coupling condenser C is often

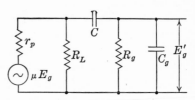

FIG. 8–6.   Equivalent circuit for one stage of Fig. 8–5.

0.05 microfarad, but a 0.1 microfarad condenser gives better low-frequency amplification. This condenser *should have mica* for a dielectric, but paper condensers may be used if their resistance is *very high*. If any leakage occurs, the positive plate voltage of the first tube will leak to the grid of the second tube. The value of the grid resistor R_g is roughly 2 to 5 times that of R_L. The condenser C_g represents the equivalent input capacitance of the second tube given by equation (8–13), page 216, plus stray wiring capacitances.

Design.—This subject has been so thoroughly covered in existing literature, such as References 6, 7, 8, and 10, that it will be but briefly summarized. Furthermore, the manuals [3] of the vacuum tube manufacturers and their application sheets clearly specify the circuit constants for best results.

In designing resistance-capacitance coupled amplifiers for audio frequencies from about 50 to 15,000 cycles, it is only necessary, for approximate results, to consider the amplification at three frequencies. These are 50 cycles, 1000 cycles, and 15,000 cycles, representing the low, intermediate, and high frequencies respectively.

Amplification at Intermediate Frequencies.—For determining the voltage amplification, the *intermediate* frequency will first be considered. The *voltage amplification* will be the ratio $A_v = E_g{}'/E_g$, where $E_g{}'$ is the voltage impressed *on the grid* of the second tube, and E_g is the voltage impressed *on the grid* of the first tube. Referring to equation (8–13) calculation shows that if the amplification *of the tube and circuit* is 8, if the grid-filament capacitance C_{gf} is 3 micromicrofarads, and if the grid-plate capacitance C_{gp} is 6 micromicrofarads, then the input capacitance will be $C_g = 3 + 6(1 + 8) = 57$ micromicrofarads. Therefore, the shunting effect of C_g (including stray capacitances of wiring) of Fig. 8–6 is negligible at 1000 cycles because the capacitive reactance is so high.

If C_g of Fig. 8–6 is negligible, then the coupling condenser C is effectively in series with the very high resistance R_g. The capacitive reactance of this condenser at 1000 cycles is negligible, and thus *for intermediate frequencies* Fig. 8–6 can be simplified to Fig. 8–7a. The amplified voltage $E_g{}'$ is the alternating voltage drop across the equivalent circuit R_e composed of R_L and R_g in parallel. The voltage amplification can be found from equation (8–11) where R_L is replaced by R_e. Thus, at intermediate frequencies,

$$A_v = \frac{\mu R_e}{(r_p + R_e)}, \qquad (8\text{–}14)$$

and this is the *maximum amplification* of the circuit.

Amplification at Low Frequencies.—For low frequencies, such as 50 cycles, the effect of C_g of Fig. 8–6 still is negligible, but the capacitive reactance of the coupling condenser C approaches in value the resistance of R_g. The simplified circuit becomes Fig. 8–7b. The voltage amplification is the ratio of E_g' to E_g. The voltage E_g' will equal the current through R_g times the resistance of R_g. The current through R_g can be found as follows: The total impedance of the circuit fed by the source of voltage μE_g will be the plate resistance r_p plus the equivalent resistance offered by the two parallel branches between points 1–2 of Fig. 7b. The total current flowing through r_p will be $I_t = \mu E_g/Z_t$, and this will divide at points 1–2 in inverse proportion to the impedances of the two paths. Thus, the current through the grid resistor R_g and the voltage drop across this resistor can be computed.

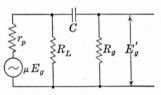

a. Intermediate Frequency

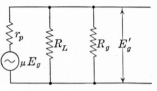

b. Low Frequency

As Terman points out,[7] the detailed calculation just discussed is seldom necessary, it being possible to estimate the characteristics quite closely. Thus, equation (8–14) gives the *maximum* voltage amplification which can be obtained. At a low frequency at which $1/(2\pi f C) = R_g$, the *actual* voltage amplification will be about 70 per cent of this maximum value (because the voltage drops across this condenser and resistor are equal and 90° out of phase). Furthermore, at a low frequency such that $1/(2\pi f C) = 2R_g$, the actual amplification is *about* 50 per cent of the maximum possible value. When the frequency is so low that the capacitive reactance of the coupling condenser rises to a very high value, the amplification becomes very low.

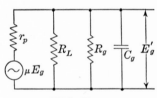

c. High Frequency

Fig. 8–7. Equivalent circuits at various frequencies for a resistance-capacitance voltage amplifier.

Amplification at High Frequencies.—At the high audio frequencies the capacitive reactance of the coupling condenser C becomes so small that its effect is negligible. The reactance of tube input capacitance C_g is lowered sufficiently that its *shunting* effect becomes appreciable, and the equivalent circuit at *high frequencies* is as indicated by Fig. 8–7c. The amplified voltage E_g' available on the grid of the second tube is equal to $I_c X_c$, where I_c is the current through the condenser C_g and X_c is the reactance of this condenser.

The circuit of Fig. 8–7c can be further simplified for deriving the expression for the voltage amplification at high frequencies as shown in Fig. 8–8. In this figure, R_e represents the equivalent parallel resistance of the load resistor R_L and the grid resistor R_g in parallel.

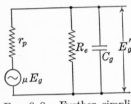

FIG. 8–8. Further simpli- fication of Fig. 8–7c.

The amplified voltage will be the alternating voltage drop across the *parallel* circuit [7] of R_e and C_g. To find this, the *total* current must first be known. This current will equal the voltage μE_g divided by the total impedance connected across this voltage value. Making these substitutions, the voltage amplification at high frequencies becomes [8]

$$A_v = \frac{\mu}{1 + r\left(\dfrac{R_L + R_g}{R_L R_g}\right) + j2\pi f C_g r_p}. \qquad (8\text{–}15)$$

With this equation, the voltage amplification at high frequencies of a resistance-capacitance coupled amplifier such as Fig. 8–5 can be calculated. Estimation of the amplification [7] can be made without the use of equation (8–15).

Resistance-Capacitance Amplifier Characteristics.—From the preceding section it is apparent that these amplifiers can be designed with a very flat frequency-amplification curve, thus producing little *frequency distortion*. Furthermore, since there are no iron-cored coils or transformers in the circuit, *non-linear distortion* is minimized. Some *phase distortion* does exist, however, since the various frequencies of a complex wave do not all travel through the amplifier at the same rate. The effects of this are unimportant in most work, but cause much serious image distortion when these amplifiers are used in television.[6]

Serious non-linear distortion will occur if the amplifier is not properly designed or is overloaded. Thus, if the magnitude of the alternating signal voltage impressed on the grid exceeds certain values, the tube will be overloaded and distortion will occur in accordance with the theory on page 129. For best results, the amplifier must be operated on the straight portion of the dynamic curve.

A peculiar type of distortion may occur if the grid is driven positive due to a *momentary* overload. The positive grid may draw a large negative charge which will not immediately leak off due to the high value of R_g of Fig. 8–5. This may block the tube causing noticeable distortion.

Common grid-bias and plate-supply batteries may be used in commercial forms [3] of resistance-capacitance amplifiers; also, the separate tubes may be connected to a common filament power supply. Nevertheless, this amplifier is quite wasteful of plate-supply voltage if improperly designed. Thus, tubes for these amplifiers should be so selected and operated that the plate current is the lowest acceptable value. This plate current flows through the load resistor R_L of Fig. 8–5, and thus an appreciable IR drop will exist for the direct plate current component. Thus, the voltage *on the plate* will equal the plate-supply battery voltage minus the voltage drop in the load resistor.

71. A-F Impedance-Capacitance-Coupled Amplifiers.—Although these are commonly called **impedance-coupled amplifiers** and **impedance-capacitance-coupled amplifiers,** such general classifications must also include the resistance-capacitance amplifier previously considered. The impedance-coupled amplifier (as it will be called for simplicity), connected as in Fig. 8–9, has an important advantage over

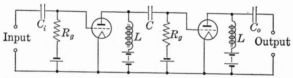

Input C_i R_g C L R_g L C_o Output

FIG. 8–9.   Two-stage inductance-capacitance-coupled audio-frequency voltage amplifier.

the resistance-capacitance type; the coupling choke L is of low resistance, thus eliminating the large IR drop and not requiring such high-voltage plate-supply batteries or such a high-voltage power supply.

The operation of this amplifier at *audio frequencies* is analogous to that of the resistance-capacitance type previously considered. The inductance of the coil L offers high reactance to the alternating component of the plate current, and thus a large alternating signal voltage drop will exist across the coil. This voltage is available for impressing on the grid of the second tube for further amplification. It is apparent that this amplifier depends on *inductance* alone for the voltage drop, suggesting the classification as an *inductance-capacitance-coupled amplifier*. This type amplifier may be made selective by "tuning" the output with a condenser connected across the coupling coil L.

In some amplifiers of this general type, a second choke coil is placed in the branch of Fig. 8–9 containing the grid resistor R_g. Thus, there are two further classifications: the type of Fig. 8–9, known as **impedance-resistance-capacitance-coupled amplifier,** and the type just discussed called a **double impedance-capacitance-coupled amplifier.**

By proper design,[10] this type amplifier can be constructed with response curves of various shapes in the low-frequency region.

Design.—The exact design of such amplifiers is complicated by many factors,[10] but simple approximations [7, 8] giving satisfactory results can be made. Such approximations will be briefly summarized.

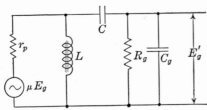

FIG. 8–10. Circuit equivalent electrically to one stage of Fig. 8–9. The coupling inductor is assumed to be pure inductance.

The operation of a triode with a resistance load was quite fully covered in the preceding discussions (page 126). Little has been said, however, regarding the operation with an impedance load such as a choke coil. For this condition, the dynamic grid voltage-plate current characteristic will not be a straight line (approximately) as for the pure resistance load, but will be an ellipse.[8, 9]

A simplified circuit of the impedance-coupled amplifier is shown in Fig. 8–10. In this circuit, L is the high-inductance coupling choke of about 100 henrys. This choke will have an effective resistance which varies with current magnitude and with frequency, but this resistance will be neglected. The condenser C, the grid resistor R_g, and the input capacitance C_g are all substantially the same as for the resistance-coupled amplifier (page 217).

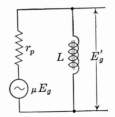

FIG. 8–11. Circuit equivalent to Fig. 8–10 if the effects of C, R_g, and C_g are neglected.

To find the *maximum possible voltage amplification*, the ratio of the output voltage E_g' to the input grid voltage E_g must be found. This voltage E_g' would equal the alternating signal voltage drop across the choke coil L if effects of C, R_g, and C_g were negligible. The circuit would then reduce to Fig. 8–11. For this figure, the voltage drop across the reactance, ωL, would be assumed equal to E_g' of Fig. 8–10, and would be

$$E_g' = IX_L = \frac{\mu E_g \omega L}{\sqrt{r_p^2 + \omega^2 L^2}}, \quad \text{and} \quad A_v = \frac{E_g'}{E_g} = \frac{\mu \omega L}{\sqrt{r_p^2 + \omega^2 L^2}}. \quad (8\text{–}16)$$

This equation would give the approximate amplification per stage at the intermediate frequencies, the actual value of E_g' of Fig. 8–10 being lower than equation (8–16) would indicate. The amplification at intermediate frequencies is affected by the value of the grid resistor R_g.

The higher the resistance, the greater will be the maximum amplification, but the *more peaked* will be the *overall* amplification. A resistor of 0.5 megohm will usually be satisfactory.

At low frequencies, the value of L must be high, chokes of several hundred henrys inductance being required for good low-frequency amplification. Also, the value of the coupling condenser C must be at least 0.05 microfarad, or the low-frequency amplification will drop essentially as explained for the resistance-coupled amplifiers.

It might appear that the higher the frequency, the greater the amplification because the reactance of the coupling choke would increase. An examination of equation (8–16) will show, however, that the amplification cannot exceed the amplification factor μ of the tube. In fact, the amplification drops at high frequencies because of the shunting effect of the input capacitance C_g of the tube. This action is analogous to that of the resistance-coupled amplifier.

Amplifier Characteristics.—If high amplification is desired, a tube which has both a high μ and a high plate resistance must be used. This high plate resistance necessitates the use of a coupling choke of high inductance. The large number of turns required will increase the distributed capacitance and lower the high-frequency response. Also, the intense magnetic field will tend to saturate the iron core, causing distortion and power loss.

Data supplied by tube manufacturers should be consulted for the best values of the circuit elements to be used. Some idea of these values has been given in the preceding pages, and further estimates can readily be made. For a tube having a μ of 10 and r_p of 10,000 ohms, a coupling choke of 100 henrys gives excellent low-frequency amplification.[8] For a tube with a higher value of μ, and with a plate resistance of 100,000 ohms, a choke coil of about 400 henrys is necessary for a good low-frequency response.

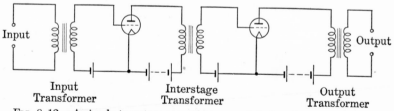

Input Transformer   Interstage Transformer   Output Transformer

Fig. 8–12.   A simple two-stage transformer-coupled class A audio-frequency voltage amplifier.

72. A-F Transformer-Coupled Amplifiers.—An amplifier with the various stages transformer coupled has many advantages over other types for certain work. Fig. 8–12 is a simple circuit of this type designed for *audio-frequency* amplification. In this circuit are included three types of transformers, an **input transformer,** an **interstage transformer,** and an **output transformer.** One important advantage of transformer coupling is that *additional voltage amplification* can be obtained in the input and interstage transformers over the voltage gain due to the amplification of the tube itself. It also provides a low resistance path for the direct plate current component, and isolates the plate of one tube from the grid of the next as far as direct current is concerned.

The circuit of Fig. 8–12 is a simple two-stage class *A* amplifier. The grids of the tubes are maintained negative at all times, and draw no current. The first transformer has a step-up ratio, increasing the voltage of the device connected to the input circuit. The reason for this is as follows: Assume that the circuit is to amplify the output of a microphone, or a phonograph, or some other *low-impedance* device, producing a relatively low voltage. The transformer is used to step-up or increase the voltage, so that less voltage amplification is needed from the tubes. Another way of describing the function of the transformer is to say that the transformer matches the low impedance of the input device to the high impedance of the grid input circuit. This viewpoint will be discussed later.

The voltage induced in the secondary of the input transformer is impressed on the grid of the first tube. This voltage is amplified to a value μE_g and this amplified voltage acts to force an alternating current through the plate resistance of the tube, and the primary of the interstage transformer. The alternating voltage drop across the primary of the interstage transformer is stepped up by the turns ratio and appears as a larger voltage across the secondary. This voltage is then impressed on the grid of the second tube where it is amplified as before. An alternating current flows through the primary of the output transformer, and the drop across the primary is usually stepped down and appears across the output terminals.

The reason for the step-down ratio is as follows: An amplifier is usually designed to drive some device such as a loud speaker. Dynamic loud speakers are low-voltage high-current devices. A step-down ratio gives this. Or, the transformer has matched the impedance of the tube to that of the load. It should be mentioned that, in an actual amplifier for driving a loud speaker with a microphone or a phonograph pickup, more than two stages would be necessary.

An analysis of the statements just made regarding the operation of the amplifier of Fig. 8–12 shows that from the input terminals to the grid of the second tube, voltage amplification was desired. (The last tube must supply *power* to the load.)   It may appear possible to omit the first tube and the associated equipment, and just have an inter-stage transformer with such a high ratio that the voltage is increased by the transformer itself until it is sufficient to drive the output tube. This is *theoretically* possible, because the grid of the output tube takes negligible power.   It is *not possible* to do this for at least one practical reason.   The secondary of the transformer would require so many turns and the distributed secondary capacitance would be so large that the voltage could not be stepped up to the *terminal* voltage value desired.

Thus, for purely practical reasons the amount of voltage gain obtainable by an unequal transformer ratio is limited.   In past years it was common to build interstage transformers with a ratio of 1 to 6, but those for high-quality use on the market today have ratios of 1 to 3 or less.   Similarly, in the input transformer there is a practical number of secondary turns which should not be exceeded or the distributed capacitance will be excessive.

Transformers as Impedance Matchers.—The preceding discussion shows the necessity for studying transformers themselves before further considering their use in amplifiers.

A transformer consists essenti-ally of a primary winding and a secondary winding on a closed core of laminated iron.*   The iron is of excellent magnetic quality, and it may be assumed, for the moment, that all the magnetic lines of force produced by the primary windings N_p link with each of the secondary

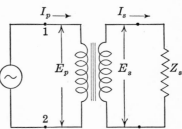

FIG. 8–13.   Transformer circuit.

windings N_s.   It will also be assumed that the losses in the trans-former are negligible.   In such a transformer, the ratio of the voltages across the primary and secondary varies directly as the ratio of turns. The currents, however, vary inversely as the ratio of turns.   That is,

$$\frac{E_s}{E_p} = \frac{N_s}{N_p}, \quad \text{and} \quad \frac{I_s}{I_p} = \frac{N_p}{N_s}. \tag{8–17}$$

The transformer of Fig. **8**–13 is connected to a load of Z_s ohms, and a current of $I_s = E_s/Z_s$ will flow.   The *current* in the *primary* will be $I_p = I_s N_s/N_p$, and (in terms of the secondary voltage) the *voltage* across the *primary* will be $E_p = E_s N_p/N_s$.   Now the *primary im-*

---

* It is quite common and very convenient to speak of the *iron* core of a transformer. Actually, the core would be of silicon steel laminations or of other magnetic material.

pedance will be $Z_p = E_p/I_p$, and hence

$$Z_p = \frac{E_p}{I_p} = \left(\frac{E_s N_p}{N_s}\right)\left(\frac{N_p}{I_s N_s}\right) = \frac{E_s N_p{}^2}{I_s N_s{}^2} = Z_s\left(\frac{N_p}{N_s}\right)^2. \quad (8\text{–}18)$$

This equation shows that the impedance which would be measured (with the generator disconnected) at the primary terminals 1–2 of an *ideal* transformer would be the impedance Z_s of the secondary times the ratio of the turns squared. Thus, the transformer may be regarded as an *impedance changer* and used to match circuits and obtain maximum power transfer in accordance with the theory on page 131.

In the use of transformers as impedance changers, it should be recalled that an *ideal* transformer can change the magnitude of an impedance, *but it cannot change the phase angle.* Thus in Fig. 8–13, if Z_s is pure resistance, then for the ideal case, Z_p measured at points 1–2 will also be a pure resistance, but of a larger or smaller value depending on the ratio $(N_p/N_s)^2$. Of course, in an actual circuit the phase angle between the current and voltage (and thus the angle of the load) is changed somewhat, but only to the extent that the transformer is imperfect. This effect will depend, for given conditions, on the frequency.

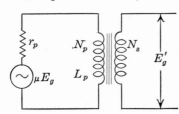

FIG. 8–14. Simplified circuit for computing the approximate gain per stage of a transformer-coupled voltage amplifier.

Approximate Transformer-Coupled Gain.—The gain per stage of a transformer-coupled amplifier can readily be calculated if the effects of the losses, the magnetic leakages, and the distributed and stray capacitances are neglected. The equivalent circuit is shown in Fig. 8–14.

Thus, the alternating current flowing in the circuit due to the alternating signal voltage E_g on the grid of the first tube is $I = \mu E_g/\sqrt{r_p{}^2 + \omega^2 L_p{}^2}$. The voltage E_p *across the primary* of the interstage or coupling transformer would be

$$E_p = IX_L = \frac{\mu E_g \omega L_p}{\sqrt{r_p{}^2 + \omega^2 L_p{}^2}}. \quad (8\text{–}19)$$

The voltage $E_g{}'$ across the secondary (which is applied directly to the grid of the second tube) will be $E_p N$, where $N = N_p/N_s$. Hence, the voltage gain per stage will be

$$A_v = \frac{E_g{}'}{E_g} = \frac{\mu \omega L_p N}{\sqrt{r_p{}^2 + \omega^2 L_p{}^2}}. \quad (8\text{–}20)$$

This equation shows that for low frequencies where ω is small, the primary inductance must be *high* or the amplification will be low. As the frequency is increased the amplification would continue to increase, rapidly at first, and then approaching an asymptotic value.

Transformer Equivalent Circuit.—The transformer is an *electrical network* having two input and two output terminals.[9, 11]   Although an audio-frequency transformer may be well designed and constructed, it is far from being ideal.   The primary and secondary windings contain resistance and there are also losses in the iron core.   Distributed capacitance exists between adjacent windings of the primary and of the secondary; also, stray capacitance exists between the primary and secondary coils.   Furthermore, all of the magnetic lines of force produced by the primary do not link the secondary.   All of these effects cause the characteristics of an audio-frequency transformer to be those of an electrical network, the characteristics of which vary with the test frequency.

For determining the network equivalent to a transformer, the theory of *coupled circuits* must be studied.   It is impossible to include this subject, and the excellent treatment [9] by Everett is recommended. As is shown in this reference, the circuit of Fig. 8–15a, representing a vacuum tube connected to a load through a transformer, is equivalent to Fig. 8–15b.   In this equivalent circuit all values are expressed in terms of the primary circuit.   The effect of the distributed and stray capacitances is neglected.

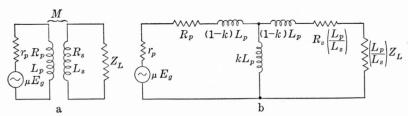

Fig. 8–15.   Actual and equivalent circuits for a vacuum tube connected to a load Z_L through an *ideal* transformer.   (Adapted from Reference 9.)

The terms R_p and R_s are the direct-current resistances of the primary and secondary.   The alternating resistance components due to eddy-current and hysteresis losses in the iron core are neglected, an assumption usually justified.   Their effect on the equivalent circuit is discussed in References 7 and 8.

The terms $(1 - k)L_p$ are due to the fact that all of the magnetic lines of force set up in the metal core by the current in the primary do not link the secondary.   The term k is the **coefficient of coupling,** and although in a well-designed audio-frequency transformer it may exceed 99 per cent, this coefficient is always less than unity. It is apparent that as the coupling increases, the term $(1 - k)L_p$, termed the **leakage inductance,** decreases. From coupled-circuit theory [9] it can be shown that $kL_1 = MN_p/N_s$, and that $L_p/L_s = N_p^2/N_s^2$.

As previously mentioned, all distributed and stray capacitances are neglected in Fig. 8–15. Their effects are very important, however, and they are included in Fig. 8–16. The condenser C_1 represents the distributed capacitance between the turns of the primary. The condenser C_2' represents the *combined effect* of the stray mutual capaci-

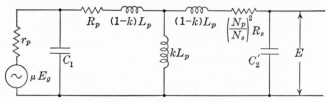

FIG. 8–16.   Equivalent circuit for a transformer-coupled amplifier including the effects of stray and distributed capacitances. Losses due to hysteresis and eddy currents are neglected.   (Adapted from Reference 9.)

tance (C_m) between the primary and secondary windings, in addition to the distributed capacitance (C_2) between the secondary turns, and the input capacitance of the grid circuit of the second tube. This value of C_2' can be shown [7, 8, 9] equal to $C_2' = (N_s/N_p)^2C_2 + (1 \pm N_s/N_p)^2C_m$.

The value C_m may be made so low as to be negligible by grounded electrostatic shields placed between the primary and secondary windings. The $\pm$ sign occurs because the primary and secondary windings may be connected so that the voltage across the mutual capacitance C_m is the sum or the difference between the primary and secondary voltages. The value C_2 is the sum of the equivalent grid input capacitance C_g which includes the amplifying effect of the following stage (page 215), the distributed capacitance of the secondary winding, and stray wiring capacitance.

The output voltage E of Fig. 8–16 is *not* the voltage impressed on the grid of the second tube because the circuit shown is the equivalent network expressed in terms of the *primary circuit*. The amplified voltage E_g' actually impressed *on the grid* of the following stage would be EN_s/N_p.

Design.—Just as for the other amplifiers discussed in the preceding pages, this subject has been covered elsewhere [7, 8, 9, 10] so adequately that this treatment will be very brief. The method of approximate analysis applied to the other amplifiers may be extended to the transformer-coupled amplifier. This material will be included in the following paragraphs.

Amplification at Low Frequencies.—For low frequencies the circuit of Fig. 8–16 can be represented approximately by Fig. 8–17a. The reactance of the condenser C_2' will be so great that the circuit to the right of points 1–2 can be neglected. Thus, equation (8–20) will apply approximately. Assume that a tube with a μ of 10 and r_p of 10,000 ohms is used with a 1 : 3 ratio transformer having a primary inductance of 50 henrys. At 50 cycles, $\omega L_p = 2\pi f L_p = 15{,}700$ ohms. From equation (8–20),

$$A_v = 10 \times 15{,}700$$
$$\times\, 3/\sqrt{(10{,}000)^2 + (15{,}700)^2} = 25.3.$$

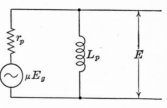

a. Low Frequencies

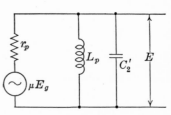

b. Intermediate Frequencies

This value is higher than would be obtained in practice, chiefly because the effect of the primary resistance R_p has been neglected. This resistance value can be added to the plate resistance r_p, lowering the value of the voltage amplification a small amount. For low frequencies the amplification will be as shown between regions A and B of the typical transformer response curve of Fig. 8–19.

It is apparent that if the current through the primary of the transformer (that is, through L_p of Fig. 8–17a) is increased by any means, then the drop across L_p and the voltage amplification will be increased. Thus, a large condenser C connected in series with the primary of the transformer as in Fig. 8–18 will lower the impedance of the load circuit connected to the tube,

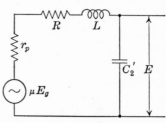

c. High Frequencies

Fig. 8–17. Circuits for analyzing the performance of transformer-coupled amplifiers. These are substantially equivalent to Fig. 8–16 at the frequencies indicated.

and will increase the current flow as desired. With this arrangement the direct component of the plate current cannot flow through the transformer, and must be fed through the high-inductance choke coil L. This connection also keeps the direct component from causing magnetic saturation effects in the iron core of the transformer. Hence, for the same amount of distortion the core may be smaller when the circuit of Fig. 8–18 is used.

An examination of Fig. 8–17a will show why transformer-coupled amplifiers do not employ high-gain tubes with *high plate resistances*. If such tubes were used with the type of transformers employed today, then the low-frequency response would be very poor because most of the voltage μE_g available would be lost within the tube. If special transformers were designed with very high primary impedances, then the distributed capacitance between the large number of turns would be great and distortion would result at the higher frequencies.

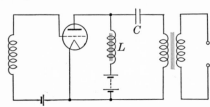

FIG. 8–18. Method of transformer coupling to prevent the flow of direct current in the primary.

This also brings out another important point in transformer design: For best results the number of primary turns should be small, and the high inductance achieved by the use of cores of high permeability. Special alloys such as Permalloy [12] have been developed and are used in high-grade interstage transformers, especially where light weight is desired.[13] This alloy is also extensively used in transformers for other communication purposes.

Amplification at Intermediate Frequencies.—For the intermediate frequencies of from about 200 to 3000 cycles the equivalent circuit for a transformer-coupled amplifier is about as shown in Fig. 8–17b. The reasons for this are as follows: At 1000 cycles, the reactance of a 50-henry primary will be 314,000 ohms; also, at this frequency the capacitance of C_2' (which is given on page 228, and may total as much as 0.002 microfarad) will be about this same value. Thus, at the intermediate frequencies a very "broad" anti-resonance condition (or parallel resonance) will occur between L_p and C_2' giving a *very high equivalent impedance* between the points 1–2 of Figs. 8–16 and 8–17b. Also, this impedance will be largely resistive, as for any anti-resonant circuit.

When a tube works into a load having a resistance high in comparison with the plate resistance of the tube, the voltage amplification approaches the amplification factor of the tube (page 212). Thus, for the intermediate frequencies, the amplification of the tube and transformer is very nearly $A_v = \mu N$, where μ is the amplification factor of the tube and N is the ratio of turns. Thus, for the transformer previously considered, the theoretical voltage amplification is $A_v = 10 \times 3 = 30$. The characteristics of a transformer-coupled amplifier at the intermediate frequencies will be as shown from B to C of Fig. **8–19.**

Amplification at High Frequencies.—At the higher frequencies of from about 3000 to 10,000 cycles (depending on the design) the equivalent circuit of a transformer-coupled audio-frequency amplifier is approximately as shown in Fig. **8–17c.** In this figure, L represents the leakage inductances, R the primary and secondary resistances, and

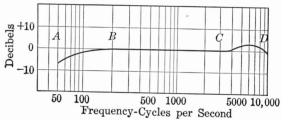

Fig. 8–19.   Typical response curve for an inexpensive interstage transformer.

C_2' the total equivalent capacitance of the secondary of the transformer. As shown on page 228, this includes the distributed secondary capacitance, the mutual stray capacitance between primary and secondary, and the input capacitance of the tube connected to the secondary. The branch L_p of Figs. **8–17a** and b is neglected because its reactance becomes very high at these frequencies.

At high frequencies, the units L and C_2' of the equivalent circuit of Fig. **8–17c** will become series resonant, and the current will tend to increase. This increase will be limited largely by the plate resistance of the tube r_p, and by the equivalent primary and secondary resistance represented by R. This increased current will cause a larger IX voltage drop across the condenser C_2', and hence an increased voltage will be impressed across the grid of the second tube. This will cause the "peak" C to D in the amplification curve of Fig. **8–19.** After passing through this resonant condition, the amplification decreases rapidly because the current decreases beyond resonance, and because the reactance of the condenser C_2' decreases rapidly at high frequencies. Thus, the amplifier will not pass the high frequencies.

For improving the frequency response, several practicable solutions are available. *First,* if the value of C_2' can be decreased by reducing any of the factors (such as the stray mutual capacitance between primary and secondary or the distributed secondary capacitance) which compose it, then the resonant frequency will be higher. Grounded electric shields between the windings, and special design of the secondary will achieve this. *Second,* if the leakage inductances can be reduced, the effect will also be to cause the resonance peaks to occur at higher frequencies. Cores of good magnetic material and good design of windings will increase the coupling and reduce the leakage flux and the so-called leakage inductances of Fig. 8–16. A resonance peak at a higher frequency means that amplification will occur over a wider frequency range before cut-off occurs. *Third*, increasing the resistance of the secondary will reduce the current flow at resonance, and thus the IX drop across C_2' will be less and the resonance peak will be reduced.

A secondary winding of high resistance is obtained by the use of very small wire, the practical limit being manufacturing operations. It might appear that a high-resistance primary or a tube with a high plate resistance would also be desirable, but these would impair the low-frequency response.

A high resistance of 0.5 to 1.0 megohm is often connected across the secondary of an audio-frequency transformer. This would be in parallel with the condenser C_2' of Fig. 8–17c. The effect of this would be *first* to reduce the resonance peak and hence improve the frequency-response curve, and *second* to lower slightly the response at all other frequencies.

Transformer-Coupled Amplifier Characteristics.—From the discussions given in the preceding pages an estimate can be made of the amplification ratio of audio-frequency transformer-coupled stages at various frequencies. If desired, these ratios can be calculated throughout the audio frequencies by several methods.[9]

Characteristics are shown in Fig. 8–19 for a typical stage of transformer coupling, using inexpensive transformers. It should not be expected that all similar amplifiers will show such distinct resonance peaks, or a dropping off at low frequencies. Transformers are now available commercially which are far superior to those of a few years ago.

On the other hand, an amplifier constructed with transformers which are *purported* to have flat characteristic curves may not have high quality. As mentioned on page 209, a flat curve indicates that the *frequency* distortion should be low, but it does not specify what the *non-linear distortion* will be. In other words, a transformer with a very small core and other defects might give a frequency-response curve which was quite flat *if operated at low signal levels*, but if operated at the levels at which it *might be rated*, the non-linear distortion might be very high. Also, a poorly balanced transformer, or one which was unshielded, might pick up bad hum.

It is apparent from the discussions of the preceding pages that the interstage transformer is a coupling device. Although its *individua* characteristics might be of some value in analytical work, the operation of the transformer is so closely related to the rest of the circuit that it should not be tested alone.   In other words, the interstage transformer is designed to function under certain conditions, and it should be tested under similar conditions.   Frequently one requirement is that direct current should flow in the primary.

The circuit of Fig. 8–20 is suggested as reflecting actual conditions and as being quite satisfactory for determining the gain per stage at various frequencies.   A value of voltage E_g is selected such that the tube will be at all times operated on the essentially linear portion of its

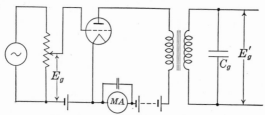

Fig. 8–20.   Circuit for measuring the gain per stage of an audio-frequency amplifier.

characteristic curve, so that the tube itself will cause little distortion. The voltmeter used for measuring E_g should be of such a type that it does not influence the output wave form of the oscillator supplying the test voltage.   The condenser shunting the milliammeter may be omitted if the deflection of this instrument is unaffected by the alternating component.   The condenser C_g represents the equivalent grid input capacitance (page 216), and any stray wiring capacitances.   If desired, the secondary of the transformer can be connected to a second tube, and the voltage impressed on the grid of this tube measured. The impedance of the voltmeter for measuring E_g' must be very high, depending on the degree of accuracy desired.   A vacuum-tube voltmeter or other similar device having a resistance input of over several megohms is recommended for high accuracy.   An analysis of the frequency distortion can be made by determining the ratio E_g'/E_g at various frequencies.   If a pure sine wave is impressed across the input, and if a wave analyzer is used to study the output, the non-linear distortion can also be found.

Measuring Transformer Characteristics.—It may be desired to test the transformer without a tube in the circuit, and this can be done according to Fig. 8–21.   The condenser in series with the oscillator is to prevent direct current from flowing through it.   The battery, rheostat, and milliammeter are for supplying and controlling the direct component through the primary to stimulate the direct plate current flowing during actual operation.   The resistor r_p is equal to the average value of the plate resistance of the tube with which the transformer is designed to operate.   The condenser C_g is equal to the combined equivalent capacitance of the tube into which the transformer is designed to work and any wiring capacitance.

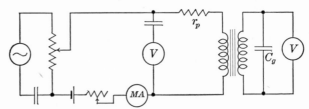

FIG. 8–21.   Circuit for obtaining the voltage ratios of an audio-frequency interstage transformer.

The condenser in series with the voltmeter in the primary circuit is to keep the direct voltage from affecting the readings.   If the voltmeter has high resistance, and if the condenser is reasonably large the reading of the voltmeter will be unaffected.   A simple calculation will prove this point.   The voltmeter across the secondary must have very high input resistance, usually above several megohms, if the true transformer ratio is to be determined.   Vacuum-tube voltmeters are well suited for such work.   A harmonic or wave analyzer with high input resistance serves well for this output voltmeter; with it an analysis can also be made to determine the non-linear distortion by measuring the magnitude of the harmonics present in the output.   Fig. 8–21 can be simplified by removing the equipment for supplying direct current to the windings, and by removing the condenser C_g if these refinements are not desired.

Various other circuits have been developed which are entirely satisfactory for measuring voltage ratios of audio-frequency transformers.   In some of these circuits one voltmeter or other indicating device is alternately shifted from the primary to the secondary circuit. In making such tests care should be taken to assure that when the indicating device is placed on the secondary it does not offer a load sufficient to cause the primary voltage to drop, thus giving incorrect ratios.

Determining Transformer Constants.—From the discussion starting on page 229, and from Fig. 8–17, it is apparent that the characteristics of an audio-frequency transformer depend largely on only a few factors; these are, *first*, the primary inductance, *second*, the distributed secondary capacitance, and *third*, the direct-current resistance of the primary and the total leakage inductance L.   These may be calculated [10] if a transformer is being designed, and measured [14] for the finished product.

The inductance of the primary must be measured with a direct current of the same magnitude flowing as is anticipated during actual use. This inductance is properly called the **incremental inductance,** and is the inductance of a coil with a magnetic core which is measured with alternating current while direct current flows through the windings. This inductance will vary with *both* the direct current and the alternating current through the coil. A low frequency should be used to make the measurements because at higher frequencies the effect of distributed capacitance becomes pronounced.

The accurate measurement of high values of incremental inductance is not simple. The method to be outlined has proved entirely satisfactory if followed carefully. The circuit is arranged as in **Fig. 8–22,**

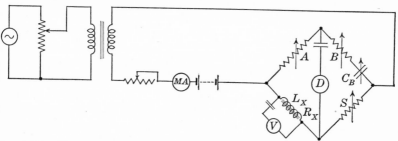

FIG. 8–22. Circuit for measuring the inductance and the effective resistance of a choke coil or of the primary of a transformer.

and is known as a Hay bridge. The oscillator is operated at about 100 cycles, although 60 cycles may be used, or a higher frequency (up to several hundred cycles) is satisfactory. The voltage divider and 1 : 1 ratio transformer select the proper amount of alternating voltage and isolate the oscillator from the direct current flowing. Other connections for supplying the direct current are possible.[7] One element of the bridge, the resistor S, must carry this direct current. The arms A, B, and S are all shown as variable resistors, but not all of them need be.

The detector of balance, D, is a very important device. A telephone receiver may be used if a test frequency of several hundred cycles is employed. The condenser isolates the detector from the direct current, but a transformer may be used if desired. The most satisfactory detector is a vacuum-tube voltmeter or voltage amplifier and indicating device *which can be tuned* for the test frequency. This eliminates the effects due to the harmonics. A wave analyzer is very satisfactory for this purpose. The voltmeter across the inductance should have a high input impedance, and should be of the vacuum-tube type. A voltage amplifier and a copper-oxide voltmeter are very satisfactory.

In operation the direct current is held constant by varying the rheostat, and the alternating voltage drop across the coil under test is held constant by varying the voltage divider across the oscillator. The bridge arms are then varied and balance is obtained. At balance the indication of the detector is a minimum, and the unknown values are as follows:

$$L_x = ASC_B, \qquad R_x = ABS\omega^2C_B^2, \qquad \text{and} \qquad Q = \frac{1}{(B\omega C_B)} \cdot \quad (8\text{–}21)$$

When A, S, and B are in ohms, C_B is in farads, and $\omega = 2\pi f$ where f is the test frequency, the inductance and effective alternating-current resistance will be in henrys and ohms. The value Q is the dissipation factor or constant as discussed on page 242.[10] The values given by equation (8–21) are approximate. For a derivation of these formulas, Reference 15 is suggested. Much information will also be found in Reference 16.

The method of determining the inductance of the primary of an audio-frequency transformer was explained in detail because of its application to studying audio-frequency choke coils and other high inductances. Methods for determining the other transformer constants will now be considered.

The leakage inductance for L of Fig. 8–17c can be determined by measuring the inductance between the primary terminals with the secondary short circuited.[14] As Terman points out, these measurements are independent of frequency and of saturation of the magnetic core, because the *leakage* path is in air. No direct current need flow through the windings for these measurements.

The value of the distributed capacitance C_s of the secondary is computed from the formula

$$C_s = \frac{1}{(\omega^2 L_s)}, \qquad (8\text{–}22)$$

where L_s is the leakage inductance, and ω^2 is equal to $2\pi f$, where f is the frequency (high) at which L and C_2' of Fig. 8–17c are in resonance. The value of C_s would equal C_2' minus the other contributing capacitances (page 228).

73. Radio-Frequency Voltage Amplifiers.—The preceding pages of this chapter were devoted to *audio-frequency voltage* amplifiers, leaving *power* amplifiers for a subsequent chapter. The following pages of this chapter will consider *radio-frequency voltage* amplifiers of the class A

type as employed in *radio receivers*.   Other types of radio-frequency amplifiers will be discussed in the following chapter.   Radio-frequency voltage amplifiers may be either *tuned* to pass a certain band of frequencies, or may be *untuned*.

The radio-frequency voltage amplifier for message reception has two important functions.   *First*, it amplifies the weak voltages induced in the antenna, and *second*, it provides selectivity, passing only the signal frequencies desired and greatly attenuating all frequencies outside this band.   For best reception, the radio-frequency amplifier in a receiving set should have as its characteristic the solid curve *a* of Fig. **8–23**, passing *only* the band of frequencies included between the two vertical lines.   For broadcast reception this would be (page 313) represented by the following $C + V, C, C - V$, where C represents the carrier and V the voice frequencies.   Thus, if a station were operated at a carrier of 550 kilocycles, and if the voice band were 5000 cycles wide, then the width of the band amplified should be at least 10,000 cycles wide, extending from 545 to 555 kilocycles. If the broadcast station were of the high-fidelity type, transmitting a wider band, then the receiver

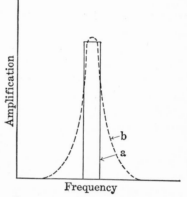

Fig. 8–23.   Theoretical (a) and actual (b) amplification curves for a radio-frequency voltage amplifier.

should also pass a wider band for true reception.   It is not practicable to design a circuit with this ideal characteristic in radio receivers. The response of a typical receiver is as shown in curve *b* of Fig. **8–23**.

The types of radio-frequency amplifier circuits which have been used are many and varied.   In their final analysis, however, they can be classified under three main headings.   These are (as for audio-frequency amplifiers) resistance-capacitance, impedance-capacitance, and transformer-coupled amplifiers.   Of these three, the first and last types are the most important.   Resistance-coupled amplifiers are largely used for television purposes.[10]   Transformer-coupled amplifiers are widely used in radio-receiving sets.

Regeneration at Radio Frequencies.—As was mentioned on page 216, and as shown on page 228, the small **interelectrode capacitances** between the tube elements are not entirely negligible, especially at the higher frequencies such as used in radio.   These interelectrode capacitances are particularly bothersome in the triode.   When the load is inductive so that the input impedance of the *triode* contains a negative resistance term, part of the output of the tube is fed back into the grid input circuit through the grid-plate capacitance in phase with the applied grid voltage.   Thus, under certain conditions this electrical feedback will cause the tube to **oscillate** or **regenerate.**   In radio-frequency amplifiers using *triodes*, special precautions must be taken to prevent such oscillations.

In the *screen-grid tetrode*, the screen quite effectively shields the plate, and furthermore, this screen is connected to ground through a low-impedance path.   Such a path is obtained by connecting a condenser to ground across any impedances which may be in the *screen-grid* circuit.   Thus, feedback is prevented quite easily except at very high frequencies and when the tube is operated in circuits where a very high amplification or gain is attempted.   In the voltage-amplifying, suppressor-grid pentode, the screen grid also shields the plate.   In addition, the suppressor grid provides additional shielding and feedback is further reduced.   Thus, a higher amplification per stage is possible, and this is one important reason why the suppressor grid pentode is finding such wide application as a radio-frequency voltage amplifier in modern radio-receiving sets.

Neutralization.—Because tetrodes and pentodes have not been practical in large power-handling capacities, triodes are very extensively used as radio-frequency amplifiers in radio-transmitting sets.   Special precautions, termed **neutralization,** must, therefore, be taken to prevent regeneration.   There are three methods of controlling feedback so that with triodes regeneration is avoided:

First, introducing resistance into the grid circuit to overcome the negative grid input resistance.

Second, keeping the equivalent reactance of the load in the plate circuit capacitive, or so nearly capacitive that the input resistance (page 216) is not sufficiently negative to cause regeneration.

Third, balancing out the voltage which is fed back into the grid input circuit through the grid-plate capacitance.

Of these three methods of neutralization to prevent regeneration, the third is the most satisfactory in radio-frequency amplifiers. Several systems [6, 7, 8, 9, 10] of neutralization have been developed but only two will be discussed.

The neutralizing circuit of Fig. 8–24 was developed by Rice, and can be explained as follows: The incoming radio-frequency signal to be amplified is induced by coupling into the coil in the grid circuit, thus impressing the signal between the grid and cathode.   This signal is then amplified, and since there is a load in the plate circuit, the increased voltage of the plate will also vary as the signal impressed on the grid, but 180 degrees out of phase with it.

This alternating plate signal voltage will cause an alternating signal current to flow to the cathode through a path provided by the stray grid-plate capacitance C_{gp} and L_1. The resulting voltage drop across L_1 (which is between the cathode and grid) will be an alternating signal voltage, and is impressed on the grid as for amplification. Furthermore, a study will show that the phase relation of this voltage is such that it will in turn tend to cause the plate voltage variations to increase, and thus the circuit will tend to oscillate.

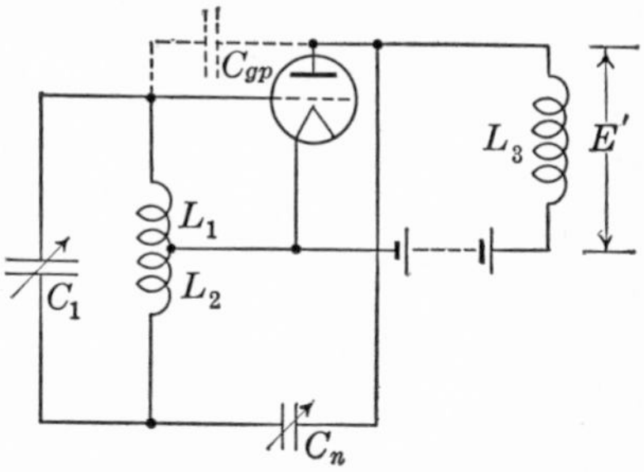

But as Fig. 8–24 is connected, alternating signal current also flows back from the plate through the variable condenser C_n and coil L_2.

FIG. 8–24. Circuit developed by Rice for neutralizing feedback due to grid-plate capacitance thus preventing regeneration. Coils L_1 and L_2 are *closely coupled*. The input circuit would be coupled with coil L_1; the amplified output voltage is E'.

A signal voltage drop also occurs across L_2, but this coil is *not* between the grid and cathode. The coupling between L_1 and L_2 is made quite high,

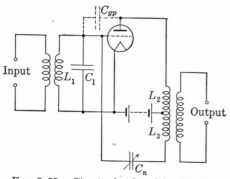

FIG. 8–25. Circuit developed by Hazeltine for preventing regeneration due to feedback through the grid-plate capacitance. Coils L_2 and L_3 are closely coupled.

and they are so connected that the signal current changes in L_2 induce voltages in L_1 which are equal in magnitude but 180 degrees out of phase with the voltage drop across L_1 due to the current flowing through the grid-plate capacitance. In this way the resultant voltage drop across L_1 *due to feedback* is largely cancelled and reduced so that regeneration is prevented.

The so-called **neutrodyne** circuit of Fig. 8–25 was developed by Hazeltine for preventing regeneration. Using a method similar to that just employed, the operation of this circuit is as follows: Signal current will tend to flow back through the grid-plate capacitance C_{gp}, and as previously explained; such current would cause a signal voltage drop across the parallel circuit $L_1 - C_1$ and this voltage would be impressed between the grid and cathode and would be amplified. This action would cause regeneration.

The coupling between the output coil L_2 and the coil L_3 is close, and a voltage will be induced in L_3 (due to the current in L_2). This voltage is 180 degrees out of phase with the voltage across L_2, and hence with the alternating signal plate voltage. Thus, the plate voltage is tending to send a current through the tube capacitance C_{gp} and down through the coil $L_1 - C_1$, and also the voltage induced in coil L_3 is tending to send an equal, but a 180 degree out-of-phase current (regulated by the neutralizing condenser C_n) through the same circuit. The result is that the feedback current and voltage are reduced to the point where regeneration does not occur.

Equivalent circuits based on the impedance bridge and on three-winding or bridge transformers are sometimes used to explain neutralization. These will be found in certain of the references listed previously. In some of these explanations the effect of the mutual inductance due to the close coupling between the coils ($L_1 - L_2$ of Fig. 8–24 and $L_2 - L_3$ of Fig. 8–25) has been neglected. It is apparent that this effect must be considered since the circuits here discussed will not function to prevent regeneration without close coupling between the coils.

74. R-F Resistance-Coupled Voltage Amplifiers.—An amplifier of this type is *untuned*, and the circuit is similar to Fig. 8–5. With this circuit, the equivalent input capacitance of the second tube offers such low reactance at radio frequencies that the output drops off as was explained (page 219).

Much progress has recently been made in the design of these amplifiers for wide-band amplification. For television purposes, resistance-capacitance-coupled amplifiers must be used to pass the wide "video" band for driving the cathode ray tube to reproduce the television image. This video band, which corresponds to the demodulated audio-frequency component of a radio program, may be 1,000,000 or more cycles wide depending on the definition desired. Furthermore, the amplification must be accomplished without excessive velocity distortion or phase shift.[17]

This wide-band transmission in resistance-capacitance-coupled amplifiers is accomplished in one of two ways. *First*, if a small amount of inductance is added *in series* with the coupling resistor (R_L of Fig. 8–5), this branch and C_g of Fig. 8–6 can be made *anti-resonant* in the high-frequency region, causing a high equivalent load impedance for the tube, thus maintaining its amplifying efficiency. *Second*, a small amount of inductance can be added *in series* with the grid of the second tube, and this can be designed to become *resonant* in the high-frequency region. This will result in a larger alternating signal current flow through, and voltage drop across, the input grid capacitance C_g and thus greater amplification at higher frequencies.[6] Although these explanations are brief, the theory will be understood if the audio-frequency resistance-capacitance-coupled amplifier is reviewed.*

75. R-F Impedance-Coupled Voltage Amplifiers.—An amplifier of this type, connected essentially as in Fig. 8–9, will operate at the lower radio frequencies. The theory given for audio frequencies can be extended to radio-frequency amplification. These amplifiers may be *untuned,* or *tuned,* the selective effect of the last type being due to a condenser connected across the coupling inductor L of Fig. 8–9. Even the "untuned" type is selective to some extent due to the distributed capacitance between the windings of the coupling inductor L becoming anti-resonant with the inductance of L at some radio frequency. Coils and transformers with air cores are usually employed at all except the lowest radio frequencies, because of the high losses which occur in magnetic materials. Special cores of powdered and compressed iron have been developed, however, which have some advantages for cores of coils and transformers at the radio-broadcast frequencies.[18]

Anti-Resonant or Parallel Circuits.—In order fully to understand transformer-coupled amplifiers, parallel anti-resonant circuits and coupled circuits must be thoroughly understood. Those desiring to review these subjects should consult such references as 7, 8, 9, 11, and 19. Very briefly, if a circuit were arranged as in Fig. 8–26a, if the magnitude of the impressed voltage were held constant and the frequency were varied, and if the magnitude of the current flowing to the circuit and its phase relations with the voltage were observed, curves such as Fig. 8–26b could be calculated. (The same curve could be found directly with an impedance bridge.)

These curves show that at some frequency the current in the condenser (assumed 90° ahead of the voltage) is equal and opposite to the current through the coil (assumed, for the moment, to be 90° behind the voltage). At this frequency the two currents will cancel, and the ammeter reading will equal zero. The impedance of the parallel circuit as viewed from points 1–2 will accordingly be infinite at this frequency of anti-resonance, so-called because the parallel circuit offers *maximum* impedance instead of minimum impedance as does the series resonant circuit.

* Those interested in the design of amplifiers for television purposes should consult the two excellent articles by F. Alton Everest entitled "Wide-band Television Amplifiers," *Electronics,* January and May, 1938.

Of course, condensers and particularly coils have appreciable losses, especially at radio frequencies, and thus the ammeter reading does not go to zero, nor does the impedance go to infinity. But, for condensers and coils having low losses, the impedance at the anti-resonant point may rise to a *very* high value. Furthermore, at this frequency the reactance is approximately zero as Fig. **8**–26b indicates, and hence at the anti-resonant point, the impedance of a parallel circuit is not only high, but also, it appears to be *pure resistance*. Thus, when a tube or other device is working into a parallel circuit of capacitance and inductance, this circuit offers a pure resistance load at the anti-resonant frequency.

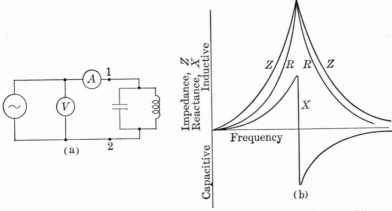

Fig. **8**–26.   Parallel or anti-resonant circuit (a), and characteristics (b).

The losses in good mica condensers, such as extensively used in radio circuits, are negligible. The losses which occur in the coils must be considered, however, and the ratio $\omega L/R$, or reactance to resistance, is a measure of the quality of a coil for circuit work. This ratio is designated as Q. Thus if a good condenser, and a coil having a high Q, are connected in parallel, the resistance will be high at the anti-resonant frequency and the circuit will be highly selective. If a coil with a low Q is used, the curve such as Fig. **8**–26b will be less steep, and the circuit will be less selective.

If the circuit of Fig. **8**–26a is coupled inductively to another similar parallel circuit or to any other circuit to which it will transfer power, this is equivalent to increasing the losses in the first circuit, and hence to making the curve of Fig. **8**–26b less steep.

76. R–F Transformer-Coupled Voltage Amplifiers.— *Untuned.—* An amplifier of this type is shown in Fig. **8**–27a. The tube shown is a suppressor-grid, voltage-amplifying pentode. With this type tube,

the effects of the interelectrode capacitances are of little importance at least in the broadcast range.   For an approximate solution, this circuit can be represented as in Fig. 8–27b.   Attention is called to the fact that this neglects all distributed and stray capacitances, and that the solution is valid only when this assumption is justified.

With the output terminals *open-circuited*, the approximate magnitude of the induced sec-ondary voltage can be found as follows: The magnitude of the alternating current flowing in the primary will be (see page 226) $I = \mu E_g / \sqrt{r_p{}^2 + (\omega L_p)^2}$, and the open-circuit secondary volt-age will be

$$E_0 = I\omega M$$

$$= \frac{\mu E_g \omega M}{\sqrt{r_p{}^2 + (\omega L_p)^2}}. \qquad (8\text{–}23)$$

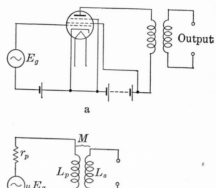

FIG. 8–27.   Actual and equivalent circuit for an *untuned* radio-frequency transformer-coupled amplifier using a pentode.

The approximate voltage amplification can be found as the ratio of E_0 to E_g.

At frequencies where the effects of capacitances are appreciable, the equation just given will not hold.   This is especially true if the fre-quency is such that the inductance and distributed capacitance of the coils become anti-resonant.   Also, if the secondary of the coil is con-nected to a tube or circuit having considerable input capacitance, then the secondary becomes tuned to some frequency and the equation is no longer valid in the region of that frequency.

Tuned Secondary.—These are used very extensively in radio receiv-ing sets, and as mentioned on page 237, much of the *selectivity* and *fidelity* depends upon the design of these amplifiers.

An amplifier with a tuned secondary is shown in Fig. 8–28a and its approximate circuit in Fig. 8–28b.   This amplifier also employs a suppressor-grid voltage-amplifying pentode.   The variable output condenser C *represents* all secondary capacitances, and would include the distributed secondary capacitance, the wiring capacitance, and the input capacitance of the following tube or circuit.

As mentioned on page 242, at anti-resonance the impedance of the parallel circuit $L_s - C$ will be very high.   A high voltage at *this anti-resonant* frequency will therefore exist across this circuit.   Italics were used because, as explained on page 237, the band at which the amplification is substantially constant must be wide enough to provide good fidelity.

The method of solving Fig. **8**–28b for the approximate voltage amplification is as follows: The inductance and resistance of the primary are neglected, because they are in series with r_p which is very high for the screen-grid tetrodes and for the suppressor-grid pentodes used as voltage amplifiers. Then, at the anti-resonant frequency for which the secondary is tuned a high impedance value is offered. This is transferred to the primary * and the total primary impedance becomes

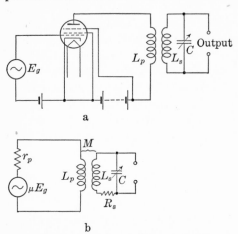

a

b

FIG. 8–28. Actual and equivalent circuit for a *tuned* radio-frequency transformer-coupled voltage amplifier using a pentode.

$$Z_p = r_p - \frac{Z_m{}^2}{Z_s}, \quad (8\text{--}24)$$

where Z_m is equal to $j\omega M$, and Z_s is the total *series* impedance of the secondary, which at anti-resonance is substantially equal to R_s. Substituting this value in equation (**8**–24),

$$Z_p = r_p - \frac{(j\omega M)^2}{R_s} = r_p + \frac{\omega^2 M^2}{R_s} = \frac{(R_p R_s + \omega^2 M^2)}{R_s}. \quad (8\text{--}25)$$

The total equivalent primary impedance is given by equation (**8**–25); therefore, the primary current is $I_p = \mu E_g/Z_p = \mu E_g R_s/(R_p R_s + \omega^2 M^2)$. The magnitude of the (open-circuit) voltage induced in the secondary due to the current I_p in the primary is $\omega M I_p$ or

$$E = \frac{\mu E_g R_s \omega M}{(R_p R_s + \omega^2 M^2)},$$

and this will cause a current flow at *anti-resonance* in the secondary of

$$I_s = \frac{\mu E_g R_s \omega M}{R_s(R_p R_s + \omega^2 M^2)} = \frac{\mu E_g \omega M}{(R_p R_s + \omega^2 M^2)}.$$

The voltage drop IX_c across the condenser is the amplified voltage impressed on the grid of the second tube, and, since $X_c = (1/\omega C)$,

---

* These steps involve coupled-circuit theory, and will be found fully explained on page 79 of Reference 8, and page 200 of Reference 9 (first edition).

this amplified voltage will be

$$E_g' = \frac{\mu E_g \omega M}{(R_p R_s + \omega^2 M^2)\omega C} = \frac{\mu E_g M}{(R_p R_s + \omega^2 M^2)C}$$

$$= \frac{\mu E_g \omega^2 M L_s}{(R_p R_s + \omega^2 M^2)}, \quad (8\text{--}26)$$

where $\omega L_s = 1/\omega C$ at anti-resonance as is approximately true. The ratio of the voltage gain per stage is E_g'/E and can be found from equation (8–26).

The derivation just given is particularly interesting, but much greater simplifications can be made. Thus for a screen-grid tetrode or pentode such as would be used in Fig. 8–28, the plate resistance is so very high that $\omega^2 M^2$ can be neglected in the denominator of the last expression of equation (8–26), and the voltage amplification then becomes [10]

$$A_v = \frac{E_g'}{E_g} = \frac{\mu \omega M \omega L_s}{r_p R_s} = g_m \omega M Q. \quad (8\text{--}27)$$

This substitution is possible because $g_m = \mu/r_p$ (page 115), and $Q = \omega L/R$ (page 242). This equation is the approximate voltage amplification per stage for a circuit such as Fig. 8–28, when the secondary is adjusted to anti-resonance for the frequency $\omega = 2\pi f$.

A very complete analysis of radio-frequency transformers will be found in Reference 8. It is also of interest to note that in the radio-frequency transformers employed in some television amplifiers (used before demodulation) a high resistance is added in parallel with the tuned circuit such as shown in Fig. 8–28. This is to make the resonance curve (page 242) less peaked, and thus the circuit will pass a wider frequency band. This should not be confused with the statements on page 240, which apply to the amplifiers for passing the *video frequencies* (corresponding to audio frequencies) obtained after demodulation.

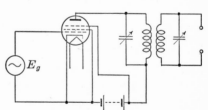

Fig. 8–29. A radio-frequency transformer-coupled voltage amplifier with tuned primary and secondary.

Tuned Primary and Secondary.—As mentioned on page 237, the ideal response curve for a radio-frequency amplifier for program reception would be flat-topped, and with straight sides. This would give high fidelity and selectivity. The circuit of Fig. 8–29 more closely achieves this ideal than the amplifiers previously considered. Both the primary and secondary of the transformer are tuned, and the flatness of the top of the response curve is determined by the mutual inductance M between the windings. This circuit arrangement is widely used in the intermediate-frequency amplifiers of modern superheterodyne receiving sets. In these amplifiers (page 358) the frequency range is fixed, and the *relative* width of the band passed must be greater than at the higher frequencies.

There are two general methods for computing the voltage gain of the amplifier. One of these considers the problem from the standpoint of coupled circuits (References 8 and 10), the other, from the standpoint of band-pass filter theory (Reference 20). The amplifier is sometimes called a **band-pass amplifier.** Neither of these derivations will be included here, as they are somewhat involved and will be best understood by consulting the references given.

REFERENCES

1. American Institute of Electrical Engineers. *Definitions of Electrical Terms.*
2. Institute of Radio Engineers. *Reports of the Standards Committee.*
3. R.C.A. Manufacturing Co. *Receiving Tube Manual.*
4. Pidgeon, H. A. *Simple theory of the three-electrode vacuum tube.* Jl. of the Soc. of Motion Picture Engineers, Feb., 1935, Vol. 24.
5. Pidgeon, H. A. *Theory of multi-electrode vacuum tubes.* Electrical Engineering, Nov., 1934, Vol. 53.
6. Pender, H., and McIlwain, K. *Electrical Engineers' Handbook.* Vol. 5, Electric Communication and Electronics.
7. Terman, F. E. *Radio Engineering.* McGraw-Hill Book Co.
8. Glasgow, R. S. *Principles of Radio Engineering.* McGraw-Hill Book Co.
9. Everitt, W. L. *Communication Engineering* (Both Editions). McGraw-Hill Book Co.
10. Henney, K. *Radio Engineering Handbook.* McGraw-Hill Book Co.
11. Albert, A. L. *Electrical Communication.* John Wiley & Sons.
12. Elmen, G. W. *Magnetic alloys of iron, nickel, and cobalt.* Electrical Engineering, Dec., 1935, Vol. 54.
13. Ganz, A. G., and Laird, A. G. *Improvements in communication transformers.* Electrical Engineering, Dec., 1935, Vol. 54.
14. Terman, F. E. *Measurements in Radio Engineering.* McGraw-Hill Book Co.
15. Hague, B. *Alternating Current Bridge Methods.* Pitman & Son.
16. General Radio Co. *Instructions for Operating Universal Bridge.*
17. Robinson, G. D. *Theoretical notes on certain features of television receiving circuits.* Proc. I. R. E., June, 1933, Vol. 21, No. 6.
18. Polydorff, W. J. *Ferro-inductors and permeability tuning.* Proc. I. R. E., May, 1933, Vol. 21, No. 5.
19. McIlwain, K., and Brainerd, J. G. *High frequency alternating currents.* John Wiley & Sons.

20. Christopher, A. J. *Transformer coupling circuits for high-frequency amplifiers.* Bell System Technical Journal, Oct., 1932, Vol. 11, No. 4.

SUGGESTED ASSIGNMENTS

1. Obtain the constants of a pentode audio-frequency voltage amplifying stage from a Tube Manual or other source, and calculate the voltage ratio and the voltage gain in decibels by both the methods discussed in the text.

2. Design a resistance-capacitance coupled battery-operated amplifier to fulfill certain specified requirements.

3. Derive the equation for the low-frequency amplification of a resistance-capacitance-coupled amplifier.

4. Derive the equation for the high-frequency amplification of a resistance-capacitance coupled amplifier.

5. On page 222 it is stated that the dynamic characteristic curve for a tube with an impedance load is an ellipse. Why does this fact not enter in the design of transformer-coupled amplifiers?

6. Following the method of Everitt, calculate the complete characteristics of a transformer-coupled amplifier stage. Check your calculations by an approximate analysis.

7. Derive the equations listed as equation (8–21), page 236.

8. Obtain the constants of a pentode radio-frequency, transformer-coupled stage from a Tube Manual or other source, and calculate the voltage amplification per stage.

9. Approximately determine the voltage gain in decibels of the voltage-amplifying portion of an audio-frequency speech amplifier such as suited for sound amplification purposes in an auditorium.

10. Approximately determine the radio-frequency voltage amplification in decibels of the voltage-amplifying portion of a tuned radio-frequency broadcast receiving set.

CHAPTER 9

VACUUM–TUBE POWER AMPLIFIERS

Audio-frequency and radio-frequency *voltage* amplifiers were discussed in the preceding chapter. Such amplifiers are used to *increase* the weak alternating signal voltage, such as the output voltage of a microphone, until this voltage is sufficiently strong to drive a *power* amplifier. *Voltage* amplifiers are of the class *A* type, because such amplifiers, when properly operated, must not greatly distort the voltage wave.

The purpose of the *power* amplifier is to furnish the power to drive a device such as a loudspeaker, or a circuit element such as a transmitting antenna. Class *A* amplifiers are also used as *power* amplifiers, but their efficiency is low because a large direct plate current component· flows even when there is no alternating signal voltage impressed. Class *AB*, *B*, and *C* amplifiers are widely used for power amplifiers, because the efficiency of these amplifiers is higher than for the class *A* type (page 210).

Audio-frequency power amplifiers will be discussed first, and then radio-frequency power amplifiers will be treated. It will only be possible to discuss amplifiers using conventional tubes. Additional information on this subject and on certain special tubes will be found in Reference 1.

77. A-F Class *A* Triode Power Amplifiers.—As defined on page 210, for a tube operated as a class *A* amplifier the direct grid-bias voltage is of such value that *plate current* flows through the tube at all times. The exciting alternating signal voltage applied to the grid should be such that the grid is *never* driven positive. The *positive* half cycle of the signal voltage *subtracts* from the direct grid bias making the total grid voltage *less* negative and *more* plate current flows. The *negative* half cycle of the signal voltage *adds* to the grid bias making the total grid voltage *more* negative and *less* plate current flows. An alternating-current component, which is almost an exact replica of the impressed signal voltage, therefore flows in the plate circuit, and this alternating component is used to drive a loudspeaker or other device.

The explanations just given were further discussed on page 129, and illustrated by Fig. 5–17. As there shown, the tube operates on the *dynamic* rather than the static curve. The way in which the output signal is distorted due to non-linearity of the dynamic curve was also shown.   Now it may appear that since the power amplifier tube works into an output transformer the dynamic curve would *not* be as in the figure to which reference was made. That the load *is* resistive will now be shown.

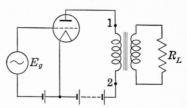

In Fig. **9**–1 is indicated a triode driven by an alternating signal voltage E_g and connected through an output transformer to a load R_L. Assume that R_L represents the moving voice coil of a dynamic loudspeaker.   Then, the transformer will have a step-down ratio to match

FIG. 9–1.   The load reflected into the plate circuit equals R_L multiplied by the turns ratio squared for an ideal transformer.

the impedance of the plate circuit to that of the load to obtain maximum power transfer in accordance with the theory on page 225.

Now the impedance measured (with the tube disconnected) across the primary of the transformer at points 1–2 with the voice coil R_L connected to the secondary is the load on the tube.   If R_L is largely pure resistance, as in the case of a voice coil, then the load impedance measured at points 1–2 will be largely pure resistance, and will be $R_L' = R_L N^2$, where N is the turns ratio.   Any deviation from this will be due to imperfections *in the transformer.*

To check these statements, approximate measurements were made of the impedance of the voice coil of a commercial dynamic loudspeaker for a radio-receiving set.   The impedance at 500 cycles was 10 ohms, almost pure resistance.   Measurements were then made across the primary of an inexpensive impedance-matching transformer with the 10-ohm coil connected as indicated in Fig. **9**–1.   Again using 500 cycles, the load impedance as *reflected into the primary* was 1810 ohms resistance and 450 ohms inductive reactance.   Furthermore, this reactance would have been lower with a better power-output transformer. Thus, for approximate calculations it can be assumed that the load on a tube connected as here considered is *largely pure resistance.*

Although this is for class *A* tubes, it applies in general to *all* similarly connected power-output tubes and power-output transformers.   In power-output transformers (as distinguished from interstage transformers, page 223) the number of primary and especially secondary turns is small.   This is because the plate resistance of *power* tubes is low compared to *voltage amplifying* tubes, and because the power-output transformer must usually step voltages down to drive some low-impedance electromagnetic device requiring a large current rather than step voltages up to drive the grid of a following tube.

The types of audio-frequency, class A amplifiers which will be treated in the following sections are (1) the single triode, (2) triodes in parallel, (3) triodes in push-pull, (4) the single pentode, and (5) push-pull pentodes.

Single Triode Amplifier.—In accordance with the theory of the preceding section, and with equation (5–15), page 126, the approximate equivalent circuit of a power-output triode connected to a resistance load through a transformer is as shown in Fig. 9–2, and the power output in watts is approximately

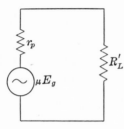

$$P = \frac{\mu^2 E_g{}^2 R_L'}{(r_p + R_L')^2}, \qquad (9\text{–}1)$$

FIG. 9–2. Equivalent circuit for Fig. 9–1.

where R_L' is the load resistance *reflected into the primary* (page 226), and E_g is the *effective* value of the impressed grid signal voltage.

As previously discussed, when a tube has resistance in its plate circuit (as it effectively has when connected as just shown) the tube operates on the *dynamic* rather than the static curve (page 129). If the distortion is to be kept low, the tube must be operated on the essentially *straight portion* of this dynamic curve. For *graphically* determining the optimum load resistance, for calculating the power output, and for finding the per cent distortion, load lines plotted on a family of static curves with *plate voltage* on the X axis and *plate current* on the Y axis are used. The methods to be outlined for plotting these have been summarized from Reference 2.

The problem is generally as follows: To find the value of load resistance to use with a triode so that the maximum power output is obtained *without* the per cent of second harmonic distortion (which is usually the most troublesome harmonic, page 252), exceeding five per cent, a value which is usually permissible.

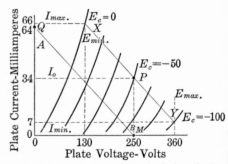

FIG. 9–3. Graphical method for finding the power output and per cent second harmonic distortion for a triode. (Adapted from Reference 2.)

In the solution of the problem, the static plate voltage-plate current family of curves such as Fig. 9–3 is used. Assume a bias voltage, plate

voltage, and load resistance (roughly twice the plate resistance).   For
Fig. 9–3 these values are − 50 volts, + 250 volts, and 3900 ohms.
Draw the line *A–B* as indicated.   The point *M* is where the plate
voltage is 250 volts and the plate current zero, and point *Q* is where
the plate current equals 250/3900 = 64 milliamperes.

Next, draw line *x–y* parallel to *A–B* and through point *P* corresponding to the voltage values selected.   It is assumed that the maximum alternating signal voltage applied to the grid *will be sufficient to
drive the grid to zero and to twice the direct bias voltage.*   Thus, line *x–y*
terminates on the $E_c = 0$ and $E_c = - 100$-volt curves.   These points
should be extended to the plate-current axis as indicated, giving the
$I_{max.}$ and $I_{min.}$ lines shown.   Also, the I_0, $E_{max.}$, and $E_{min.}$ lines should
be drawn.   Under these conditions, the power output is

$$\text{Power Output} = \frac{[(I_{max.} - I_{min.})(E_{max.} - E_{min.})]}{8}. \tag{9-2}$$

For Fig. 9–3, this equals $[(66 - 7)(360 - 130)]/8 = 1700$ milliwatts.

The per cent *second harmonic* distortion is determined approximately by the relation

$$\text{Second Harmonic Distortion} = \frac{\left[\dfrac{(I_{max.} + I_{min.})}{2}\right] - I_0}{(I_{max.} - I_{min.})} \times 100. \tag{9-3}$$

For Fig. 9–3, this becomes

$$\frac{\left[\dfrac{(0.066 + 0.007)}{2}\right] - 0.034}{(0.066 - 0.007)} \times 100 = 4.2 \text{ per cent.}$$

Since this value does not exceed 5 per cent, the conditions for operation
assumed would be satisfactory; otherwise, new operation conditions
would have to be selected and a new check made.   Usually 5 per cent
distortion is not exceeded when R_L' equals about twice r_p.

The derivation of equation (9–2) is simple, being as follows: Power
in watts is given by the relation *EI*, where *E* is the *effective* voltage, *I*
is the *effective* current, and the circuit is of pure resistance.   Thus,
$(I_{max.} - I_{min.})/2\sqrt{2}$ is the *effective* current *I*; also, $(E_{max.} - E_{min.})/2\sqrt{2}$
is the *effective* voltage *E*.   When these values are substituted in the
relation $P = EI$, equation (9–2) results.

Second-Harmonic Distortion.—The way in which distortion is
caused in a triode because the dynamic characteristic curve was not a
perfectly straight line was illustrated by Fig. 5–17, page 130.   Equation (9–3) can be proved correct by analyzing this figure.

This distorted output wave is reproduced in Fig. 9–4. It will be noted that the wave is non-symmetrical with respect to the X axis;

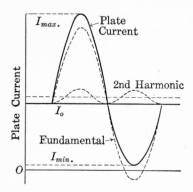

the upper half cycles are larger than the lower ones. As is well known, any recurring wave can be analyzed into a fundamental and harmonics. Assuming that only a second harmonic exists in the distorted wave, the wave is composed of a fundamental and a second harmonic as shown by the dotted lines.

The reason the axis of the second harmonic does not coincide with that of the fundamental is as follows: When distortion occurs in a

Fig. 9–4. The second harmonic component causes the plate current to be non-symmetrical about the X axis, I_0.

triode operated in class A, some rectification results because the positive and negative halves of the cycle are not the same. If the distortion is small, then a milliammeter in the plate circuit of a triode amplifier will show a negligible increase in current, but if the distortion is considerable, a very noticeable increase in plate current will occur when the signal voltage is impressed. This increase in current is equal to the *amplitude of the second harmonic*.

As Fig. 9–3 shows, with no alternating signal voltage on the grid, the plate current is I_0. With a signal, the *average* value of the plate current is $(I_{max.} - I_{min.})/2$, and this also equals the amplitude of the fundamental component. The amplitude of the second harmonic will be $\frac{1}{2}[(I_{max.} - I_{min.})/2] - I_0$, and this value, divided by the amplitude of the fundamental and multiplied by 100 gives the per cent second harmonic as indicated by equation (9–3). For additional information on this derivation, References 3, 4, and 5 are recommended.

Parallel Triode Amplifier.— If the power output of one tube is insufficient, two or more triodes can be connected in parallel as indicated in Fig. 9–5. For the same per cent distortion, this combination provides twice the output of a

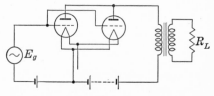

Fig. 9–5. Triodes are sometimes operated in parallel to increase the power supplied to the load R_L.

single tube, for the *same value of* alternating signal voltage applied to the two grids *in parallel* as previously applied to a single tube. If the total input grid capacitance is to be considered, it is about twice the effective input capacitance of one tube.

The two plates are in parallel and hence the equivalent plate resistance of the two tubes (looking back into the tubes from the output terminals) is one-half that of each tube.   Since each tube will generate a voltage of magnitude μE_g between the filament and plate, the equivalent circuit will be as shown in Fig. 9–6.   The value of R_L' (which is the load resistance reflected into the primary) should be *about* the same as the plate resistance of *one* tube for satisfactory power output conditions.   Actually it seems that a value equal to one-half that determined for one tube alone as on page 250 should be used.   Little information is available on this point however.   The expression, corresponding to equation (9–1) for the power output can be readily derived.

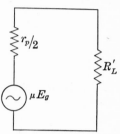

FIG. 9–6.   Equivalent circuit of two triodes in parallel.

Tubes are not now so extensively operated in parallel as formerly. Larger tubes having greater power-handling capacities are now available, and push-pull operation has certain important advantages.   As an illustration of the problems of early radio, for the first transatlantic *telephone* tests made, several hundred tubes, each of about 25 watts capacity, were operated in parallel in the final stage.

Push-Pull Amplifiers.—A circuit with two triodes in push-pull for audio-frequency power amplification is shown in Fig. 9–7.   The two

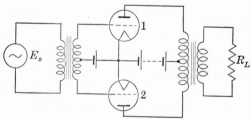

FIG. 9–7   Two triodes connected for push-pull class *A* operation.

tubes and corresponding transformer windings are assumed to be identical so that the amplifier is *balanced*.   Such an amplifier has many advantages over the parallel type as will now be explained.

The grids of the two tubes are biased negatively to *about* one-half the cut-off value.   One-half the alternating signal voltage induced in the secondary of the input transformer is impressed on the grid of *each* tube.   The grids never should be driven positive.   With no signal impressed, the plate current drawn by each of the *balanced* tubes is the same, and since this direct component flows in opposite directions through each of the identical halves of the primary of the ouptut transformer, no resultant magnetizing effect is produced. Smaller magnetic cores may, therefore, be used before magnetic saturation and distortion results.

When an alternating signal voltage is impressed on the two grids, they are driven alternately more positive and less positive. Thus, as the plate current in one tube *increases*, that in the other tube *decreases*. The net magnetizing effect in the transformer is the same as if an alternating current of *twice the value of either alternating plate-current component flowed through one-half of the primary winding.*

The power output of two tubes in class *A* push-pull is *considerably greater* than twice that of a single tube in class *A*. This is *contrary* to the popular opinion, and to explain the reason therefor requires considerable detail as will now be shown.

Operation of Push-Pull Amplifiers.—This is fully illustrated by Fig. 9–8 and the explanation here given closely follows the excellent treatment given by Glasgow.[5] The *dynamic* characteristics are plotted with the curve for tube 2 inverted. The current variations in each tube when an alternating signal voltage is impressed on the grids are shown by the curves: plate current—tube 1, and plate current—tube 2.

As illustrated, these two plate currents are badly distorted because the tubes are operated with alternating signal voltages (on the grids) which are so large that operation is over more than the (essentially) linear part of the dynamic curves. As was indicated by Fig. 9–4, this will be largely a second-harmonic distortion. As Fig. 9–8 shows, however, these second-harmonic components existing in the plate current of each tube *are balanced out in the transformer.* This is *one reason* that the power output of two tubes in push-pull may be greater than twice the output of one tube; *the second-harmonic distortion is balanced out.* A *second*, and perhaps more fundamental reason will be given later.

As mentioned in the preceding section, the net magnetizing effect of the separate alternating plate-current components is the same as if an alternating current of twice the value of either component flowed through one-half of the primary winding. This is equivalent to saying the net magnetizing effect is as if a combined resultant current flowed as shown in Fig. 9–8 *from a source which had a dynamic curve which was the resultant of the dynamic curves of the two separate tubes.*

If this resultant dynamic curve were an ideal curve as shown by the broken line, then the resultant current for the two tubes would be a pure sine wave composed only of a fundamental. The resultant dy-

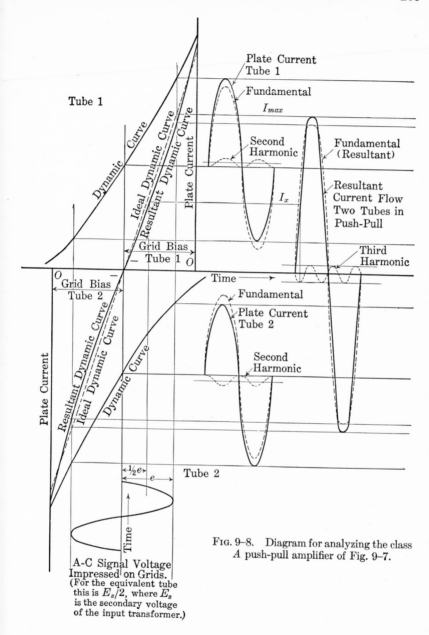

FIG. 9–8.   Diagram for analyzing the class *A* push-pull amplifier of Fig. 9–7.

namic characteristic is slightly curved as Fig. **9**–8 shows, and therefore a third-harmonic distortion (and under overloads also a fifth harmonic) exists in the output, as this figure indicates.

Equivalent Circuits for Push-Pull Triodes.—It is apparent that a push-pull audio-frequency power amplifier could be designed (page 258) from the *dynamic* curves of Fig. 9–8. Much time would be consumed

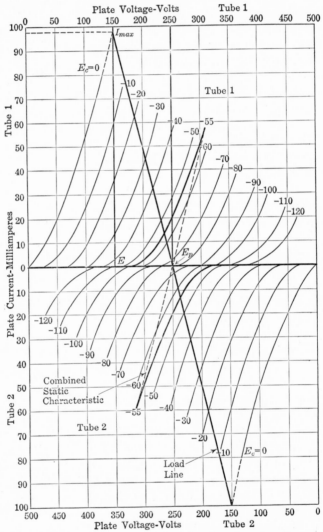

Fig. 9–9. Static curves for the design of a class *A* push-pull amplifier.

in plotting these *dynamic* curves, and thus the *static* curves are commonly used. This method was reported by Thompson.[6]

The static curves are plotted as shown in Fig. 9–9, with the curves of one tube inverted as before. The combined static curves (only one of which is shown by the broken line) represent the characteristic of *an equivalent tube.* Now the plate resistance of each tube is the reciprocal of the slope of the static curve at the point of operation (page 114). Hence, the *apparent* plate resistance of triodes in push-pull would be the reciprocal of the slope of the *combined static curve shown by the broken line.* For Fig. 9–9 this value is about 1000 ohms. The corresponding value of the tube plate resistance determined from the slope of an *individual* static curve (not the combined curve) is about 1700 ohms.

The method of determining the value of the load for a push-pull circuit will now be considered. For a *single class A tube,* it may be necessary to try several values of load resistance before one is found with which the second-harmonic distortion is less than five per cent. This value of load resistance which gives maximum *undistorted* power output (but not necessarily maximum power output) for a *single* class *A* tube is usually about twice the plate resistance. With push-pull tubes, the second-harmonic distortion is balanced out in the transformer. Thus, a value of load resistance may be selected which is *equal* to the apparent plate resistance, and thus the *maximum possible* power output can be obtained. This is the *second important reason* for the high output of push-pull tubes.

It is now possible to draw an equivalent circuit as shown in Fig. 9–10. As has been mentioned, the two tubes in push-pull class *A* act like one fictitious tube on which is impressed *one-half* of the total alternating input signal voltage * E_g, and which has a static curve as shown by the dotted line of Fig. 9–9. This fictitious tube was shown to have an *apparent* plate resistance r_p' of about 1000 ohms. In accordance with the statements of the preceding paragraph, the selected load resistance should also be 1000 ohms.

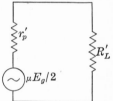

Fig. 9–10. One possible equivalent circuit for a class *A* push-pull amplifier.

This value of R_L' is not the *plate-to-plate* load which should be used with the two tubes in push-pull. The value of the actual plate-to-plate load equals $4R_L'$. The reason for this is as follows: As previously mentioned, this fictitious tube from which the equivalent current of Fig. 9–8 flows, operates into *one-half* of the primary. Thus, for an output transformer of 1 to 1 overall ratio, if one-half of the primary turns is used, the ratio becomes 1 : 2, and an impedance on the secondary will be reflected as *one-fourth* the value (see page 226) when measured across

* In these discussions E_s represents the impressed alternating signal voltage, and E_g the value of the signal voltage on the secondary of the transformer.

one-half of the primary in the manner the fictitious tube operates. Thus, the actual plate-to-plate load connected across the transformer secondary is $4R_L'$ as previously mentioned (see page 249). In practice, the output transformer of Fig. 9–7 often has a high turns ratio so that the load, which is usually a low-impedance dynamic speaker voice coil, is reflected into the primary as the correct load resistance.

There is a second possible equivalent circuit for the push-pull amplifier as shown in Fig. 9–11. In this, R_L represents the plate-to-plate load of $4R_L'$ as previously determined. The values of r_p are the plate resistances of the tubes as ordinarily determined. The alternating signal voltage impressed on the *two* tubes in push-pull is now E_g instead of $E_g/2$ as for Fig. 9–10.

Push-Pull Power Output Calculation.—Either of the equivalent circuits may be used to give the power output of a push-pull amplifier. Using the circuit of Fig. 9–10, and assuming an alternating signal voltage of $E_g = 110$ volts peak or 77.7 volts effective value, a bias of -55 volts, and a $\mu = 3.5$, the output would be $I = 77.7 \times 3.5/(2 \times 2000)$ = 0.068 ampere. The power delivered to the load would be

$$I^2R_L' = 0.00462 \times 1000 = 4.62 \text{ watts.}$$

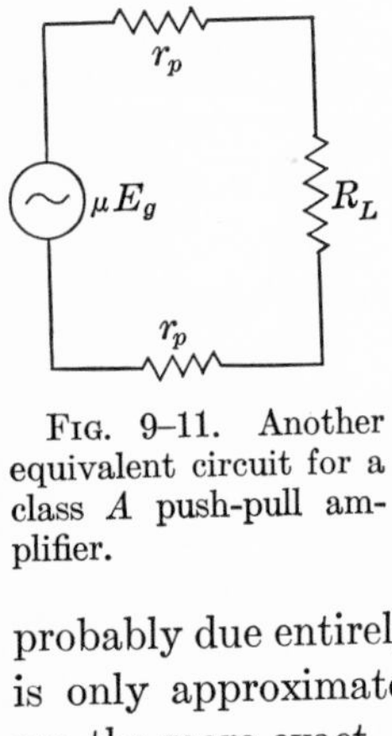

Using the circuit of Fig. 9–11, the current would be

$$I = \frac{77.7 \times 3.5}{(2 \times 1700 + 4000)} = 0.0367 \text{ ampere.}$$

The power delivered to the load R_L would be $I^2R_L = 0.00135 \times 4000 = 5.38$ watts. These two calculations are not in very close agreement, probably due entirely to the fact that the plate resistance of 1700 ohms is only approximate. The calculations of the preceding paragraph are the more exact.

Fig. 9–11. Another equivalent circuit for a class A push-pull amplifier.

Although much detail has been required to explain the operation of push-pull amplifiers,* they can readily be designed from simple calculations as explained in Reference 2 from which the following is summarized. Using the static curves for the tube (such as the upper set of curves of Fig. 9–9), erect a vertical line at $E = 0.6E_p$, where E_p is the operating plate voltage. (Both E and E_p are shown on Fig. 9–9.) Draw a load line from $I_{\max}$. to E_p. The tangent of the angle (that is,

* E. W. Houghton has shown in the June 1937 Electronics that the detailed plotting of plate characteristic curves in order to determine the circuit constants is unnecessary. His article is recommended to these interested in the design of push-pull circuits.

E_p/I_p) that this line makes with the vertical when *multiplied by four* is the value of the plate-to-plate load resistance to be used in accordance with the explanations previously given.   For Fig. **9**–9 this is 100/0.096 = 1040 ohms.   (In the preceding discussion, 1000 ohms was used for R_L' of Fig. **9**–10.)   The power output of the two tubes in class *A* push-pull is [2]

$$P = \frac{I_{\max.}\, E_p}{5},\qquad\qquad (9\text{–}4)$$

where the power is in watts, where $I_{\max.}$ is in amperes and E_p is in volts.

Distortion in Class A Push-Pull Amplifiers.—As has been mentioned, the second harmonics are balanced out in a push-pull stage. Likewise, power hum introduced into the plate circuit *from the power supply* is balanced out.   Any hum induced *into the grid circuit* would of course be amplified just as would any other grid signal.

Some third harmonic distortion, and a small amount of fifth-harmonic distortion is caused as discussed on page 255.   As shown in Reference 5, the per cent of third-harmonic distortion is

$$\frac{(I_{\max.} - 2I_x)}{[2(I_{\max.} + I_x)]}\qquad\qquad (9\text{–}4a)$$

multiplied by 100.   The values of $I_{\max.}$ and I_x are as indicated on Fig. **9**–8.

Thus, in summarizing, the push-pull class *A* audio-frequency amplifier using triodes offers a means of obtaining very high-quality amplification.   This amplifier is *not so efficient* as certain other types which will be considered.   Hence, push-pull class *A* power amplifiers are not so widely used as formerly except in high-quality equipment.   Before leaving the subject of push-pull amplifiers it should be mentioned that there is an increasing tendency to use such circuits for *voltage* amplification in high-quality amplifiers in addition to their use as power amplifiers as included in this chapter.

78. A-F Class *A* Pentode Power Amplifiers.—When the suppressor-grid power-output pentode is used, a large power output is obtained with a *low alternating signal voltage applied to the grid.*   This tube is, therefore, widely used as a power-output tube for radio receiving sets because it can be driven *directly from the detector* or demodulator (page 335) without an intervening audio-frequency voltage-amplifying stage.

As a single power-amplifying stage, the suppressor-grid pentode would be connected as in Fig. **9**–12 if of the separate-heater type.   If not, the suppressor grid is connected (usually internally) to the center of the filament.   An equivalent circuit for this tube is shown in Fig.

9–12, in which r_p is the plate resistance and R_L' is the load resistance R_L reflected into the primary. In accordance with the theory on page 226, $R_L' = N^2 R_L$, where N is the turns ratio of the (ideal) transformer.

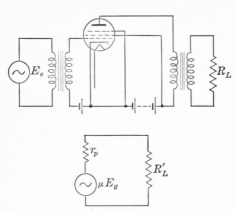

It is evident from Fig. 6–18 that, if a large value of load resistance is used, the dynamic curve will be very badly curved at the upper end. For distortionless amplification, the value of the load resistance chosen should be such as to give a straight dynamic curve on which to operate. In *triodes*, the value of load resistance chosen is as close as practicable to the plate resistance of the tube to make the power output large. As discussed on page 131, the power output is maximum when the load resistance equals the plate resistance, but in triodes the value of load resistance actually selected is about twice the plate resistance, to reduce distortion. Owing to the excessive bending of the *dynamic curve for the pentode* the value of the load resistance selected must be very much *lower* than the plate resistance of the tube. For the tube of Figs. 6–17 and 6–18 the load resistance chosen would be about 6000 ohms, although from Fig. 6–17 the plate resistance of the tube is 50,000 ohms. This mismatch causes the power output to be lower than the value theoretically obtainable (and which would result in excessive distortion). The power output under these conditions can be obtained from equation (9–1). The suppressor-grid power-output tube is widely used however, because as Fig. 9–13 shows, only a small alternating signal voltage need be applied to the control grid to drive the tube.

Characteristics of Class A Power Pentodes.—As shown in Fig. 6–18, even at the low plate resistance of 6000 ohms the dynamic curve of a suppressor-grid power pentode is not a straight line. This curve has been replotted as Fig. 9–13. When points on this dynamic curve corresponding to given values of the alternating grid signal voltage are projected, the resultant plate-current curve is obtained. If the points are projected from the *ideal* dynamic curve, a sine wave is obtained corresponding to the fundamental. The resultant wave has further been broken down into second and third harmonics (see also page 163).

Fig. 9–12. Actual and equivalent circuits for a class A power pentode.

The power output and the harmonic distortion for suppressor grid pentodes can be calculated from equations based on Fig. 6–17 and derived from Fig. 9–13. These equations are derived in Reference 5 on the basis of I_x being the plate current at $0.5e_g$, where e_g is the maximum value of the alternating grid signal voltage, assumed to be sinusoidal. Similarly, I_y is the plate current at $1.5e_g$. The equations given in Reference 2 are derived on the basis of I_x equals the plate current

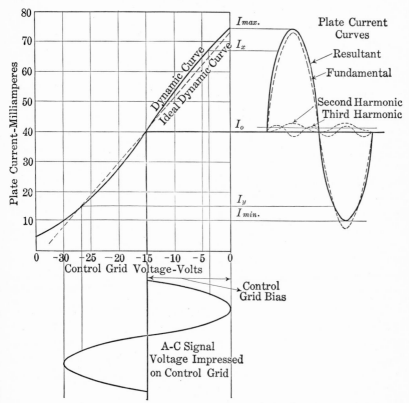

FIG. 9–13. Diagram for analyzing the performance of a power pentode.

flowing at $0.293E_c$ and I_y is the current at $1.707E_c$. The voltage E_c is the direct grid bias voltage, which equals the maximum value of the alternating sinusoidal signal voltage which when applied to the grid will just drive it to zero potential (see Fig. 9–13). These two different methods lead to the same results; attention is directed to them to prevent confusion.

Thus, *in accordance with Reference 2*, and referring to Fig. 6–17 and Fig. 9–13, the power output for a suppressor-grid pentode or a beam-power tube (which has a similar family of curves, as shown in Fig. 6–23 is

$$\text{Power Output} = [I_{\text{max.}} - I_{\text{min.}} + 1.41(I_x - I_y)]^2 \frac{R_L'}{32}. \quad (9\text{–}5)$$

This value will be milliwatts if the current is in milliamperes and the load resistance R_L' is in ohms. The value R_L' is the load resistance reflected into the primary for a transformer-coupled amplifier. From Fig. 6–17 this load resistance is equal to $(E_{\text{max.}} - E_{\text{min.}})/(I_{\text{max.}} - I_{\text{min.}})$.

The per cent distortion can be found from Fig. 9–13 by the following equations

2nd Harmonic Distortion

$$= \frac{I_{\text{max.}} + I_{\text{min.}} - 2I_0}{I_{\text{max.}} - I_{\text{min.}} + 1.41(I_x - I_y)} \times 100. \quad (9\text{–}6)$$

3rd Harmonic Distortion

$$= \frac{I_{\text{max.}} - I_{\text{min.}} - 1.41(I_x - I_y)}{I_{\text{max.}} - I_{\text{min.}} + 1.41(I_x - I_y)} \times 100. \quad (9\text{–}7)$$

The total per cent distortion; that is, the sum of the second and third harmonic distortion is equal to the square root of the sum of the per cent second harmonic squared and the per cent third harmonic squared. This is in accordance with the usual method of adding two alternating values of different frequencies.

The manner in which the harmonic output changes with various load resistances and input voltages is shown in Fig. 6–20. The peculiar shape of the second harmonic curves is explained in Reference 7.

Thus, in selecting the best value of load resistance to use with a suppressor-grid power pentode or a *beam-power tube* (page 164) several load lines for different resistance values are drawn on the family of curves such as in Fig. 6–17, page 159. For the curve giving low distortion, the distance I_0 to $I_{\text{max.}}$ will approximately equal the distance I_0 to $I_{\text{min.}}$. If the per cent distortion is desired, then equations (9–6) and (9–7) should be used.

Pentodes in Push-Pull.—Suppressor grid power pentodes are sometimes operated in push-pull circuits similar to that of Fig. 9–7. Operation may be as class A or as class AB amplifiers.[2, 8].

The third harmonic distortion in pentodes is much higher than in triodes under comparable conditions (Fig. 6–20). Odd harmonics are *not* cancelled in push-pull circuits. Also, in properly designed single-tube circuits, the second harmonic output is fairly low (Fig. 6–20). Thus from the standpoint of distortion *produced by the tubes themselves*, little advantage results from push-pull *pentode* operation. As in all push-pull operation, there are certain other advantages, such as the reduction in hum in the output transformer, thus requiring less filtering in the power-supply rectifier.

79. A-F Class *AB* Power Amplifiers.—In such amplifiers, defined on page 211, two tubes (usually triodes) are connected in a push-pull circuit such as Fig. 9–7. A *higher* negative grid bias is used than for class *A* operation, and higher plate voltage (and screen voltage if a pentode) is also used.[2] These are also called *class A prime* amplifiers.

There are *two types* of these amplifiers. In the class AB_1 amplifier, the maximum value or peak of the alternating signal voltage applied to the grid never exceeds the direct grid-bias voltage; that is, the grids are never driven positive, and *no grid current ever flows*. In the class AB_2 the maximum value or peak of the alternating signal voltage impressed on the grids *exceeds* the direct grid bias voltage and the grids are driven positive, and *grid current flows*.

The design of class AB_1 amplifiers (in which no grid current flows), follows the general method given on page 256 for the class *A* push-pull amplifier. For example, on page 256, the curves could be drawn for a plate voltage of 275 volts and a grid-bias voltage of − 70 volts. Following the method outlined, the equations on page 256 apply for class AB_1 operation. For given tubes, higher output and efficiency are obtainable with but little greater distortion than with class *A* operation.

The class AB_2 amplifier, *in which grid current flows*, requires special consideration, best explained after studying class *B* amplifiers. For this reason, further discussion of these will be deferred to page 267.

80. A-F Class *B* Power Amplifiers.—From the definitions given on page 210, the class *B* amplifier is biased about to cut-off so that plate-current flow with no alternating signal voltage on the grid is almost zero. Two tubes are used in "push-pull," and when an alternating signal voltage is impressed on the grids, each tube passes one half of the cycle. The term "push-pull" is growing in usage, but the action is not exactly the same type of push-pull explained on page 253 for class *A* amplification. The action is, perhaps, better specified by the term "push-push," which, although expressive, has not received wide acceptance. In accordance with accepted usage, the term push-pull will be used in the following discussions.

As defined, tubes operated in class *B* are biased approximately to cut-off, and hence require a large direct biasing voltage if *ordinary* triodes are used. This biasing voltage must be fixed in value, such as is supplied by a rectifier, or by batteries. Self-biasing arrangements (page 202) *cannot be used* because of the plate-current fluctuations. To avoid the use of large fixed sources of biasing voltage, special tubes have been developed for class *B* operation which *require no biasing voltage.* Examples of these are the types 46 and 59.

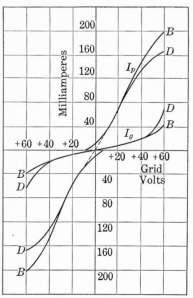

FIG. 9–14. Dynamic transfer characteristics for two type 46 tubes operated as class *B* triodes. Plate current I_p and grid current I_g for plate-to-plate loads per tube of *B*, 1450 ohms, and *D*, 2000 ohms. $E_p = 400$ volts. (Data from Reference 2.)

Operation.—In Fig. 9–14 are shown the *dynamic characteristics* of two tubes when operated with two different plate load resistances. These tubes are of the special type for class *B* operation, and as previously mentioned require no grid bias to produce (approximate) cutoff. For convenience, only two of the family of dynamic curves have been plotted. Assuming that satisfactory operation would be obtained with a *plate load* of 1450 ohms (not plate-to-plate load as will be discussed later), the output current would be as shown when the grids were driven by the alternating signal voltage.

In particular it should be noted from Fig. 9–14 that each tube passes current when its grid *is positive*, and that considerable grid current flows. Some plate current flows when no signal is impressed, but this is incidental and undesired, and is a source of distortion. The ideal class *B* tubes would have dynamic characteristics shown by the straight broken line.

Since one tube and then the other functions, the effect is the same as one tube working into *one-half* the primary. Thus, for an ideal *unity ratio* transformer, if the optimum load resistance per tube is selected, such as 1450 ohms (Fig. 9–14), then the effective plate-to-plate load would be 1450 × 4 = 5800 ohms as explained on page 257. Or, looked at in another way, if the secondary of an ideal unity-ratio transformer is terminated in 5800 ohms resistance, this value appears to be 1450 ohms when measured through one-half of the primary in the manner in which each tube functions.

An analysis similar to that of Fig. 9–8 can be used to prove that the second harmonics produced by the individual tubes are balanced out in the output transformer just as in the push-pull class *A* amplifier. This statement applies to any even harmonics and to the hum introduced by the plate supply to the class *B* stage.   Of course, any harmonics or hum impressed on the grids will be amplified just as are any other signals.

The family of plate current-plate voltage *static* characteristic curves is shown in Fig. 9–15. A load line corresponding to 1450 ohms is drawn in the usual way so that the intercepts on the *X* axis in volts divided by those on the *Y* axis in amperes equals the load resistance. Since only one tube operates at a time, it is not necessary to show inverted characteristics as for the class *A* push-pull stage of Fig. 9–9.

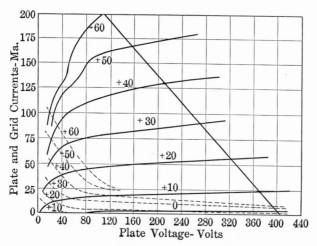

Fig. 9–15.   Static plate current (solid) and grid current (dotted) lines for the tubes of Fig. 9–14.   Values on curves are grid voltages.   Load line for 1450 ohms is shown.   (Data from Reference 2.)

Power Output.—The power output of this amplifier with large alternating signals impressed on the grid can be approximately determined in several ways.   Perhaps the easiest is as follows: Referring to either Fig. 9–14 or Fig. 9–15, for a maximum grid signal voltage on the tube of 50 volts, the corresponding peak value of plate current is about 170 milliamperes for a 1450-ohm *tube* load (not plate-to-plate).   The alternating or speech power delivered by the two tubes in class *B* would be $P = I^2R$ or $P = (0.707 \times 0.170)^2 \times 1450 = 20.9$ watts.

This calculation is based on the fact that *each* tube delivers power to one-half the primary of the output transformer for only one-half of the cycle.   As has been brought out, this is equivalent to *one* tube on which one-half of the secondary voltage of the input transformer is impressed, and which delivers power to one-half the primary for the *entire* cycle.   Thus, the plate-to-plate load would be 5800 ohms, but the reflected impedance into which the tube worked would be 1450 ohms. This calculation neglects distortion and assumes a pure sine wave output. It is not very accurate for low values of alternating signal voltage.

An equivalent circuit can be drawn for a class B amplifier as for the other amplifiers which have been studied. This is also on the basis of an *equivalent* class A tube. This equivalent tube has one-half the voltage of the secondary of the input transformer impressed on it, but works over the entire cycle into one-half of the primary of the output transformer, the secondary of which is terminated with 5800 ohms. Such an equivalent circuit for two type 46 tubes in class B (the type tubes which have just been considered) is shown in Fig. 9–16.

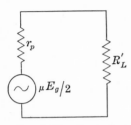

FIG. 9–16.   Equivalent circuit for two tubes in class B.

Assuming that $r_p = 17,500$ ohms, $\mu = 70$, $R_L' = 1450$ ohms, and that E_g is 100 volts, the power output of the *two* tubes is

$$P = I^2 R = \left[\frac{\mu E_g}{(r_p + R_{L'})} \right]^2 \times R_L'$$

$$= \left[\frac{70 \times 50 \times 0.707}{(17,500 + 1450)} \right]^2 \times 1450 = 24.7 \text{ watts.}$$

This value agrees fairly closely with the value previously computed of 20.9 watts. This value of 20.9 watts is more correct, because of the fact that the coefficients of a class B tube are not exactly constant. For instance, the plate resistance r_p is assumed fixed at 17,500 ohms, but an examination of Fig. 9–15 will show that it is different for the various grid voltages.

Input Power.—As Fig. 9–14 shows, the grids draw considerable current in class B tubes. This means that signal power must be put *into* the class B stage by the preceding stage; for example, 650 milliwatts [2] are required to drive the class B stage here considered. This is in contrast with class A amplifiers in which the preceding stage serves (largely) as a voltage amplifier, the negative grids taking negligible power.

The value of the input grid resistance of the class B tubes is the reciprocal of the slopes of the grid-current curves for conditions of operation. Thus the input resistance varies with the varying magnitude of the alternating signal voltage impressed on the grid. The resistance is several thousand ohms for low signals and a few hundred ohms at high signal values. Since the class B input circuit must be supplied with power, special care must be taken in the design of the preceding stage and the input transformer.   If this is not done, when the class B stage starts to draw power the alternating signal voltage will drop because of insufficient power capacity and too high impedance. This drop in voltage *causes distortion*.   References 2, 9, and 10 should be consulted for additional data on the design of the driver stage.

The class B audio-frequency amplifier early fell into disfavor with many, largely because these amplifiers were poorly designed and operated.   The output of a class B amplifier can be made to have excellent quality.   Such an amplifier is especially well adapted to use in sound amplifying systems (or public address systems), especially for a stadium where considerable power is necessary.

81. A-F Class AB_2 Power Amplifiers.—The two types of these amplifiers, class AB_1 and AB_2, were discussed on page 263.   In the AB_1 amplifier the grid is *not* driven positive by the alternating signal voltage at any time, and consequently no grid current flows.   In the AB_2 amplifier, the grid *is* driven positive and grid current does flow.   The operation of the class AB_1 system is similar to push-pull class A, and will not be considered further.   The operation of the class AB_2 is similar to the class B amplifier and will now be discussed.

In the class A amplifier, plate current always flows.   This is equivalent to saying that plate current flows for 360 degrees of the input cycle.   In class B operation, the tubes are biased to the cut-off value so that plate current flows only for one-half cycle or for 180 degrees.   In class AB_2 operation the direct grid bias is such that plate current flows for *less* than one cycle but *more* than one-half cycle; that is, the **angle of flow** is less than 360 degrees but greater than 180 degrees.

In the class A push-pull amplifier, it was found (page 257) that the apparent plate resistance of the tubes, or what might be termed the plate resistance of a tube equivalent to the two in push-pull, was reduced to about one-half the value of the plate resistance of a single tube.   In the class B push-pull amplifier, since one tube works and then the other (rather than both together as in class A push-pull) the effective plate resistance of the equivalent class A tube (page 210) *is the same as* the plate resistance *of one* of the class B push-pull tubes. Since the class AB_2 tubes operate at some point between class A and class B, the plate resistance of an equivalent class A tube must also be between these two extremes, the exact value being determined by the grid bias for the conditions of operation.   Thus, the power output equation on page 266 can be used to give the power output in class AB_2 operation if the correct value of r_p is known.   The method of finding this correct value is explained in Reference 9.

With the exception just given, the design of class AB_2 amplifiers is very similar to class B systems, although the requirements are not so severe. As in the class B system, power must be supplied the class AB_2 stage when the grids are driven positive, and this power must come from the preceding driver stage.

82. Radio Transmitters.—Audio-frequency power amplifiers were treated in the preceding pages of this chapter. The following pages will be devoted to *radio-frequency power* amplifiers. Before considering these, however, it is advisable to present the schematic of several radio transmitting sets to clarify the discussions.

In a radio transmitting set (or radio transmitter) for *voice* communication, the voice frequencies are used to **modulate** (see Chapter 11) a high-frequency carrier so that the voice signals may be transmitted through space at high frequencies. There are many reasons why such a frequency translation is necessary. Among these are the following: Energy could not be effectively radiated from ordinary antennas at the low audio frequencies; also, if translation to the various radio-frequency channels were not effected, all stations would operate over *the same frequency band* with resulting confusion of signals, and without the possibility of selecting one station and excluding others.

As will be shown in Chapter 11, in the process of modulation, new frequencies *are created* which did not exist *in the input.* Modulation may be correctly regarded as a *useful* form of non-linear distortion (page 209). Thus, if a *broadcast station* operates at a carrier frequency of 1,000,000 cycles, and if the voice frequencies impressed on the stage *in which the modulation occurs* vary from 100–5000 cycles, then the output from the antenna will contain frequencies as follows: The carrier plus the voice, varying between the limits of 1,000,100 to 1,005,000 cycles; the carrier of 1,000,000 cycles; and the carrier minus the voice, varying between the limits of 995,000 to 999,900 cycles. The first group of these is called the **upper side band,** and the last the **lower side band.** The output wave in the antenna circuit containing these three components would appear as in Fig. 9–17. In any system there

Fig. 9–17. Showing the shape of a wave before and after modulation. The unmodulated portion at the left contains only the carrier; the modulated portion contains *three* components: The carrier frequency; the carrier plus the voice (upper sideband); the carrier minus the voice (lower sideband). The carrier-frequency component *does not* vary in amplitude in the modulated portion. The *apparent* change in amplitude is due to the presence of the sidebands.

are also other unwanted components which will be neglected since they are usually suppressed.

There are two general types of radio transmitters in use. In one, modulation occurs in the last stage (before the antenna) and this is called **high-level modulation.** In the other, stages of amplification intervene between the modulating stage and the antenna, and this is

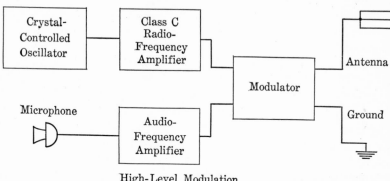

High-Level Modulation

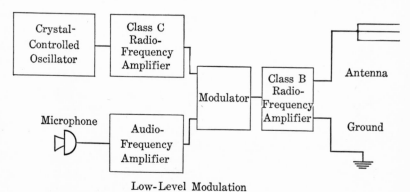

Low-Level Modulation

FIG. 9–18.   Illustrating two typical systems for radio transmitting sets for voice communication.

called **low-level modulation.** Schematic drawings of the two systems are shown in Fig. 9–18.

Very briefly, a typical *high-level modulation* transmitter operates as follows: The output of the crystal-controlled oscillator (page 295) drives a class *C* radio-frequency power amplifier. The audio-frequency amplifier is driven by the microphone. This amplifier is of the type

A large high-vacuum triode with external water-cooled copper plate (tubular portion below) and copper-glass seal. Used as radio-frequency class B and C power amplifiers. Rating as follows: Filament, 60 amperes at 20 volts; maximum plate current, 3 amperes; maximum plate voltage, 20,000 volts. (Courtesy Western Electric Co.)

previously discussed, and may be class *A* voltage stages driving a class *AB* or class *B* push-pull power-output stage. The outputs of the radio-frequency and the audio-frequency amplifiers are fed into the *stage where modulation occurs*, and this stage is directly connected to the antenna. This stage has been called a **modulator** in Fig. 9–18, and is defined [11] as "a device to effect the process of modulation." In other words, the *modulator* is the stage in which the process of *modulation* is brought about. This point is stressed, because the audio-frequency *driving stage* is often incorrectly referred to as a modulator.

The operation of the typical *low-level modulation* transmitter is evident from the preceding discussion. Modulation occurs at a low power level, however, and class *B* radio-frequency stages are used to increase the power until it is sufficiently high to be impressed on the antenna circuit.

Although it is possible to do so, class *A* power amplifiers are not ordinarily used at *radio* frequencies because of their low efficiency as compared with class *B* and *C* amplifiers.

83. R-F Class *B* Power Amplifiers.—As shown in Fig. 9–18, this type amplifier is used in low-level modulation transmitters to increase the power output of the *modulating stage* to a level sufficient for impressing on the antenna. Although for *audio frequencies* two tubes in push-pull must be used in each stage to prevent distortion (since each tube passes only one-half of each cycle), for radio-frequency amplification one class *B* tube per stage is sufficient. Two class *B* tubes are often used in "push-pull," however.

The reason a single tube may be used is illustrated by Fig. **9–19.** A modulated wave containing the *carrier* and the *upper* and *lower side-bands* is shown driving the grid of a tube which is biased approximately to the cut-off point and therefore operating in class *B*.   It is assumed that the carrier wave *has been* modulated by a pure sine wave of, for example, 1000 cycles per second.   The load in the plate circuit is so chosen that the dynamic characteristic curve is approximately a straight line, at least until the vicinity of cut-off.   As Fig. 9–19 indi-

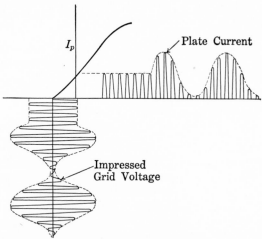

FIG. 9–19.   In the class *B* amplifier the plate current is badly distorted.   The anti-resonant tuned load circuit selects only the desired frequency components and does not transmit the undesired products of distortion.

cates, the radio-frequency components will be distorted but the tuned load circuit acts as a filter and largely suppresses the undesired harmonics.*   Two tubes in class *B* "push-pull" tend to reduce the radio-frequency distortion making filtering less difficult.

Characteristics.—The usual plate circuit load, as indicated in Fig. 9–20, is a parallel circuit which is *anti-resonant* (in *current* reso-

---

* An alternate point of view describes the modulated wave as a single radio-frequency sine wave varying in amplitude, so that the maximum (and rms) value of a single r-f cycle is proportional to the instantaneous value of the modulating signal frequency voltage. Thus if there is no distortion the *envelope* of the carrier frequency wave will have the wave form of the signal voltage.

From this point of view there is no distortion since the average current (average through one cycle of the radio frequency) will follow the carrier envelope, and if this envelope is undistorted there will be a current of the wave form of the original signal voltage.

The two points of view are completely interchangeable both physically and mathematically.   Where trouble has been encountered with this alternate point of view, as in the historical "Stenode" discussion, it has usually been because the variable amplitude sine-wave was treated as an ordinary steady state sine-wave, and circuit behavior predicted on that basis.   This is not permissible; a transient point of view must be adopted.   If the proper mathematical treatment is used the answers derived from the two points of view are identical.   See Chapter 11.

nance) to the carrier frequency. *To this frequency*, and *to the side bands* which are also being amplified, this load circuit is essentially a *pure resistance* of the correct value to load the tube properly. To the harmonics of the radio frequency, the load is reactive and of a low value; hence, the harmonics are amplified very little. The resistance value includes the reflected effect of the connected load resistor which represents the antenna or the following amplifier stage to which the circuit shown is supplying power. In this connection it will be recalled that for a class B or C amplifier, the grid is driven positive, and input power is required so to drive it.

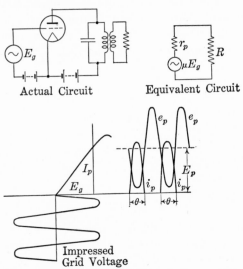

Actual Circuit   Equivalent Circuit

Impressed
Grid Voltage

Fig. 9–20. Actual and equivalent circuit and diagram showing the shape of the plate current and instantaneous plate voltage. The effect of the tuned anti-resonant plate load causes the instantaneous plate-voltage variations to exceed the plate-supply voltage E_p.

Since the load is essentially pure resistance to the alternating component *in the plate circuit*, the amplifier can be represented by the equivalent circuit of Fig. 9–20. It should be kept clearly in mind that this load resistance *presents itself only to the alternating component.* To the direct component, the coil offers a path of negligible resistance, and hence negligible *direct voltage drop appears across the load circuit.*

Now assume that a pure sine-wave voltage E_g is impressed on the grid of the tube which is biased to the cut-off value for class B operation. The instantaneous current in the plate circuit will flow for a time equal to about one-half cycle and represented by the angle θ, sometimes called the angle of flow. Although this plate current appears to be "spurts," it is a recurring phenomenon and can be analyzed [12] into a fundamental (of the same frequency as the alternating signal voltage applied to the grid), and a series of harmonics. Thus, the *instantaneous voltage* e_p between the plate and cathode is composed of the constant direct plate voltage E_b and the value of the fundamental alternating current component at that instant.

In particular, it will be observed that the potential e_p of the plate is *minimum* while plate current flows through the tube. The power loss *within the tube* is, therefore, kept low. The plate efficiency of the tube is accordingly high, having a theoretical maximum value [9] of 78.54 per cent. The efficiencies actually obtained in practice are somewhat lower. For further information on this subject and for information on the design of class *B* circuits for radio-frequency power amplifiers, References 5, 9, 13, and 14 are recommended.

84. R–F Class *C* Power Amplifiers.—The circuit for the class *C* amplifier is the same as Fig. 9–20 for a class *B* amplifier, the essential difference being that the grid of a tube in class *C* is biased with a direct voltage considerably beyond the cut-off point, so that the plate current flows only for a small part of the cycle as Fig. 9–21 indicates. Since the angle of flow is so small, the distortion is *very* great. Such an amplifier cannot, therefore, be used for voice frequencies, or for a voice-modulated carrier. As Fig. 9–18 indicates, the class *C* amplifier is used in radio-telephone transmitters for amplifying a *single frequency*, such as the carrier wave. It is also used as an amplifier in radio-telegraph transmitters.

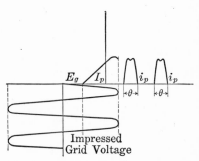

Fig. 9–21. For class *C* amplification the plate current may show "dips" if the tube is driven with a large grid voltage as indicated. The angle θ is less than in Fig. 9–20 for the class *B* amplifier. The instantaneous plate-voltage variations are similar to those shown in Fig. 9–20.

Of course this single-frequency wave is badly distorted, and harmonics are produced. The load circuit is made anti-resonant to the fundamental frequency, however, and thus the harmonics are effectively filtered. As mentioned when discussing the class *B* amplifier, it should be remembered that any continuously-recurring current can be analyzed into a fundamental and harmonic components.[12]

If the grid of the tube is driven sufficiently positive, a "dip" will occur in the *plate current* as in Fig. 9–21. This is caused by reaching the region of saturation on the grid voltage-plate current characteristic curve. This curve may drop as shown because the positive grid is drawing many of the electrons available from the filament (page 124). A similar "dip" may occur in the *grid current curve* if secondary emission from the grid causes the grid voltage-grid current curve to drop as explained on page 125.

Characteristics.—As previously mentioned, this amplifier operates into an anti-resonant circuit which is so adjusted that the load offered to the fundamental (which it is desired to amplify) is essentially a pure resistance of high value. The equivalent circuit of Fig. 9–20, and the accompanying explanations, will also apply to the class *C* amplifier. The efficiency of this amplifier is higher, however, reaching about 80 per cent under good conditions. For data on the design of these amplifiers, and for other information, the references listed on page 273 are suggested.

In the preceding explanations, the use of the term "tank circuit" to describe a circuit composed of inductance and capacitance in parallel has been avoided. Also, no reference has been made to "fly wheel action." It is assumed that the theory of a parallel circuit is understood, a brief explanation having been given on page 242. Often, in communication work, it is advisable to consider a network, such as a parallel anti-resonant circuit and its coupled load, from the standpoint of the impedance offered at the frequency under consideration, rather than to attempt to analyze what is occurring in each element. This method of presentation has been followed.

Neutralization.—Screen-grid tetrodes, usually requiring no neutralization (page 238) can be used for radio-frequency power amplification. They are, however, difficult to construct with outputs greater than 500 watts,[9] and thus triodes must be used. In the larger sizes these are water-cooled tubes as discussed on page 270. Triodes *must be neutralized* to prevent radio-frequency feedback and resulting undesired oscillations as discussed on page 238.

85. Measurements of A-F Distortion.—The three types of distortion were discussed on page 209. *Frequency distortion* means that all frequencies are not amplified (or attenuated) the same amounts. In audio-frequency amplifiers this usually causes the low-frequency and the high-frequency response to be less than at the intermediate frequencies. *Non-linear distortion,* usually occurring in the tubes and transformers, changes the wave shape, causing harmonic components to exist in the output which were not in the input. *Delay distortion* means that some frequency components are not propagated through an amplifier at the same rate as are others. Thus, the various frequency components arrive at the output terminals with different phase relations than they had at the input.

Frequency distortion can be determined by measuring the input and output voltages at various frequencies. From these data, curves can be plotted showing the gain (or loss) at various frequencies. It is customary to plot these curves with decibels (page 206) on the Y axis, and with the frequency to a logarithmic scale on the X axis. Vacuum-tube voltmeters, and in some instances copper-oxide voltmeters, are very well suited for such measurements. Various substitution methods [15] also may be used. It is important *not to overdrive* the amplifier when such tests are made, and to terminate it with the proper load.

Non-linear distortion can be measured by analyzing the wave form of the output when the amplifier is driven with a *pure sine wave* voltage. If a sinusoidal voltage is not available, then both the input and output waves must be analyzed, the difference in harmonic content being due to the distortion of the amplifier. It is also important that the amplifier is not overdriven, and that it is correctly terminated. Very satisfactory wave analyzers [15] are available commercially at a reasonable cost. If such an instrument is not obtainable, the dynamometer method [16] is very satisfactory.

With this method, the current to be analyzed is passed through one coil of a dynamometer instrument, and the current from a variable-frequency oscillator is passed through the other coil. As the frequency of the oscillator is varied, the dynamometer instrument will deflect when the oscillator frequency approaches that of the fundamental or of one of the harmonics of the wave to be analyzed. The magnitude of the deflection is proportional to the product of the magnitude of the current from the oscillator and that of the harmonic. A continuously-variable beat-frequency oscillator is well adapted to such measurements.

The phase relations caused by delay distortion can be determined by a phase-shifting bridge arrangement. For a convenient method of accomplishing this, and for additional data regarding the methods of measurement previously discussed, Reference 15 should be consulted.

It is no longer necessary to judge the characteristics of an amplifier by ear. Such tests are often misleading because they include the distortion present in phonograph pickups, records, microphones, loud speakers, and the rooms in which the tests are made. Also, such tests depend on the judgment of the listener. Laboratory equipment is now available at a very low cost by which reliable quantitative tests readily can be made.

86. Typical A–F Class *A* Amplifier.—All the elements of this type amplifier have now been dscussed in the preceding pages of this text.

To indicate how these are sometimes combined in practice, the circuit diagram of Fig. 9–22 is included. This particular circuit was chosen because of its simplicity. This circuit and the data listed are reproduced by permission from the Thordarson No. 346-A Sound Amplifier Manual.

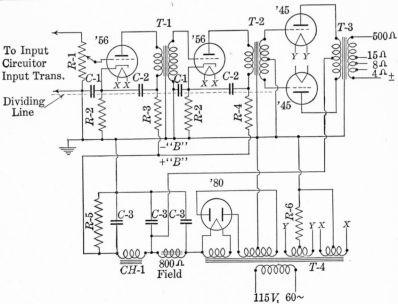

FIG. 9–22. Circuit diagram of an audio-frequency amplifier. Diagram and equipment essentially as listed in Thordarson 346-A Sound Amplifier Manual.

T-1	Interstage transformer 1 to 3 ratio
T-2	Interstage transformer 1 to 3 ratio
T-3	Output transformer
T-4	Power transformer, 700-volt, center-tapped secondary
CH-1	Filter choke, 22 henrys at 35 milliamperes
R-1	500,000-ohm volume control
R-2	2500-ohm carbon resistor, 1 watt
R-3	25,000-ohm carbon resistor, 1 watt
R-4	15,000-ohm carbon resistor, 1 watt
R-5	30,000-ohm wire-wound resistor, 10 watts
R-6	750-ohm wire-wound resistor, 10 watts
C-1	4-mfd. electrolytic condenser, 25 volts
C-2	2-mfd. electrolytic condenser, 450 volts
C-3	8-mfd. triple electrolytic condenser, 450 volts.

Operation is from a 115-volt, 60-cycle alternating-current source. The rectifier unit functions in accordance with the theory on page 183. The choke noted as "field" is the field of a dynamic loud speaker. When connected in this manner, the loud-speaker field serves as a choke coil and also provides the field magnetizing current. If desired, this field may be replaced with a 15-henry choke and sufficient resistance to bring the total resistance equal to the 800 ohms indicated for the field.

As will be noted, the plate supply for the push-pull type 45 tubes is taken immediately behind the first filter choke. This is permissible for at least two reasons. *First,* less filtering is required because the signal level is high in the output stage and hence more "ripple" can be tolerated. *Second,* in the push-pull stage, hum is reduced, and hence less filtering is needed (page 259).

The resistor R-5 is the so-called "bleeder" resistor. Its purpose is to put a continuous load on the filter and thus improve the regulation (by decreasing the voltage rise with no load). The resistor R-6 is center-tapped to the filament supply for the push-pull stage, and there-

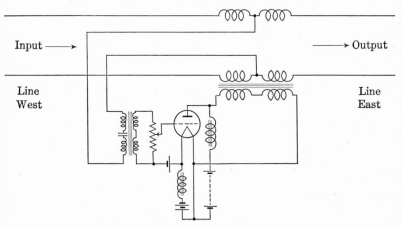

FIG. 9–23. Simplified diagram of a two-way, one-element telephone amplifier or repeater.

fore acts as a biasing resistor. The resistors R-2 are also biasing resistors functioning as explained on page 202. The condensers C-1 and C-2 are decoupling capacitors used to prevent "motor-boating" as explained on page 204.

87. Two-Way Amplifiers or Repeaters.—As mentioned on page 206, one of the first commercial uses of the thermionic vacuum tube was as an amplifier or **repeater** for telephone circuits. Such amplifiers are placed at regular intervals in open-wire and cable telephone circuits to strengthen the speech currents which have been attenuated by the line losses. Since conversation is *generally* two-way, the so-called repeaters must amplify in both directions. The word generally is inserted, because in many cables four-wire telephone circuits [17] are used, two wires for talking in one direction, and two wires for the other.

Two general schemes [10, 17] are used for two-way amplifiers or repeaters for two-wire telephone circuits. The first of these is the so-called type 21 repeater (two-way, one-element) shown in Fig. 9–23. To explain its operation, suppose that an attenuated speech signal comes in from *line west*. This will induce a signal voltage onto the grid of the amplifier, and this will be amplified in the vacuum tube and introduced through the output transformer onto the line. If the impedances of the line west and line east are the same, one-half of the amplified output signal will flow in *each direction*, and no signal will be reintroduced into the grid input circuit. If these impedances are not the same, or if for any other reason the circuit is unbalanced, then the amplified output signal *will* induce a voltage in the input circuit, and the circuit will oscillate or "howl" as it is called in telephone circles.

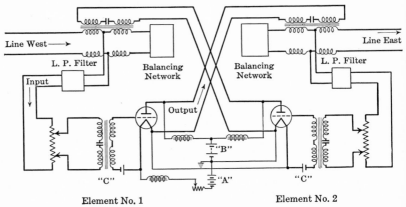

FIG. 9–24. Simplified diagram of a two-way, two-element telephone amplifier or repeater.

The second repeater is the type 22 (two-way, two-element) shown in Fig. 9–24. Again assuming a signal coming in on line west, this will induce a signal voltage on the grid of tube No. 1. This will be amplified and impressed as indicated on the line east. The important advantage of this circuit over the simpler one of Fig. 9–23 is that the lines are balanced by individual balancing networks. For oscillations and howling to occur, an unbalance must exist at *both* output transformers. With such a circuit, therefore, a much higher gain or amplification can occur at each repeater point.

88. Feedback Amplifiers.—As has been discussed previously (page 202), if energy is fed from the output circuit back into the input circuit of an amplifier, the circuit might oscillate. This *positive* feedback action would result if the phase relation is such that the energy fed back will *increase* the impressed signal strength.   If the phase of this feedback is such as to *oppose* the applied signal, the output will be *decreased* instead of increased.   This is a *negative* feedback.

On first thought, it would seem undesirable ever to *reduce* the gain of an amplifier by negative feedback, but such is not the case.   In an amplifier [18, 19, 20] developed by Black, negative feedback is employed with much success.   The amplifier is designed with excess gain, and this is reduced by controlled negative feedback.   As explained in the references given, this new-type feedback amplifier is far superior to other types.   The noise level of the amplifier is reduced and the frequency characteristics are improved.   The harmonic output and delay distortion are lower than in conventional amplifiers.   The variations in gain (amplification) are made quite independent of supply-voltage fluctuations.

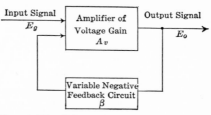

FIG. 9–25.   Schematic circuit of the controlled negative feedback amplifier.

This negative feedback principle is illustrated in Fig. 9–25. The alternating input signal voltage E_g is impressed on the amplifier of total voltage gain A_v.   The output voltage of the amplifier *without* feedback would be $E_g A_v$, but *with negative* feedback it will be reduced to some value E_0.   The controlled negative feedback circuit impresses a certain portion of this output voltage βE_0 back on the input terminals in such a manner that the net input signal to the amplifier is reduced.

With *negative* feedback adjustment, the magnitude of the output voltage is $E_0 = (E_g - \beta E_0)A_v$.   The ratio E_0/E_g will be the actual voltage gain of the amplifier with negative feedback.   Thus,

$$\text{Voltage gain with negative feedback} = \frac{A_v}{1 + A_v}. \qquad (9\text{–}8)$$

For *negative* feedback, the voltage gain is reduced because of the denominator; for *positive* feedback, the voltage gain is increased because the sign of β is changed and the denominator becomes less than unity.[18]   Under these conditions the system becomes unstable and tends to oscillate.

With a large amount of *negative* feedback, the term βA_v becomes large, and the voltage gain is reduced, approaching the value $1/\beta$. The importance of this is that the amplification is largely independent of the value A_v (equation **8–11**), which means that the gain of the negative feedback amplifier will not vary to an appreciable extent with the circuit conditions which determine A_v, and therefore the amplifier will be very stable.

In vacuum-tube amplifiers, distortion of the wave shape is caused by the non-linear grid voltage-plate current characteristic, and occurs in the *plate circuit*. The *negative* feedback amplifier reduces distortion in the following way: A portion of the distorted output signal is introduced by the negative feedback circuit into the grid circuit of the tube. When this is amplified in the tube, it tends to cancel distortion in the output. This is expressed by the relation [18]

$$\text{Distortion with negative feedback} = \frac{d}{1 + \beta A_v}. \qquad (9\text{--}9)$$

In this expression, d is the distortion without negative feedback. An equation can also be written expressing [18] the relation between the signal-to-noise ratios with and without feedback.

The generalized treatment [18] places negative signs in equations (9–8) and (9–9), and considers that β is either positive or negative; also, different symbols are used. In these pages, the discussion has been limited almost entirely to negative feedback, and the symbols used conform with the rest of the book. Although these amplifiers were largely developed for use in telephone repeaters the principle is now used in amplifiers for many other purposes, and current literature contains many articles describing their use.

This negative feedback amplifier can be made to amplify over a very wide frequency range, such as for the entire video (corresponding to audio) frequency band in television which must be at least 1,000,000 cycles wide for good image definition. These amplifiers are used on the new experimental coaxial cable [21] between New York and Philadelphia. This cable will handle at least 240 commercial telephone message channels, or will handle one television channel about 1,000,000 cycles wide. This *entire* band is amplified at each repeater point by one amplifier of the controlled negative feedback type. This amplifier is also well suited for use as a repeater (amplifier) on cable circuits in which carrier frequencies are employed.

The Compandor.—This is in reality a system rather than a single piece of equipment. It was originally designed for improving the signal-to-noise ratio of trans-atlantic radio-telephone conversations. It has also been applied to other fields, for instance, in the recording and reproduction of high-quality phonograph records.

In speech, or in the rendition of a musical number, the power level varies greatly (page 308). In the cutting of phonograph records, if the extreme volume level variations are recorded, there is danger of overcutting the grooves. If a *volume compressor* is used in cutting the record, however, the peaks of power will be reduced and the overcutting prevented. If a *volume expander* is used in playing the record, the original naturalness will be restored. Other applications are possible.

The compressing and expanding features are automatically controlled. Rectifiers are used to produce a bias voltage proportional to the signal strength. This bias voltage is impressed on the grids of vacuum tubes so connected that volume compression and expansion are achieved.

REFERENCES

1. Pidgeon, H. A., and McNally, J. O. *A study of the output power obtained from vacuum tubes of different types.* Proc. I.R.E., Feb., 1930, Vol. 18.
2. R.C.A. Manufacturing Co. *Receiving Tube Manual.*
3. Kilgour, C. E. *Graphical analysis of output tube performance.* Proc. I.R.E., Jan., 1931, Vol. 19.
4. Pidgeon, H. A. *Simple theory of the three-electrode vacuum tube.* Jl. of the Soc. of Motion Picture Engineers, Feb., 1935, Vol. 24.
5. Glasgow, R. S. *Principles of Radio Engineering.* McGraw-Hill Book Co.
6. Thompson, B. J. *Graphical determination of performance of push-pull audio amplifiers.* Proc. I.R.E., April, 1933, Vol. 21.
7. Pidgeon, H. A. *Theory of multi-electrode vacuum tubes.* Electrical Engineering, Nov., 1934, Vol. 53.
8. R.C.A. Manufacturing Co. *Class AB Operation of Type 6F6 Tubes Connected as Pentodes.* Application Note No. 54, Dec. 20, 1935.
9. Henney, K. *Radio Engineering Handbook.* McGraw-Hill Book Co.
10. Pender, H., and McIlwain, K. *Electrical Engineers' Handbook—Vol. 5. Electric Communication and Electronics.* John Wiley & Sons.
11. Institute of Radio Engineers. *Reports of the Standards Committee.*
12. Jolley, L. B. W. *Alternating Current Rectification.* John Wiley & Sons.
13. Fay, C. E. *The operation of vacuum tubes as class B and class C amplifiers.* Proc. I.R.E., March, 1932, Vol. 20.
14. Everitt, W. L. *Optimum operating conditions for class C amplifiers.* Proc. I.R.E., Feb., 1934, Vol. 22.
15. Terman, F. E. *Measurements in Radio Engineering.* McGraw-Hill Book Co.
16. Nicholson, M. G., and Perkins, W. M. *A simple harmonic analyzer.* Proc. I.R.E., April, 1932, Vol. 20.
17. Albert, A. L. *Electrical Communication.* John Wiley & Sons.
18. Black, H. S. *Stabilized feedback amplifiers.* Electrical Engineering, Jan., 1934, Vol. 53.
19. Black, H. S. *Feedback amplifiers.* Bell Laboratories Record, June, 1934.
20. Terman, F. E. *Feedback amplifier design.* Electronics, Jan., 1937.
21. Strieby, M. E. *A million-cycle telephone system.* Electrical Engineering, Jan., 1937.

22. Mathes, R. C., and Wright, S. B. *The compandor—an aid against static in radio telephony.* Electrical Engineering, June, 1934, Vol. 53.

NOTE: Since this manuscript was prepared "Fundamentals of Vacuum Tubes" by A. V. Eastman (McGraw-Hill Book Co.) has been published. This book contains much excellent material on amplifier design. Regarding the controlled feedback amplifier, its commercial applications are increasing, and much technical information is being published in the communication journals.

SUGGESTED ASSIGNMENTS

1. Obtain the required data for a power-output triode from a tube manual, calculate the power output under given conditions by equation (9–1) and by equation (9–2), and compare the results.
2. Referring to Fig. 9–4, page 252, derive equation (9–3).
3. Derive an equation for the power output of triodes in parallel.
4. Derive equation (9–4).
5. Referring to page 263, assume class AB_1 operating conditions for two tubes and calculate the power output. Obtain the required data from a tube manual.
6. Explain the steps involved in the design of a driver stage for a class B amplifier.
7. Explain the steps involved in the design of a class C radio-frequency power amplifying stage.
8. About what should be the maximum gain of each repeater in an open-wire telephone line? Why is this so? Why is it not practicable to do all the amplifying at the terminals, rather than install repeaters at various points along the line?
9. Prepare a bibliography and briefly abstract the articles which have appeared on the feedback amplifier.
10. Explain how it is possible, with the compandor system, to carry on satisfactory trans-atlantic radio-telephone conversations under otherwise prohibitive static conditions.

CHAPTER 10

OSCILLATORS

The vacuum-tube oscillator is extensively used in communication as a source of alternating-current power. The frequency of the oscillator may be *fixed* at some desired value, or may be *variable* over a wide range. An **oscillator** is defined [1] as "a nonrotating device for producing alternating current, the output frequency of which is determined by the characteristics of the device." In one sense the oscillator is a converter, since it changes the direct-current power from the batteries or other supply source to alternating-current power.

Thermionic vacuum-tube oscillators are almost universally used to supply power for communication circuits. The frequencies which can be produced may be as low as a *fraction of a cycle* per second, or they may be billions of cycles per second.

It is difficult to classify oscillators rigidly from the frequency standpoint, but classification, even though somewhat arbitrary, will be helpful. Oscillators generating frequencies of from about 20 to 15,000 cycles per second are called **audio-frequency oscillators.** Those producing frequencies from about 15,000 to (for example) 50,000 cycles are often classified as **carrier-frequency oscillators,** because of their use in carrier-frequency telephony [2] over telephone and power lines. Oscillators with frequencies from 50,000 to about 1,500,000 cycles are commonly called **radio-frequency oscillators.** **Short-wave** or **high-frequency oscillators** may be classified as those operating at from 1,500,000 cycles to 30,000,000 cycles. Above this band are the **ultra-short-wave** or **ultra-high-frequency oscillators** operating from 30,000,000 to 300,000,000 cycles per second, and above these the **microray oscillators** of the Barkhausen type operating up to several billion cycles per second.

Considered from one standpoint, the vacuum-tube oscillator is merely an amplifier in which part of the output voltage is properly reintroduced into the grid input circuit so that the tube drives itself. The tube may be operated as a class *A, B,* or *C* amplifier. In a high-quality *audio-frequency* oscillator, the oscillator tube would *probably* be operated in class *A* with the grid driven *slightly* positive. For the other oscillators, the tube would *probably* be operated in class *C* because both high efficiency and satisfactory quality can be obtained with such operation at these higher frequencies. The word *probably* was inserted because there are exceptions to these statements, but in general they apply.

Very little (or no) power is required to drive a tube operated as a class A amplifier. Although more input power is required for a class C amplifier, it is, of course, less than the output. Thus, if in either instance part of the output is *properly* fed back into the input, the tube will oscillate at some frequency determined by the electrical constants of the circuit. Furthermore, since there is an excess of power, the oscillator can also be used to supply power to external circuits.

As was shown on page 237, feedback through the interelectrode capacitances will cause a tube to oscillate. This method of producing oscillations will not be discussed further. The oscillators of practical importance are those in which the feedback is intentional and controllable, and accomplished by circuit arrangements external to the tube itself. An exception to this is included on page 297.

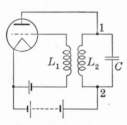

FIG. 10-1.   Connections for a simple vacuum-tube oscillator.

89. The Vacuum Tube as an Oscillator.— The circuit of Fig. 10-1 is an oscillator of a simple type, and is convenient for explaining the principles involved. This discussion will assume that the grid of the tube is so biased (as indicated) that operation is as a class A or linear amplifier. In actual operation the grid must go slightly positive, but this consideration will be reserved for page 285.

The parallel or anti-resonant circuit L_2–C in the plate circuit is tuned to be anti-resonant for some frequency, and this tuning *largely* determines the frequency of oscillation. At this anti-resonant frequency the input impedance, to the parallel circuit, measured between points 1–2 is a *high* value of almost *pure resistance* in accordance with the explanation on page 241. To all other frequencies, the impedance is reactive, and is smaller than that offered to the frequency to which it is tuned. Thus, when a complex current containing many frequency components is passed through the parallel circuit L_2–C of Fig. 10-1, *a large voltage will appear between points 1–2 for the frequency at which the circuit is anti-resonant.* For other frequencies the voltage drops between points 1–2 will be less.

This value of resistance of the tuned circuit L_2–C at anti-resonance is the plate-circuit load into which the oscillating tube operates. The frequency at which the resistance is maximum occurs when the inductive susceptance of the branch L_2 approximately equals the capacitive susceptance of the branch C. If the losses in the coil L_2 and the condenser C are low (as is usually the case), the equation for the frequency of anti-resonance becomes

$$f = \frac{1}{(2\pi\sqrt{L_2C})} \cdot \qquad (10\text{--}1)$$

Since the final frequency adjustments are made by varying the value of capacitance slightly, this equation is entirely satisfactory for most purposes.

The value of the equivalent resistance of the parallel circuit at anti-resonance is determined by the usual method of solving parallel circuits. This is explained in simple terms in such books as Reference 3. Other explanations, more from the communication stand-point, are given in References 4, 5, 6, and 7. So long as the grid is negative, the presence of the coupled coil L_1 has little effect on the circuit L_2–C, except at very high frequencies where stray capacitances may become of importance. When the grid goes positive (as in actual operation), this is approximately equivalent to coupling a low re-sistance to the L_2–C circuit by the coil L_1. This will lower the equiva-lent resistance and change the frequency of anti-resonance of the parallel tuned circuit L_2–C in accordance with coupled-circuit theory.[4, 5, 8]

Thus, when the circuit of Fig. 10–1 is energized, a complicated transient current will flow through the parallel circuit L_2–C. A much larger voltage will exist between points 1–2 for the component of this current for which L_2–C is anti-resonant than for other frequency components. A larger voltage at this anti-resonant frequency will be induced in L_1, and if the *connections to the grid are correct*, this voltage will cause a further amplified voltage of this anti-resonant frequency to exist between the plate and cathode. This will cause a plate current flow at the anti-resonant frequency, which will again induce a voltage in the grid circuit, and the oscillations will continue to increase. If the connections to the grid are such that the oscilla-tions do not build up, these connections must be reversed.

In the first paragraph of this section it was stated that the tube considered was being operated as a class A amplifier. This is only partly true; the grid must be driven positive and some distortion must occur for the following reasons: It is apparent that the increasing of the oscillations discussed in the preceding section cannot continue indefinitely. They will continue to increase, however, until the grid goes positive and draws power. When this happens, the input resistance of the grid circuit drops to a comparatively low value.

This will couple a low value of resistance to the anti-resonant tuned circuit and reduce the value of the equivalent load resistance offered the tube by the tuned circuit, making the tube a less efficient *voltage* amplifier. Also, when grid *current* flows, voltage drops will occur and the alternating voltage applied to the grid will be less than when it does not flow. These factors combine to cause the oscillations to increase to a certain value and then become stable.

No method of drawing power from the oscillator of Fig. 10–1 is shown therein; several schemes can be used. *First*, a load can be connected across points 1–2. *Second*, an output coil could be coupled with L_2, and power drawn from this coil. *Third*, a transformer could be connected in series with the plate lead. All of these methods will affect the circuit constants and the oscillations produced. As an illustration, the second method will couple the load resistance to the coil L_2, and will change the anti-resonant frequency of the tuned circuit.[3, 4, 5, 8] Methods of drawing power from an oscillator to avoid such difficulties are discussed on page 291.

Theory.—The complete solution of oscillator circuits is very complex.[7] By means of several assumptions, van der Pol has given the solution of certain oscillator circuits.[9] The treatment most readily understood, however, is probably that of van der Bijl given in Reference 10. This treatment will be followed closely in the succeeding pages. A similar discussion is included in Reference 6.

The oscillator circuit of Fig. 10–1 can be simplified to that of Fig. 10–2. The tube is represented by the fictitious generator μE_g in series with the plate resistance r_p. The resistor R_2 is the *effective* or alternating-current resistance of the coil L_2. If this coil has a magnetic core, this value includes the core losses caused by hysteresis and eddy currents.

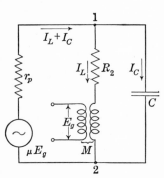

Fig. 10–2. Equivalent circuit for Fig. 10–1.

The purpose of this analysis is to find an expression for the conditions under which the circuit of Fig. 10–2 will produce sustained oscillations. Three assumptions will be made: *First*, the grid is at all times maintained negative; *second*, the effect of the interelectrode capacitances is negligible; *third*, the impedance between points 1–2 of Fig. 10–2 is substantially pure resistance at the frequency of oscillation. The branch currents will be as indicated.

The current I_L in the coil L_2 will induce an instantaneous voltage in the grid of magnitude

$$e_g = M \frac{di}{dt}, \tag{10-2}$$

where M is the mutual inductance between L_1 and L_2, and di/dt is the rate of change of current I_L at that instant. For steady-state conditions, this equation becomes

$$E_g = MI_L\omega, \tag{10-3}$$

where E_g is the magnitude of the *effective* value of the voltage induced in the grid circuit by the current I_L in coil L_2, and ω equals 2π times the frequency of oscillation.

Now a voltage E_g impressed on the grid will cause a voltage of magnitude μE_g between the cathode and plate in accordance with the equivalent generator viewpoint (page 125). Thus, from equation (10-3) it can be written that

$$\mu E_g = \mu MI_L\omega. \tag{10-4}$$

By applying Kirchhoff's laws and writing two voltage equations for Fig. 10-2, van der Bijl shows that the *condition for oscillation* is

$$r_p = \frac{\mu M}{CR_2} - \frac{L_2}{CR_2}, \tag{10-5}$$

and that the *frequency* of oscillation is

$$f = \frac{1}{2\pi} \sqrt{\frac{1 + \dfrac{R_2}{r_p}}{L_2 C}}. \tag{10-6}$$

The fact that the amplification factor μ occurs in equation (10-5) proves that the ability of a tube to oscillate depends on its ability to amplify. The fact that r_p is included in equation (10-6) shows that the plate resistance of the tube affects the frequency of oscillation. This in turn means that any conditions of operation which vary r_p will cause the frequency to change.

It is also shown by van der Bijl that

$$g_m = \frac{\mu}{r_p} \geqq \frac{L}{r_p M} + \frac{CR_2}{M} \quad \text{or} \quad g_m \geqq \frac{CR_2}{M - \dfrac{L}{\mu}}, \tag{10-7}$$

where g_m is the control grid-plate transconductance (mutual conductance) of the tube, and is equal to μ/r_p as discussed on page 115.

These equations may be interpreted as follows: For the condition of oscillation, the grid-plate transconductance of the triode shown in Fig. 10–1 must be equal to, or greater than, either of the expressions on the right of equation (10–7). Thus, there are *circuit conditions* under which a tube *will not oscillate*, even if the connections are correct.

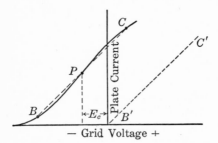

FIG. 10–3. Grid voltage-plate current (E_g-I_p) curve for a triode, illustrating its use as an oscillator.

In Fig. 10–3 is shown the E_g-I_p curve for the triode of Fig. 10–1 under a given set of conditions of operation. Suppose that the tube is biased E_c volts negative so that operation is at point P. The slope of the curve *at this point* is the value of the grid-plate transconductance (page 113). This holds for the condition of small current variations, that is, small oscillations. As previously shown (page 285), however, the oscillations will increase until the grid is driven positive. Thus, the equivalent slope of the curve is no longer as at point P, but is as shown by the line B–C extending between the minimum and maximum points of the current fluctuations. Hence, as the intensity of the oscillations increases, the slope of the line and the equivalent tube transconductance become less.

Referring again to equation (10–7), these relations state that the grid-plate transconductance of the tube must equal or exceed certain values, determined by the circuit constants, for oscillations to be sustained. These values, to the right of the equality signs, are shown by van der Bijl to have the dimensions of a conductance. These parts of the expressions included in equation (10–7) can, therefore, be plotted as on Fig. 10–3 as a line B'–C'.

To summarize van der Bijl's discussion, if the conditions of equation (10–7) are satisfied, the tube will oscillate, and the oscillations will increase until the slope of the line B–C representing the equivalent conductance of the triode is parallel to the line B'–C' which is determined by the right-hand parts of equation (10–7). These parts of the equation are determined by the circuit constants, and by the amplification factor of the tube.

Phase Relations.—The instantaneous current and voltage variations in an oscillator similar to Fig. 10–1 are also given by van der Bijl in Reference 10. These relations are shown in Fig. 10–4.

When the tube is not oscillating, the voltage on the grid is equal to the bias voltage E_c as shown by the broken line.   When some of the output signal is impressed on the grid, by inducing a voltage in coil L_1, the instantaneous potential of the grid will vary as shown in e_g.

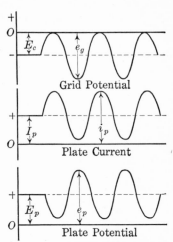

Since the tube is being operated essentially as a class A amplifier, when it is not in oscillation the plate current will be as shown by the broken line I_p. When in oscillation, the plate current will vary as indicated by i_p.   When the grid goes less negative the plate current will increase, and when it goes more negative, the current will decrease.

Very little resistance is offered to the direct component of the plate current by the coil L_2; hence, when the tube is not in oscillation, substantially the entire battery voltage of Fig. **10–1** is impressed *on the plate.* This is represented by E_p of Fig. **10–4**.

Fig. 10–4.   Instantaneous variations in the voltages and potentials of an oscillating triode.

When the tube is oscillating, however, and therefore operating as a linear amplifier, the instantaneous plate potential (that is, the voltage between the plate and cathode) will vary as shown by e_p.

It will be noted that the instantaneous voltage e_p *rises above* the value of the direct voltage E_p on the plate. This phenomenon can be explained as follows: As Fig. **10–4** indicates, the plate current consists of a direct and an alternating component. As explained in the preceding paragraph, almost the entire battery voltage E_B appears as E_p on the plate.   On this is superimposed the voltage drop caused by the alternating component flowing through the anti-resonant cir-

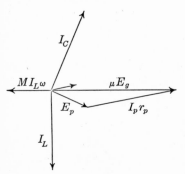

Fig. 10–5.   Vector diagram for the triode oscillator.

cuit L_2–C which is largely pure resistance at the fundamental frequency of oscillation.   It will be noted that the plate-potential variations of the plate are 180 degrees out of phase with those of the grid.   This is a condition necessary for oscillation.

The phase relations in a vacuum-tube oscillator of Figs. **10-1** and **10-2** can also be represented by the diagram [4, 5, 10] of Fig. **10-5**. It is assumed that the only current flowing is a sinusoidal alternating current of the fundamental frequency, and that the tube is operating as a linear class A amplifier. The magnitudes and phase relations of the *effective* values are shown.

In drawing the diagram, it is convenient to take the voltage μE_g generated by the fictitious generator as a base. As mentioned earlier in this section, the alternating voltage on the grid of magnitude $MI_L\omega$ is 180 degrees out of phase with the voltage μE_g. Since this voltage must be 90 degrees behind the current I_L in coil L_2 which induces it, the current I_L must have the position shown.

Now the alternating voltage across points 1–2 of Fig. **10-2** must be the alternating voltage E_p on the plate of the tube of Fig. **10-1**. If the coil L_2 were pure inductance, then E_p would be exactly 90 degrees ahead of I_L; since the coil also has an effective resistance R_2, this angle must be less than 90 degrees as shown. The current through the condenser I_c must lead E_p by 90 degrees, because the condenser has negligible losses. The alternating current I_p flowing in the plate circuit is the vector sum of I_L and I_c. This current will cause an internal voltage drop $I_p r_p$ across the plate resistance of the tube, and this drop will be in phase with I_p and will subtract from the voltage μE_g to give the alternating plate voltage E_p.

In the preceding discussion all references to oscillator "tank circuits" and "circulating currents" have been carefully avoided. The anti-resonant circuit composed of L_2 and C in parallel is often called a "tank circuit," especially in radio literature. While such explanations may be helpful for certain purposes, they hide the true nature of the basic principles involved. It is significant that the standards [1, 11] contain no definition of a tank circuit.

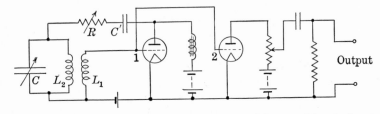

Fig. **10-6.** Circuit of an audio-frequency oscillator. The output terminals may be connected to additional voltage and power-amplifying stages.

90. Audio-Frequency Class A Oscillator.—A large variety of oscillator circuits are available for this use. The circuit of Fig. **10-6** is

one of the best audio oscillators, especially as a stable source of audio frequencies of low harmonic content such as desired for laboratory measurements. Similar oscillators [12] were early developed for high-quality work. The one in Fig. 10–6, known as a **resistance-stabilized oscillator,** is fully described by Terman in Reference 13.

Tube 1 is the amplifier tube, and tube 2 is an isolating or **buffer tube.** Its purpose is to isolate the tube from all variations in load, so that the stability of the oscillations will not be affected. The grid of this isolating or buffer tube is driven in accordance with the grid potential variations of the oscillating tube.

The oscillating tube (number 1 of Fig. 10–6) functions in accordance with the oscillator theory discussed above. The bias voltage is so adjusted that the tube operates as a linear or class A amplifier, producing but little distortion. As has been shown (page 285), the oscillations, to become stable, must increase until the grid is driven slightly positive, and hence some distortion must occur. That is, some harmonics of the fundamental frequency will exist in the plate current of the oscillating tube, and will flow through the blocking condenser C', the feedback resistor R, and the anti-resonant circuit composed of C and L_2 in parallel. Since this parallel circuit is tuned to the fundamental, it will offer a large value of substantially pure resistance to the fundamental, but the impedance offered to the harmonics will be low. The voltage drop *due to the fundamental will be large,* and a relatively large voltage of the fundamental frequency will be impressed on the grid of the second tube. The voltage drop across L_2–C due to the harmonics will be small, and they will be amplified but little.

91. Design of Resistance-Stabilized Oscillators.—This subject is fully discussed [13] by Terman, and need not be repeated in detail. A few of the basic principles will, however, be summarized.

Since the grid of the oscillating tube goes slightly positive, the bias voltage selected is slightly less than that which would normally be chosen for class A operation. The blocking condenser C' should have low reactance at the frequency of operation, and the reactance of the choke coil in series with the battery should be high. These precautions tend to make the amount of feedback entirely dependent on the feedback resistor R, and thus avoid phase shifts; that is, changing the grid and plate voltage variations from the theoretical 180 degree relation. For audio frequencies, the coils L_2 and L_1 may be a one-to-one ratio transformer with an iron core; such close coupling increases the frequency stability. The losses in the coils and the iron core should be low so that the impedance of the anti-resonant circuit L_2–C will be high for the fundamental frequency. This is commonly stated by saying the circuit should have a high Q ratio. Also, the ratio of L_2/C should be low. Various values of L and C will satisfy equation 10-1, but a low ratio will improve frequency stability. This is because low reactance will be offered to frequencies other than the one for which the circuit is anti-resonant.

If the conditions just enumerated are satisfied, the tube will oscillate, if, when a voltage of value E_g is impressed on the grid, a voltage of the same value E_g is developed across the tuned parallel circuit L_2-C. Under these conditions, the starting feedback resistance is given by the relation

$$R = R_L(\mu - 1) - r_p, \qquad (10\text{-}8)$$

where R_L is the resistance of the tuned circuit at anti-resonance, μ is the amplification factor of the tube, and r_p is the plate resistance of the tube. This equation can be derived on the basis that the tube generating a voltage μE_g is driving a series circuit composed of r_p, R_L, and R.

Triodes with an amplification factor or μ of about 10 are very satisfactory for these oscillators. With such tubes, the resistance of the plate circuit (load resistance) at anti-resonance should be from about 10,000 to 50,000 ohms. The corresponding value of the feedback-resistor R is several hundred thousand ohms. Although the discussions just given apply largely to audio-frequency oscillators, these oscillators can readily be made to operate up to several hundred thousand cycles. The circuit of Fig. 10-6 is designed to supply the driving voltage for additional voltage and power-amplifying stages.[13]

92. Class C Oscillators.—The oscillator described in the previous pages was a special class A type for generating high-quality audio and carrier-frequency signals. Oscillators for radio-frequency generation are usually class C amplifiers (page 211) in which some of the output is fed back into the grid circuit.

The tubes of most radio-frequency oscillators are operated in class C largely because higher efficiency can be obtained. Higher efficiency can also be obtained with audio-frequency class C oscillators, but at these low frequencies the class C oscillator is not used because the distortion present in the output is excessive. At the high radio frequencies the distortion is also great, but the frequency discrimination offered by the anti-resonant or parallel tuned circuit is sufficient to make the output good and class C operation satisfactory.

Since the class C oscillator is a self-excited class C amplifier, the discussions for the amplifier given on page 273 also apply to the oscil-

lator.   The tube is biased to about twice cut-off, and the plate current
flows in "spurts" as shown in Fig. 9–21.   Owing to the fact that plate
current flows *only* when the plate voltage is at low values, the losses
within the tube are decreased and the efficiency is high.   With a class
A oscillator the efficiency is less than 50 per cent, but with the class *C*
oscillator it may be 80 or 90 per cent.

In the class *A* oscillator previously considered, a constant grid-bias
voltage, such as supplied by batteries, was used.   In the class *C*
oscillator, however, the grid bias is usu-
ally obtained by the so-called grid leak-
condenser method.   With this method
(Fig. 10–7), when the tube is not oscillating, the bias on the grid is zero, and hence
oscillations will be self-starting when the
circuit is energized.   If the tube is biased
initially to about twice cut-off, then oscillations will not start because no plate
current will flow through the tube.

The way in which the grid leak-condenser combination functions to bias the

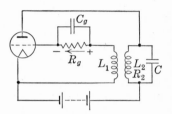

FIG. 10–7.   A class *C* oscillator, self biased by the grid
resistor-grid condenser combination.

tube is essentially as follows: When the tube is first energized the bias
is zero and oscillations will start.   These will increase as explained on
page 285, and the grid will be driven positive.   This will cause a
rectified *grid current* to flow in "spurts," and this will have a direct-
current component I_g (see page 178).   This grid current will be electrons flowing *to the grid* inside the tube, which is equivalent to
conventional current flowing *to the grid* from outside the tube.   This
current will cause an $I_g R_g$ drop across the resistor as shown in Fig.
10–7.

Thus, the grid condenser C_g acts as a low-impedance path for the
alternating components of the grid current, but the direct current
must pass through the grid resistor R_g to produce the required $I_g R_g$
voltage drop to bias the tube.[4, 5, 8]   In this connection it should be
mentioned again (page 178) that even the intermittent grid current,
flowing for only a small part of a cycle, contains both direct and alternating components.

The value of the grid condenser C_g is not at all critical, but its
impedance at the fundamental frequency of operation should be very
low in comparison with the value of the grid resistor.   If the capacitance is too great, however, intermittent operation and blocking of
the tube may result.   Grid condensers of 100 to 250 micro-microfarads
are often used with the smaller tubes.[14]

The value of the grid resistor for a given bias can be determined if the value of the direct component of the grid current is known or can be reliably estimated. The selection is often based on experience and empirical data since the value needed is not critical.[15] A value of 10,000 ohms for the bias resistor is often satisfactory, but for tubes with remote cut-off points, a value up to 25,000 or even 50,000 ohms must be used.

Design.—Information on this subject is conveniently available in a number of sources,[4, 5, 6, 14] and only a few of the important points will be summarized here.

Experience with oscillator design has indicated that the class C oscillator will be unstable if the ratio of $\omega L_2/R_2$ is less than about 12. The value of R_2 is largely determined by the load, usually inductively coupled to L_2. This reflected load resistance acts like a resistance in series with the coil, and thus reduces the ratio $Q = \omega L_2/R_2$ to lower values than for the coil and condenser alone. A ratio higher than about 12 is satisfactory from a stability standpoint, but as the ratio is increased, so are the magnitudes of the currents I_L and I_c of Fig. 10–5. Excessively large currents are undesirable.

As previously mentioned, the sizes of the grid resistor and condenser are not critical, providing the requirements previously given are satisfied. If either C_g, R_g, or both of these is too large, however, then **intermittent operation** may result. This phenomenon [4] can be explained as follows: After stable operation has been reached, the grid has assumed an equilibrium bias value. If now the amplitude of oscillation should be reduced by any slight change in circuit conditions, the grid bias voltage must also reduce itself. This it cannot readily do if the condenser or resistor is too large, and the tube may stop oscillating until the bias voltage across $R_g - C_g$ reduces to the value where oscillations will again start. Ordinarily, intermittent operation results only in erratic performance.

The similar phenomenon of **blocking** also causes oscillations to stop, but often with more disastrous results. Thus, if the grid resistor is too large so that the current of electrons flowing to the grid is low, if the grid is driven highly positive by the alternating voltage impressed on it, and if at this instant the plate potential is high, the *secondary emission current from the grid to the plate may exceed the electron flow from the cathode to the grid.* If this occurs, the grid current will reverse, the grid will be biased positively by this reversed-current flow through the large grid resistor, the plate current will rise to a high value, and the tube will be overheated. This will cause the evolution of occluded gases (page 67) and probably ruin the tube.

Blocking can be prevented by proper design, and by not attempting operation at too high efficiencies. In order for blocking to occur, the grid must emit electrons. Modern air-cooled tubes are treated to prevent grid emission, and blocking cannot occur with such tubes.[4]

In addition to the books referred to on page 294, much information on the design of class C oscillators and amplifiers will be found in the journals, particularly the Proceedings of the Institute of Radio Engineers.[15, 16, 17]

93. Typical Oscillator Circuits.

—The types of circuits which have been developed for vacuum-tube oscillators are great in number.[4, 6] Some of these are, however, merely derived from certain fundamental types. Of the basic types, three are shown in Fig. 10–8. These are the Meissner, the Hartley, and the Colpitts circuits, named after the men who invented them, and who were among the first to study vacuum-tube oscillators.

The operation of these oscillators is based on the principles which have previously been discussed, and no additional comments will be made. If further information is desired, the references listed on page 294 should be consulted.

Constant-Frequency Oscillators. —This subject was carefully investigated by Llewellyn and is covered by Reference 18. His method

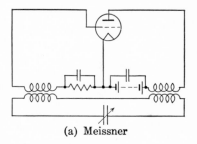

(a) Meissner

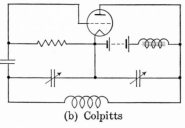

(b) Colpitts

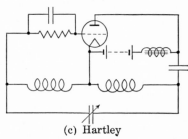

(c) Hartley

Fig. 10–8.   Basic oscillator circuits.

of obtaining frequency stability consists in general of placing a simple phase shifting network between the tube and tuned circuits. This makes the frequency of oscillation independent of the tube resistances. Terman has published information [19] on resistance-stabilized oscillators.

Crystal-Controlled Oscillators.—Although by careful design and operation, oscillators, such as those just described, can be made to have remarkable frequency stability, the exacting requirements of modern radio engineering have made necessary the use of oscillators whose frequency stability is better than that obtainable by the use of tuned circuits alone. Thus, a crystal oscillator used by the Bureau of Standards for the broadcast of standard-frequency signals, was stable within 1.5 parts in a million for over a year, and its stability was greater than 2 parts in 100,000,000 for several hours.[7] Of course, such extremely high stability is neither needed nor obtained in commercial radio systems, but that attained is, nevertheless, very high. For example, radio broadcast stations are permitted a frequency variation of but 50 cycles from their assigned carrier frequency. Since their carrier frequency may be a million cycles or more, this is a very small percentage change.

Crystal oscillators are based on the discovery, made by the Curies, that if certain crystals are subjected to mechanical stresses, potential differences will be produced between opposite crystal surfaces. The effect is a reversible one; if the direction of the force is reversed, then, the polarity of the potential difference will be changed. Furthermore, if a voltage is applied to the opposite faces of a crystal, the dimensions will be changed. These effects are very pronounced in Rochelle salts which are used as the generating units in the various crystal microphones. The effect also exists to a lesser degree in quartz, but, since this substance is better suited mechanically, it is used in radio circuits.[4, 5, 6, 7, 8]

If a quartz crystal is placed between two condenser plates on which is impressed an alternating voltage of *varying* frequency, nothing of importance occurs until a certain critical frequency value is reached. At some frequency, at which the crystal is *mechanically* resonant, the crystal will vibrate at the exact frequency of the applied alternating voltage. If the crystal is thin, and if the voltage is high, the vibrations may be of sufficient magnitude to shatter the crystal. The resonating properties of such crystals were early studied by Cady. An authoritative article on the history and application of piezoelectricity was recently published.[20]

The method of mounting a crystal between the metal plates of the crystal holder, and its connection in an oscillator circuit are shown in Fig. 10–9. A triode is used in this circuit, but tetrodes and pentodes also are used extensively.[14] The electrical circuit equivalent to the mechanical oscillating circuit of the quartz crystal is also shown in Fig. 10–9.

The theory of operation of this crystal oscillator is as follows: It was mentioned on page 237, that if the load on a tube were inductive, then the tube would feed back through the internal electrode capacitances, and would oscillate. Thus, if the anti-resonant parallel circuit

L–C of Fig. **10**–9 is tuned to a frequency slightly *higher* than the natural frequency of the crystal, the equivalent impedance of the L–C load at the crystal frequency would be inductive. Hence, at the natural frequency of the crystal, feedback will occur through the interelectrode capacitances of the tube of Fig. **10**–9, and the circuit will oscillate *at the crystal frequency*. Other crystal oscillators use feedback through an external circuit.

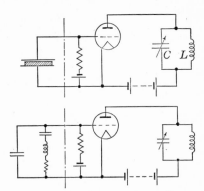

The methods of cutting and grinding the crystals so that they will have the correct natural frequency, and the arrangements for mounting these crystals are discussed in detail in the references given in the preceding section.

Fig. 10–9. A crystal oscillator, showing the crystal replaced by its equivalent electrical network in the lower illustration.

Crystals cut from the same specimen, but in different planes, exhibit different properties, especially with respect to frequency variations with temperature. One type cut has a *positive* temperature coefficient, and another a *negative* coefficient. Thus for precise work, temperature control is necessary. This also provides a method of final adjustment of the frequency of oscillation. Certain special methods of grinding have been developed [21] which make possible crystals with almost zero temperature coefficients.

In transmitters employing crystal control, the crystals are usually used with tubes below 50-watt ratings; with larger tubes the crystals are too likely to be broken. These are called **master oscillators,**[1] and are used to drive class *C* radio-frequency amplifiers (page 273).

Quartz crystals for very high frequencies must be extremely thin and fragile. They can, however, be used for control at very high frequencies, up to at least 15,000,000 cycles for experimental work. Crystals of tourmaline [7] can be used instead of quartz at higher frequencies.

Oscillator Control Using Resonant Lines.—There are practical objections to the use of a crystal oscillator for short-wave commercial transmitters such as those employed in transoceanic radio telegraph work. Among these is the fact that large amounts of amplification are required, resulting in high operating costs and in increased possibilities of equipment failure.[22] For those high frequencies, a length of transmission line,[23] sharply resonant at some frequency, may be used instead of crystal control. Such systems [24] have proved very satisfactory in high-power commercial short-wave radio transmitters. These lines control the frequency of oscillators which operate at high power levels and hence little additional amplification is required.

Transmission lines of the coaxial-cable type are usually employed, since with these the outer conductor also acts as a shield. These resonant lines are so designed that dimensional changes with temperature variations are controlled. Such variations in dimensions would change the frequency at which the line is resonant, and hence the frequency of oscillation.

Magnetostriction Oscillators.—If a magnetic field is applied to a rod of magnetic material, the dimensions of the rod will be changed *very slightly*. Since any rod has a frequency at which it is *mechanically* resonant, this property can be used to control the frequency of a vacuum tube oscillator. This oscillator was developed by Pierce and reported [25] in 1929.

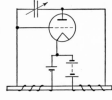

Fig. 10–10. A magnetostriction oscillator.

A simplified diagram of a magnetostriction oscillator is shown in Fig. 10–10. The rod is often clamped securely at the center. If the rod is permanently magnetized, or magnetized by a direct-current winding, the rod will vibrate at its natural mechanical frequency when a current of the resonant frequency is passed through the coil. Since the magnetostriction rod is very sharply resonant, it can be used to hold the frequency of the circuit of Fig. 10–10 very stable, just as does the quartz crystal previously considered.

This oscillator serves as a frequency standard in the range above tuning-fork controlled oscillators and below the range of crystal-controlled oscillators; that is, from about 1000 cycles to 100,000 cycles. A very good analysis of magnetostriction oscillators is given in Reference 13.

Electron-Coupled Oscillators.—As was mentioned on page 291, a buffer or isolating tube must be used between an oscillator tube and the load to prevent variations in the load impedance from affecting the frequency of oscillations. Oscillators may be electron coupled in such a manner that the usual buffer stage may be omitted. This subject was discussed [26] by Dow, and also has been treated in detail [13] by Terman.

These oscillators employ either tetrodes or pentodes.[13] A circuit using a screen-grid tetrode is shown in Fig. 10–11. In this the cathode, control grid, and screen grid act as a conventional triode oscillator. For *alternating voltages*, the screen grid is effectively at ground potential through the condenser C_1, and hence acts as a shield between the oscillator and the output circuit; that is, the plate.

When the plate is thus shielded from the oscillator circuit by the screen grid, the only coupling is due to the electron current flow which largely passes through the screen grid to the plate; hence the wording "electron coupled." When the plate voltage is sufficiently high so that the plate current does *not* vary with plate voltage changes, then any changes occurring in the output or load circuit cannot be reflected back into the oscillator circuit and affect its frequency stability.

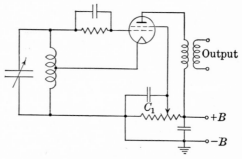

The variable voltage divider shown in Fig. **10–11** is to adjust the ratio of the screen-grid to plate voltage. For some particular ratio of

FIG. 10–11. An electron-coupled oscillator using a screen-grid tube.

these voltages, the frequency will be found to be independent of the supply voltage variations.[13]

Dynatron Oscillators.—In discussing the screen-grid tetrode on page 147 it was indicated that secondary emission *from the plate* causes the plate current to *decrease* with *increasing* plate voltages. This occurs, of course, only over a small portion of the characteristic, the exact region depending on the electrode voltages. If the current *decreases* with *increasing* plate voltage and *increases* with *decreasing* plate voltage, the tube must act as a negative resistance (in the sense that ordinary resistance is positive) over *this particular region*. Use is made of this interesting property in the **dynatron oscillator,** so named by Hull who first described its operation. Although screen-grid tetrodes are usually employed, a triode, in which the grid is made more positive than the plate, and therefore will exhibit secondary emission phenomena, also may be used.[6]

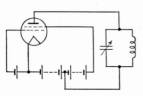

FIG. 10–12. Circuit for a simple dynatron oscillator.

A simple dynatron oscillator circuit using a screen-grid tetrode is shown in Fig. **10–12**.

When adjusted for operation over the negative-resistance region, the dynatron functions as follows: When the *absolute magnitude* of the negative resistance is *less* than the resistance offered by the parallel or anti-resonant circuit, oscillations will start. These will increase until the variations over the curve are such that the effective negative resistance for these increased oscillations is equal to the resistance offered by the anti-resonant circuit.[13] The oscillations then become constant at this value. The frequency of oscillation is fixed by the adjustment of the anti-resonant circuit. Oscillations are most stable when the operation is at the middle of the negative resistance region of the plate-current curve of Fig. 6–5. A rather complete discussion of this subject is given by Terman in Reference 13.

94. The Multivibrator.—This device is not an oscillator in the sense that the frequency is controlled by a tuned circuit. The **multivibrator** is merely a *two-stage resistance-coupled amplifier* in which the output of the second tube is fed back into the first. Since in a vacuum-tube amplifier the plate-voltage changes are 180 degrees out of phase with the grid-voltage variations, two tubes will shift the phase 360 degrees. Thus, the output of the last of the two tubes will have the correct phase relation for driving the first tube.

The output of the multivibrator is a badly-distorted, square-topped wave which contains many harmonics. This fact, and the fact that the frequency of oscillation of the multivibrator can be controlled by an *injected* voltage, make this device very useful for frequency calibration and similar work. Thus, if a 100,000-cycle source of standard frequency is available, this could be injected and the tenth (or other) harmonic of the multivibrator synchronized with it. The output of the device would therefore contain a 10,000-cycle fundamental and harmonics at 10,000 cycle intervals over a wide frequency range. Very complete information on this device and its uses is given in Reference 13.

95. High-Frequency Oscillators.—It is possible to design oscillators of the general types described on page 292 to operate at very high frequencies. The conventional three-electrode tube can be used to generate frequencies up to at least 100 million cycles. Although the ordinary tube will oscillate up to this value, and even beyond,[27] above about 30 million cycles the power output and efficiency drop rapidly.[6] Special tubes, which operate satisfactorily for this high-frequency range, have been developed.

The usual difficulty, when the conventional triode is operated at very high frequencies, is due to the internal interelectrode capacitances, and to the wiring capacitances in the stem and base. These stray capacitances determine the highest frequency at which the tube will oscillate. Using the special two-tube circuit of Fig. 10–13, making possible short leads with low inductance and capacitances, Englund was able to produce oscillations with conventional tubes at wave lengths as short as 1.67 meters.[27]   With the tube bases removed, oscillation at 1.42 meters was obtained.   These wave lengths correspond to frequencies of about 180 million and 210 million cycles per second.

Much material is available on the design, construction, and operation of high-frequency oscillators; this is summarized in Reference 28, which also contains an excellent bibliography.   For operation above about 30 million cycles, special tubes, in which care has been taken to reduce the stray capacitances, are used.

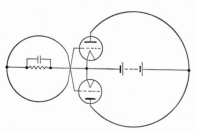

Fig. 10–13. Circuit for obtaining very high-frequency oscillations. (Adapted from Reference 27.)

In these tubes certain of the electrode leads are brought out of the sides and top of the tubes, thus eliminating stray capacitances in the stem and base.   Since each of these tubes is best over a certain range of high-frequency oscillations, different tubes are available for the various bands.[28]   In very high-frequency oscillators the **transit time** or **time of flight** of the electrons in passing between electrodes becomes comparable to the time of oscillation.   Thus, in such oscillators the plate-circuit voltage changes will not be 180 degrees out of phase with grid-voltage variations.   This is a further limitation on the operation of conventional *tuned-circuits* at high frequencies. At these frequencies, as Llewellyn shows, the amplification factor becomes a complex number.[29]

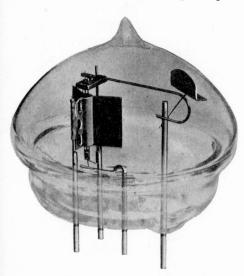

Special ultra-high frequency oscillator and amplifier triode.   Frequency limit, 750 megacycles. Peak power output, 7.5 watts.   (Courtesy Western Electric Co.)

Barkhausen Electron Oscillators.—These oscillators (often called Barkhausen-Kurz oscillators) operate at extremely high frequencies producing **ultra-short waves** or **micro-rays.** Instead of the time of flight of electrons limiting operation as described in the preceding paragraph, these oscillators *depend* on the time of flight for operation.

The conventional explanation of the Barkhausen oscillator will be found in most of the recent textbooks and handbooks on radio and allied subjects. This explanation is somewhat as follows: In certain tubes which are operated with a *negative* plate and *positive* grid, *some* of the electrons attracted by the positive grid pass through between the wires and their kinetic energy carries them on toward the plate. They never reach it, however, because it is negative, so they flow back toward the grid. They may strike the grid or may pass through and flow on toward the cathode. The attraction of the positive grid will soon bring them to rest, and they will return toward the grid, which they may strike, or again pass through. These oscillations by *some* of the electrons between the plate and grid cause a very high-frequency voltage between these electrodes. The frequency of oscillation is determined, in a tube of given geometrical construction, by the electrode voltages.

In a very complete article [30] on the subject, Llewellyn gives a far more comprehensive explanation of the theory of operation. In particular, he points out that in its commercial form the Barkhausen oscillator is not very different from the conventional type operating with *negative* grid and *positive* plate. Barkhausen oscillators are used in commercial installations such as described in References 31 and 32. With Barkhausen oscillators, wave lengths of only a *few centimeters* have been generated, corresponding to oscillations of *billions* of cycles per second.

The **Gill-Morell oscillator** is sometimes considered as a modification of the original Barkhausen oscillator. In the original electron oscillators, the external circuit was assumed to have no influence on the frequency. In the Gill-Morell oscillator,[5, 6] a Lecher wire system (two parallel wires) is used to control the frequency generated. Much information on Barkhausen and Gill-Morell oscillators is given in References 33 and 34.

Magnetron Oscillators.—The magnetron tube depends for its operation on the deflection of electrons by a magnetic field as was described on page 5. In its simplest form it consists of cylindrical plate surrounding a central cathode. A uniform magnetic field is passed through the interelectrode space in the direction of the axis of the cylindrical plate. For high-frequency oscillators a special split-plate construction is employed. This tube was first described by Hull in 1921. The split-anode construction was developed by Okabe and described in 1928 (see articles listed at end of Reference 28).

If the field is sufficiently strong the electrons will miss the plate. When used in the split-anode form, the tube is essentially a push-pull oscillator as Fig. **10–14** indicates. Oscillations can be produced by this tube in two different ways.[28] *First,* the negative resistance characteristics just beyond cut-off (obtained by varying the magnetic field) can be used, much as in the dynatron oscillator (page 299). *Second,* oscillations can be produced whose frequency depends on the transit time of the electrons.

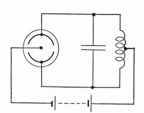

FIG. 10–14.   Circuit of a split-anode magnetron oscillator.   The heated cathode is at the center. The coil for producing the constant field is not shown.

In the first type, operation is limited [28] to about 450 million cycles. As in the triode, this is due to interelectrode capacitances and wiring inductances. For the second type, oscillations as high as *30 billion* cycles have been produced.[28] This corresponds to a wave length of *1.0 centimeter*, the shortest value yet reported (Reference 28, published in 1934).

96. Special Oscillator Circuits.—*Beat-Frequency Oscillators.*—These, logically, should be treated in this chapter. Since they involve the process of modulation (usually referred to as detection in such oscillators), and since this has not been discussed, the treatment of beat-frequency oscillators will be reserved for Chapter 11, page 332.

Saw-Tooth or Sweep Oscillators.—As will be explained in Chapter 14, it is necessary to apply a saw-tooth shaped sweep voltage to one set of cathode-ray tube deflecting plates to "stretch out" the phenomenon impressed on the other set of plates for visual study. This peculiarly shaped voltage rises slowly to a maximum value, but quickly returns to zero, thus slowly sweeping the spot across the fluorescent screen, but almost instantly returning it to zero.

Grid-controlled gas triodes (page 133) are usually employed in these sweep oscillators.[35] A simple circuit is shown in Fig. **10–15**; its operation essentially is as follows: The tube is biased so that the anode or plate must be quite positive before the tube will break down and conduct. At the instant of starting, the voltage across condenser C and hence from cathode to anode of the tube is zero.

The condenser is slowly charged through R by the battery at the right, the rate being controlled by the value of R. When the voltage across the condenser, and hence on the anode, becomes sufficient, the tube suddenly conducts and, since there is but little resistance in the circuit, quickly discharges the condenser. With proper circuit adjustments,[35] a saw-tooth shaped voltage will exist across the condenser

C.   In practice a vacuum tube is usually employed instead of the resistor *R* for controlling the current flow.

Diathermy.—By diathermy is meant [11] the "therapeutic use of high-frequency current to generate heat within some part of the body." The frequency may be as high as several million cycles per second. These high-frequency currents are passed through suitable electrodes which are often in close proximity to, but insulated from, the parts of

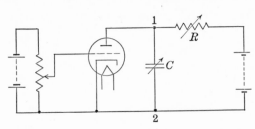

Fig. 10–15.   Oscillator employing a grid-controlled gas-filled tube for producing a saw-tooth wave for cathode-ray tube sweep circuits.

the body to be treated.   The losses produced in the body by these high-frequency currents raise the temperature of the body, often as much as several degrees.   This increased temperature has proved very useful in the treatment of certain diseases.

Oscillators similar to those discussed on page 293 are used for producing these high-frequency currents.   In Reference 7 is shown a diathermy oscillator driven directly from an alternating-current power source.

Electrosurgery, using a high-frequency "knife," is also finding use. This knife is an electrode of a high-frequency circuit fed by an oscillator. The heat generated at the point of contact of this knife electrode with the body is sufficient to cut or destroy the body tissues.   The generated heat seals the small blood vessels, effectively reducing bleeding.

REFERENCES

1. Institute of Radio Engineers.   *Reports of the Standards Committee.*
2. Albert, A. L.   *Electrical Communication.*   John Wiley & Sons.
3. Albert, A. L.   *The Fundamental Theory of Electrical Engineering.*   Ginn & Co.
4. Terman, F. E.   *Radio Engineering.*   McGraw-Hill Book Co.
5. Glasgow, R. S.   *Principles of Radio Engineering.*   McGraw-Hill Book Co.
6. Henney, K.   *Radio Engineering Handbook.*   McGraw-Hill Book Co.
7. Pender, H., and McIlwain, K.   *Electrical Engineers' Handbook.*   Vol. 5, Electric Communication and Electronics.   John Wiley & Sons.

8. Everitt, W. L. *Communication Engineering.* McGraw-Hill Book Co.
9. Van der Pol, Balth. *The nonlinear theory of electric oscillations.* Proc. I.R.E., Sept., 1934, Vol. 22, No. 9.
10. Van der Bijl, H. J. *The Thermionic Vacuum Tube and Its Applications.* McGraw-Hill Book Co.
11. American Institute of Electrical Engineers. *Definitions of Electrical Terms.*
12. King, R. W. *Thermionic vacuum tubes and their applications.* Bell System Technical Journal, Oct., 1923, Vol. 11, No. 4.
13. Terman, F. E. *Measurements in Radio Engineering.* McGraw-Hill Book Co.
14. American Radio Relay League. *The Radio Amateur's Handbook.*
15. Terman, F. E., and Roake, W. C. *Calculation and design of class C amplifiers.* Proc. I.R.E., April, 1936, Vol. 24, No. 4.
16. Everitt, W. L. *Optimum operating conditions for class C amplifiers.* Proc. I.R.E., Feb., 1934, Vol. 22, No. 2.
17. Fay, C. E. *The operation of vacuum tubes as class B and class C amplifiers.* Proc. I.R.E., March, 1932, Vol. 20, No. 3.
18. Llewellyn, F. B. *Constant frequency oscillators.* Proc. I.R.E., Dec., 1931, Vol. 19, No. 12.
19. Terman, F. E. *Resistance stabilized oscillators.* Electronics, July, 1933, Vol. 6, No. 7.
20. Tournier, M. *History and application of piezoelectricity.* Electrical Communication, April, 1937, Vol. 15, No. 4.
21. Lack, F. R., Willard, G. W., and Fair, I. E. *Some improvements in quartz crystal circuit elements.* Bell System Technical Journal, July, 1934, Vol. 13, No. 3.
22. Conklin, J. W., Finch, J. L., and Hansell, C. W. *New methods of frequency control employing long lines.* Proc. I.R.E., Nov., 1931, Vol. 10, No. 11.
23. Terman, F. E. *Resonant lines in radio circuits.* Electrical Engineering, July, 1934, Vol. 53, No. 7.
24. Hansell, C. W. *Resonant lines for frequency control.* Electrical Engineering, Aug., 1935, Vol. 54, No. 8.
25. Pierce, G. W. *Magnetostriction oscillators.* Proc. I.R.E., Jan., 1929, Vol. 17, No. 1.
26. Dow, J. B. *A recent development in vacuum tube oscillator circuits.* Proc. I.R.E., Dec., 1931, Vol. 19, No. 12.
27. Englund, C. R. *The short wave limit of vacuum tube oscillators.* Proc. I.R.E., Nov., 1927, Vol. 15, No. 11.
28. Kelley, M. J., and Samuel, A. L. *Vacuum tubes as high-frequency oscillators.* Electrical Engineering, Nov., 1934, Vol. 53, No. 11.
29. Llewellyn, F. B. *Vacuum tube electronics at ultra-high frequencies.* Proc. I.R.E., Nov., 1933, Vol. 21, No. 11.
30. Llewellyn, F. B. *The Barkhausen oscillator.* Bell Laboratories Record, Aug., 1935, Vol. 8, No. 12.
31. Karplus, Eduard. *Communication on the quasi-optical frequencies.* Electronics, June, 1931, Vol. 2, No. 6.
32. McPherson, W. L., and Ullrich, E. H. *Micro-ray communication.* Electrical Communication, April, 1936, Vol. 14, No. 4.

33. Hollmann, H. E.   *On the mechanism of electron oscillations in a triode.*
    Proc. I.R.E., Feb., 1929, Vol. 17, No. 2.
34. Anderson, J. E.   *Theory of electron oscillators.*   Electronics, Aug., 1936.
35. RCA Manufacturing Co.   *Cathode Ray Tubes and Allied Types.*   Pamphlet TS-2.

SUGGESTED ASSIGNMENTS

1. Fully explain the statements made on page 292 that a low ratio of L_2/C will improve the frequency stability of an oscillator.
2. Derive equation (**10–8**).
3. Fully design a high-quality audio-frequency oscillator such as shown in Fig. **10–6**.
4. Design a high-frequency oscillator using a transmission line for controlling the frequency.
5. Referring to page 298, what will happen if the rod of a magnetostriction oscillator is not magnetized?
6. Referring to the discussion on sweep oscillators, fully explain why a vacuum tube is usually employed instead of the current-limiting resistor R.

CHAPTER 11

MODULATORS

The purpose of any system of electrical communication is to transmit speech, music, or sounds and signals of various types. Modern systems are possible largely because of the thermionic vacuum tube. The importance of these tubes as rectifiers, amplifiers, and oscillators has been discussed in previous chapters. The uses of vacuum tubes as **modulators** will be covered in this chapter.

There are two very similar definitions of **modulation.** *First,* modulation [1] is "the process whereby the amplitude (or other characteristic) of a wave is varied as a function of the instantaneous value of another wave. The first wave, which is usually a single-frequency wave, is called the **carrier wave;** the second wave is called the **modulating wave.**" The *second* definition [2] for modulation is "the process of producing a wave some characteristic of which varies as a function of the instantaneous value of another wave, called the modulating wave." In the following pages, unless specifically stated, the *discussions will apply to* **amplitude modulated waves,**[2] which are those "whose envelope contains a component similar to the wave form of the signal to be transmitted."

To those not experienced in wire or radio communication, it may not be clear just why modulation is necessary. Just why should the voice frequencies, or the dots and dashes of a telegraphic code, be used to modulate or change the characteristics of a carrier wave in accordance with the definitions just given? There is at least *one* important reason why this is done in wire communication and *two* reasons in radio communication.

In wire communication the circuits are very long and are expensive to construct and maintain. If *more than one* telegraph message can be sent over the *same* telegraph line, or if *more than one* telephone conversation can be carried on over *one pair* of wires, great savings in plant will be effected. For voice-frequency telephone messages this is accomplished in *one carrier system* [3, 4] in the following manner: Three carrier frequencies (for example 10,000, 15,000, and 20,000 cycles) are selected. Each of these is *modulated* by one telephone conversation. By this process, the intelligence present in the low-frequency telephone conversation is *translated* to a new and higher frequency band. Since

307

the intelligence of each conversation will now exist at different frequencies, all three conversations can be transmitted simultaneously over the *same* pair of line wires.   Similar systems [4] have been designed for telegraph service.

Of course, for the conversations to be made audible at the distant city, the received signals must be **demodulated** (page 335) and returned to their original frequency band.   In ordinary telephone circuits these carrier-systems are limited somewhat by the increased losses offered at the higher frequencies.   It is theoretically possible, however, with the new coaxial telephone cable [5] installed from New York to Philadelphia to provide transmission for *240 simultaneous telephone conversations over one circuit.*

In radio or wireless communication there are at least two important reasons why modulation is necessary.   *First,* if an attempt were made to impress the voice frequencies directly on an antenna and radiate energy into space *at voice frequencies,* the system would not work because the dimensions of an antenna must be of the same order of magnitude as the length of the wave radiated.   Thus, a quarter-wave antenna for 1000 cycles would be about 46.5 miles long.   Radiation at voice frequencies is very inefficient, but it is quite effective at high frequencies.

The other reason modulation is necessary in radio is as follows: *Suppose* that a radio transmitting station *could* effectively radiate audio-frequency waves.   Then, all radio transmitting stations would radiate *in the same frequency band,* and it would be impossible to tune in one station and exclude the others.

97. The Nature of Speech and Music.—As the preceding discussions indicate, the process of modulation in carrier-telephone systems and in radio-telephone transmitters is accomplished by the speech currents corresponding to the human voice.   Before studying modulation further, it is advisable to consider the physical nature of speech. Furthermore, since broadcast stations must be designed to transmit musical programs as well, the nature of music must be investigated. In studying these, the considerations most useful in the design of vacuum-tube equipment are *first,* the frequency components present; *second,* the power level; and *third,* the variations in the power level during conversation or during the rendition of a musical program.

If the frequency range covered by speech is considered, the upper limit of the frequencies found will depend, among other factors, on the sensitiveness of the measuring equipment.   As a result of a thorough investigation [6, 7] with adequate equipment, the lowest frequencies of an average male voice were found to be *about* 100 cycles per second;

those of an average female voice are slightly higher.   The highest frequencies of the male voice found were about 8500 cycles, but those of the female voice extended to 10,000 cycles.

For music, the frequency band covered was considerably wider than for speech.   Frequencies as low as 40 cycles were found, and as an upper limit, harmonics or overtones extending to at least 15,000 cycles were readily detected.   The next step of the investigation was to determine if good quality of reproduction required that all these frequencies be transmitted electrically when reproducing speech and music.

By removing certain of the upper and lower frequencies, and by having the resulting sounds judged by experienced observers, it was found that little was lost to the quality of male speech if a band of from about 120 to 7000 cycles instead of the entire band were transmitted. For female speech, the band found necessary was 200 to 9000 cycles. For music, the required band was found to depend on the type of instrument.   In general, it was concluded that for both speech and music a frequency band transmitted of from about 60 to 8000 cycles gave a quality satisfactory for most purposes.

For commercial telephone conversation purposes, a high degree of *intelligibility* is necessary, but high quality is not; experience has shown that if the band of frequencies transmitted is from 250 to 2750 cycles, the intelligibility will be entirely satisfactory.   The tendency is to increase this band width, however.   For the transmission of speech programs and music over lines for simultaneously feeding a number of broadcast stations, two grades of service are sometimes supplied.   In the older circuits a band of from about 100 to 5000 cycles was transmitted, but in the later circuits this was extended to from 50 to 8000 cycles, in accordance with the limits prescribed in the preceding paragraph.

It is difficult in a few words to state all the facts regarding the energy levels and their variations in speech and music.   The subject is well summarized in Reference 7.   Some of the important facts are as follows: The *average* power in connected speech is 10 microwatts. Speech *peak* powers of over 100 microwatts may occur quite often. The electrical power available from a microphone depends on its efficiency in converting from acoustical to electrical power; this efficiency is very low, and with only 10 microwatts of sound energy available the electrical output is small.   The acoustical power output from an orchestra is relatively quite high, a large orchestra being capable of radiating *peak* powers of from 60 to 70 watts.   Of great importance to the communication engineer is the *variations* in the power output of an orchestra during the rendition of a program.   A medium-sized orchestra may vary as much as 100,000 to 1 (or 50 decibels) during a single selection. It has been found that little quality is lost if a volume range of only 10,000 to 1 (or 40 decibels) is provided. By an interesting system of volume compression and expansion using a *Compandor*, the volume range may be compressed for transmission and expanded after reception [8] (see page 280).

From the above considerations it is apparent that speech and music signals are quite complex. The complex *modulating* wave may vary rapidly in power level, and consists of many frequency components. Experience has shown, however, that if a circuit will satisfactorily transmit pure sinusoidal currents of frequencies distributed throughout the band occupied by speech and music, then the circuit will satisfactorily transmit the complex speech and music programs such as are broadcasted by radio stations.

98. Nature of a Modulated Carrier.—From the preceding discussions it is seen that a relatively low-frequency wave is used to modulate a high-frequency wave so that the program can be transmitted over lines or through space at higher frequencies.

There are *two* ways in which the process of modulation may be regarded. One is that the amplitude of the carrier wave is merely caused to vary in accordance with the impressed program signal. The other viewpoint stresses the fact that during the modulating process new frequencies are created. While both viewpoints may lead to the same conclusions, it is easy to form an *incomplete* mental picture of the process if modulation is regarded only as a process for varying the amplitude of the carrier. In the following pages both explanations will be given, with emphasis placed on the fact that *in the output of a modulator new frequencies exist which were not present in the input, and that these are the frequencies desired for transmitting the intelligence or the program.*

Since in the process of modulation new frequencies are produced which *were not present* in the input of either the modulating signal or the carrier wave, there is justification for regarding *any* process of modulation as a form of non-linear distortion. As explained on page 209, non-linear distortion results in the creation of new frequencies which were not present in the input.

Types of Modulation.—The three types of modulation are *amplitude*, *phase*, and *frequency* modulation. That is, intelligence existing initially at low frequencies may be translated to, and transmitted at, higher frequencies by causing the amplitude, or phase, or frequency of a carrier wave to vary in accordance with the low-frequency signal wave. Of these three types, *only* the so-called *amplitude modulation is used commercially.* Frequency modulation (page 331) has been demonstrated experimentally, and phase modulation (page 332) is theoretically possible.

Excluding the two latter types, and referring only to *amplitude modulation*, it is possible to make further classifications. These include [9] absorption modulation, plate-circuit modulation, grid-circuit modulation, and modulation by means of non-linear impedances. Another classification [10] is a division into modulated oscillators, modulated amplifiers, modulation by non-linear circuit elements, and modulation by means of variable circuit elements. A division [3] by Everett is particularly helpful in studying the subject. Other classifications have also been given.[11, 12]

Since the various possible classifications have never been standardized, there is great possibility for confusion. One of the worst obstacles in studying modulation (and demodulation as well), is the *lack of uniformity* in the descriptive terms as used by the various authorities.

For this reason, extreme care will be taken in the following pages to make clear the exact process by which modulation is accomplished. As previously mentioned, there is justification for assuming that all amplitude modulation is due to impressing voltages on *non-linear circuit elements*, whether these are circuits using vacuum tubes, saturated iron-cored inductances, or crystals of galena. Regardless of viewpoints and definitions, the fact remains that the *purpose of the process of modulation is to translate* the low-frequency signals to higher frequencies; this is done by simultaneously impressing signal and carrier voltages on a *device which distorts them so that the desired frequencies are created.*

Analysis of Modulation.—An amplitude-modulated wave will be shown (page 316) to appear as in Fig. 11–1. If such a wave is analyzed with a wave

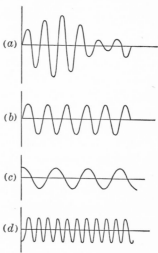

FIG. 11–1. The so-called amplitude modulated wave of (a) can be analyzed into a carrier wave (b) and lower (c) and upper (d) side bands. This can be proved by making an analysis by the Fourier series method, or with a wave analyzer. Conversely, (b), (c), and (d) can be shown graphically to combine and give the modulated wave (a). The above illustrations are *not* to scale. Note in particular that the *amplitude* of the carrier component (b) *does not vary* for a modulated wave.

analyzer (page 275), it will be found to contain *three* separate frequencies. These are, *first*, the carrier plus the modulating frequency, called the **upper side band**; *second*, the carrier; and *third*, the carrier minus the modulating frequency, called the **lower side band**. Thus, if the carrier is a 20,000-cycle sinusoidal wave as it might be in a carrier-telephone system, and if the modulating frequency is a 1000-cycle sinusoidal wave, then the upper side band will be a 21,000-cycle sine wave, the carrier will exist as before, and the lower side band will be a 19,000-cycle sine wave.

If the carrier wave is completely modulated, the minimum values of the resulting amplitude-modulated wave will just strike the zero axis.

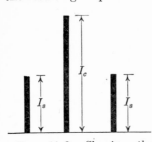

Fig. 11-2. Showing the relative heights of the carrier component I_c and the two side bands for 100 per cent modulation.

The **percentage modulation**[1, 2] is denoted by m, and is 100 per cent in the instance just given. The relations of the preceding paragraph are shown graphically in Fig. 11-2; the modulation is 100 per cent. The length of the lines represents the height of the components of Fig. 11-1. For complete modulation, the amplitude of the side bands is one-half that of the carrier as the figures indicate. If I_c represents the unmodulated carrier, and if I_s represents the height of a side band, then $m = 2I_s/I_c \times 100$. That is, the percentage modulation[1] is "the ratio of half the difference between the maximum and minimum amplitudes of a modulated wave to the average amplitude, expressed in per cent."

A simple and generalized treatment of amplitude modulation is as follows: The instantaneous value of any sinusoidal current is

$$i = I_{max.} \sin \omega t. \tag{11-1}$$

Now suppose the amplitude $I_{max.}$ is made to vary sinusoidally (by a signal of lower frequency) in any one of the several systems of modulation, the percentage modulation being m. Then, at any instant

$$I_m = I_c(1 + m \sin \omega_s t). \tag{11-2}$$

If this value is substituted in equation (11-1), then

$$i = I_c(1 + m \sin \omega_s t) \sin \omega_c t, \tag{11-3}$$

in which ω equals 2π times the frequency f, and the subscripts s and c represent the signal and carrier components respectively. Expanding equation (11-3) according to the usual method of performing trigonometric operations,

$$i = I_c \sin \omega_c t + \frac{mI_c}{2} \cos (\omega_c - \omega_s)t - \frac{mI_c}{2} \cos (\omega_c + \omega_s)t. \tag{11-4}$$

This equation shows that the wave of Fig. 11–1 contains three frequency components, the carrier represented by $I_c \sin \omega_c t$, the lower side band represented by $mI_c/2 \cos (\omega_c - \omega_s)t$, and the upper side band represented by $mI_c/2 \cos (\omega_c + \omega_s)t$. These equations prove the statements made with respect to Fig. 11–2 regarding the magnitudes of the side bands. For 100 per cent modulation the *maximum* value of each side band is $I_c/2$. For any percentage modulation m, the *maximum* value is $mI_c/2$.

In following the above discussion, it *should not be inferred* that the carrier and the two side bands are all the frequencies which ever exist in the output of a modulator. In fact, the analysis just given is a somewhat incomplete "picture," applying only to a wave containing three components such as the modulated wave of Fig. 11–1. Any of the usual methods of modulation can be represented fully only by the use of mathematical series (page 324), and hence the output wave will be badly distorted and contain many frequencies not included in an approximate analysis.

Energy Relations in Modulated Waves.—As was previously mentioned, for 100 per cent modulation the amplitude of each side band is half that of the carrier. The power contained in each component is proportional to the amplitude squared, since power varies as the current squared. If the amplitude of the carrier equal 1.0, and *each* side band 0.5, then the corresponding power relations will be 1.0 and 0.25. That is, if P represents the total power in the modulated wave, then $66\frac{2}{3}$ per cent will be in the carrier, and $33\frac{1}{3}$ per cent in the *two* side bands ($16\frac{2}{3}$ per cent in each one).

The *intelligence* or program signal power is *entirely in the side bands. No intelligence whatever is conveyed by the carrier wave.* This statement applies to code as well as voice-modulated signals. Although the carrier wave and both side bands are at present broadcast for entertainment purposes, in many other systems (pages 325 and 337), only the carrier and one side band, or *only one side band is transmitted.* Thus the final power amplifying stages handle only useful power.

From an examination of Figs. 11–1 and 11–2, it can be proved that the continuous (or average) power output with 100 per cent modulation is 1.5 times the output with zero modulation. Also, that for modulation peaks the output is four times the unmodulated carrier. This is because power is proportional to current or voltage squared.

99. Types of Vacuum-Tube Modulators.—A modulator is defined [2] as "a device to effect the process of modulation   It may be operated by virtue of some non-linear characteristic or by a controlled variation of some circuit quantity." Although this definition implies that modulation may be accomplished by two distinct methods, the two methods are really equivalent.

It is important to have clearly in mind just what part of the circuit is the modulator. Thus, in many circles it is common to *call the last audio-frequency* stage the modulator, when in reality *it is an amplifier* driving the circuit in which the distortion and modulation are produced. In the following discussions, the term modulator will be used to mean the circuit or device used to effect (or accomplish) the process of modulation. In other words, the modulator will be the *circuit which distorts* the carrier and signal waves *and produces the new frequencies* desired— the *side bands.*

Just as it is difficult to classify the methods of modulation, so is it difficult to classify the types of vacuum-tube modulators; the definitions have not been standardized. Furthermore, it is possible to explain the process of modulation from different viewpoints. In accordance with the non-linear impedance and distortion viewpoint, a satisfactory classification is given in Reference 12. The following paragraph is largely summarized from this article.

There are two distinct classes of vacuum-tube modulators which may be designated as **plate-circuit modulators** and **grid-circuit modulators.** This classification is according to the circuit in which modulation is *initially* produced, although in some tubes modulation may be produced in both the plate and grid circuits. The Heising modulator following is an example of the plate-circuit type; this scheme was used for many years in broadcast stations. The van der Bijl system (page 322), so widely used in carrier-telephone systems, is also of the plate-circuit type. An example of the grid-circuit modulator is the grid leak-condenser type once widely used as a demodulator or detector for radio reception. (From one viewpoint, modulation and demodulation are the same process, page 336.)

In the following pages, this classification will be followed. The distinction between plate-circuit modulators and grid-circuit modulators will at all times be clearly defined.

The way in which modulators are connected into the circuit of typical radio transmitters for both high-level and low-level modulation was shown in Fig. 9–18.

100. Plate-Modulated Class *C* Oscillator.—This method [13] is often called **Heising modulation,** so named after its inventor. In the past, this method was very widely used, but has been largely superseded because of frequency instability and other limitations. Other names, such as **constant-current modulation,** and **plate-circuit modulation,** have been applied to it.

A circuit of a plate-modulated class *C* oscillator is shown in Fig. 11–3. The audio-frequency input from a microphone and voltage amplifier is fed into the grid circuit of the audio-frequency amplifier.

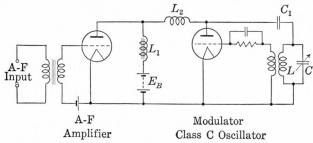

A-F   Modulator
Amplifier   Class C Oscillator

Fɪɢ. 11–3.   Circuit for a plate-modulated class *C* oscillator.

This tube is often incorrectly called the modulator tube.   It is merely an audio-frequency, class *A*, impedance-coupled, power-amplifier tube. No (intentional) distortion occurs in its plate circuit.

The modulated class *C* oscillator tube receives its plate-supply voltage from the same source E_B, and through the same coil L_1 as does the amplifier tube.   Otherwise, the circuit is that of a conventional class *C* oscillator.   Connections to the antenna would be made to the anti-resonant or parallel circuit *L–C*.   The radio-frequency choke coil L_2 prevents the flow of the high-frequency curents to the left.   The condenser C_1 prevents the flow of current from the plate-supply battery E_B, around through the circuit *L–C*.   Note in particular that *only audio-frequency components exist to the left of the radio-frequency choke L_2.*

The operation of the plate-modulated oscillator of Fig. 11–3 is essentially as follows: Negligible alternating current flows through the audio-frequency choke coil L_1.   The plate resistance (plate to cathode) of the oscillator tube is the alternating-current load for the amplifier tube.   When an audio-frequency signal is impressed on this amplifying tube, the potential of the plate of the amplifying tube will vary with the audio signal just as in any amplifying tube.   Since the two plates are tied together, the plate potential of the oscillator tube also must vary in accordance with the audio signals.

The alternating radio-frequency or carrier voltage generated by the oscillator *varies almost directly with the magnitude of the plate-supply voltage.*   Since the plate voltage is varying in accordance with the audio signal, the radio-frequency carrier voltage must also follow the audio variations, as Fig. 11–4 indicates.

The output circuit for the oscillator is through the small condenser C_1 to the parallel circuit *L–C* which is anti-resonant and hence offers a high impedance to the carrier frequency. Thus, a large voltage drop will exist across this parallel circuit *for the carrier and for the upper and*

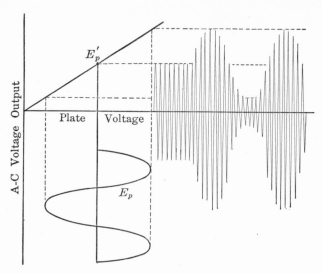

Fig. 11–4. The magnitude of the alternating voltage output of the oscillator depends on the magnitude of the direct voltage E_p'. When this is caused to vary in accordance with the audio voltage variations E_p, the alternating radio-frequency voltage *across the anti-resonant tuned circuit L–C* will be as shown. The *envelope* of the radio-frequency output voltage has the shape of the audio signal E_p. This *does not* mean that any appreciable audio-frequency component exists across the circuit *L–C*. This circuit is *tuned to the carrier* frequency and thus the only appreciable voltages existing across it are due to the carrier and the two side bands. These components are impressed on the antenna.

lower side bands, generated when the oscillator output is caused to vary at the audio rate. Of course other frequency components are also produced, but these do not appear to any great extent as voltages across *L–C*, because this tuned circuit offers low impedance to them. The fact that C_1 is small prevents the audio components from passing around through the circuit *L–C* instead of through the load offered to the amplifying tube by the plate-circuit resistance of the oscillator tube.   The condenser C_1 also prevents the flow of direct current.

This modulator once was used extensively, but is now seldom employed for at least two reasons. *First*, if 100 per cent modulation is attempted, then the oscillator plate voltage must approach zero and hence oscillations may stop. *Second*, as was mentioned on page 315, the magnitude of the plate-supply voltage is changing at an audio rate, and this will cause the *frequency* of the oscillator to vary accordingly. The output of the plate-modulated oscillator will, therefore, be frequency modulated in addition to amplitude modulated. Frequency modulation is undesired.

101. Plate-Modulated Class C Amplifier.—If a class C *amplifier* instead of a class C *oscillator* is used, the difficulties just mentioned do not present themselves. In the plate-modulated class C amplifier, the carrier-frequency grid exciting voltage is produced by a crystal oscillator and associated voltage amplifier. Thus, the carrier-frequency is held constant and the output of the modulator is not (theoretically) frequency modulated. Also, this device may be 100 per cent modulated, without fear of oscillations ceasing.

This type modulator is *very widely used at present*. It can be used in either high-level or low-level modulation circuits as discussed on page 269. Since the class C oscillator and the class C amplifier differ only in the fact that one is self excited and the other externally excited, the discussions of the preceding section can be readily extended to cover the plate-modulated class C amplifier.

The circuit of Fig. 11–3 *could* be used for a plate-modulated class C amplifier merely by separately exciting the oscillator and using it as an amplifier tube. This circuit is not desirable, however, because with it 100 per cent modulation is impossible. It is impossible because the two plates are in parallel, and for complete modulation the plate-potential variations of the class A amplifier must be from zero to twice the direct plate-supply voltage; this cannot be achieved practically. The circuit can be modified by placing a resistor in series with the choke coil L_2. The resistor is of such value that the direct voltage applied to the plate of the modulated class C amplifier tube is reduced to a value such that the modulating class A amplifier tube can swing the plate from zero to twice the direct plate-supply voltage. This resistor must be shunted by a very large condenser so that the audio-frequency currents from the class A amplifier tube have a low-impedance path to the plate circuit of the class C amplifier tube.

The three circuits shown in Fig. 11–5a, b, and c are often used for plate-modulated class C amplifiers. In each of these, the tuned circuit $L–C$ would be coupled to additional amplification for low-level modulation, or to the antenna for high-level modulation.

In the first circuit, 100 per cent modulation is possible because the autotransformer used for coupling (instead of a choke) increases the voltage impressed on the modulated class C amplifier tube. Also, this autotransformer changes the magnitude of the load resistance offered by the plate circuit of the second tube. By selecting the proper ratio of transformation, the correct load for the class A tube can be obtained.

Of all the possible schemes of coupling the driving audio amplifier to the plate-modulated class C amplifier, the last two circuits of Fig. 11–5, employing transformers, are the most satisfactory. In the first of these two, a common plate supply can be used as shown, or the plates of the two tubes may be separately supplied, thus increasing the flexibility of conditions of operation. In the last of these systems, the audio-

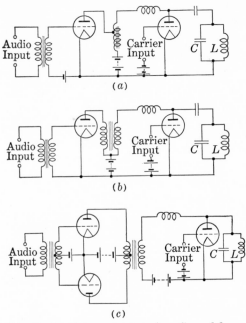

Fig. 11–5. Circuits for plate-modulated class C amplifiers. The modulated signal composed of the carrier and the two side bands exists as a voltage across the tuned circuit L–C. This would be coupled to the antenna, sometimes by inductive coupling with L.

frequency driving tubes are operated in push-pull class A, AB, or B as desired. In fact, the circuits are often adjusted so that class A operation obtains for small inputs, but for large audio-frequency signals the tubes operate as class AB or as class B. These drivers usually are audio-frequency *power* amplifiers (since they usually drive power-consuming class C stages), and the discussions given in Chapter 9, page 263, therefore apply.

Equivalent Circuit for Modulated Amplifier.—For a further explanation of the plate-modulated class C amplifier, the circuits of Fig. 11–5 may be represented by the equivalent circuit of Fig. 11–6. Although the audio-frequency signal voltage is not in series with the tuned anti-resonant circuit L–C in Fig. 11–5, the action is equivalent to the simplified circuit shown.

The grid is biased to twice cut-off, so that with a sinusoidal carrier-frequency voltage applied to the grid, less than half cycles of carrier current will flow (Fig. 11–6a) in the plate circuit *with no audio-frequency voltage applied*. This wave is, of course, badly distorted, but will contain a large carrier-frequency component (somewhat as given by equation 7–1, page 178) to which the L–C circuit is tuned. The impedance of this L–C circuit will be a large value of pure resistance *to the carrier* frequency (and to the side bands) but will offer low impedance to all other components. Thus, the voltage appearing across the circuit L–C will be largely a carrier-frequency voltage, and this will be impressed on the antenna.

When an audio-frequency signal voltage is impressed with *no carrier-frequency* voltage, the resulting plate potential will be that of the plate supply plus the signal voltage. If the magnitude of the peak values of this signal voltage is equal to the direct plate-supply voltage, the potential of the plate will vary with the audio-frequency signals from zero to twice the direct plate-supply voltage. Assuming a sinusoidal audio-frequency signal voltage, the plate potential will vary as in Fig. 11–6b.

When the carrier-frequency voltage and the audio-frequency signal voltages are impressed simultaneously, the plate current will vary as in Fig. 11–6c. This plate current is again badly distorted. Instead of containing only

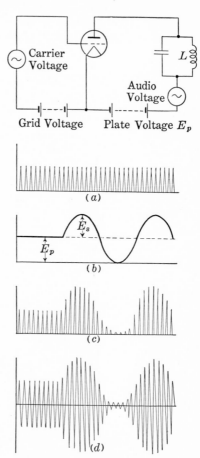

Fig. 11–6. Equivalent circuit for a modulated class C amplifier, and curves for analyzing its operation.
(a) Plate current with only carrier impressed.
(b) Direct voltage E_p and audio signal voltage E_s.
(c) Resulting plate current when carrier voltage and signal voltage are simultaneously impressed.
(d) Voltage drop across the tuned circuit composed of the inductance and the condenser.
This so-called modulated wave contains the carrier and the side bands.

harmonics of the carrier voltage as in Fig. 11–6a, it now also contains (among other frequencies) the carrier frequency, the carrier frequency *plus* the audio frequency, and the carrier frequency *minus* the audio frequency. These two last components are the desired *upper and lower side bands which convey the intelligence or musical program.* The carrier-frequency component is constant and conveys no information.

This modulated plate current of Fig. 11–6c must flow through the parallel circuit *L–C* which is tuned, and therefore anti-resonant, to the carrier frequency. The tuning must be sufficiently broad that a very high impedance of essentially pure resistance is offered, not only to the carrier frequency, but *also to the side bands.* Thus, the voltage across this parallel *L–C* circuit will be due to the combined effect of the carrier frequency and the side bands, and this is the voltage *impressed on the antenna.* This wave shape, both before and after modulation, is shown in Fig. 11–6d. The tuned circuit offers low impedance to all the other components of the complex wave of Fig. 11–6c, and hence they are not radiated in the same magnitude as are the desired frequencies. If it were not for the selective action of this tuned circuit, the transmitter would radiate at various frequencies, instead of radiating at the frequency of the side bands and the carrier.

It is of interest to investigate the power relations in a plate-modulated class *C* amplifier. As mentioned on page 313, the power relations in a completely-modulated wave are as follows: If the power output of the carrier is assumed 1.0, then that of each side band is 0.25, and the total *average* power output of the modulated wave would be 1.5. The carrier wave *is unaffected* by the process of modulation, the power output being 1.0 before and after modulation. The power supplied the side bands must, therefore, be furnished by the audio-frequency driving or modulating amplifier.

Information on the design of plate-modulated class *C* amplifiers is given by Terman in Reference 10. Additional information will be found in such publications as the Proceedings of the Institute of Radio Engineers, and the Bell System Technical Journal. Rather complete design and construction information of a practical nature is given in Reference 14.

102. The Grid-Modulated Class *C* Amplifier.—In the plate-modulator just described, the carrier was impressed on the grid circuit, and the audio-frequency variations on the plate circuit. Modulation was effected in the plate circuit. In the system now to be described, *both frequencies* are impressed *in the grid circuit* of a class *C* amplifier, and modulation is again effected *in the plate circuit.* This is often called grid modulation, a term not in agreement with the classification on page 314. It is plate modulation by *grid injection*. A simplified equivalent circuit is shown in Fig. 11–7.

In this figure is also shown the method of distorting the carrier and audio-frequency impulses to produce the side bands and thus accomplish modulation. As indicated, the tube is biased to twice cut-off. The magnitude of the carrier voltage depends on the type of system desired. In one,[10] the magnitude of the carrier voltage is so adjusted that the grid is never driven positive, even on modulation peaks. In the other,[9] the magnitude of the carrier voltage is such that the grid may be driven slightly positive even with no audio-frequency excitation. This latter scheme is shown in Fig. 11–7.

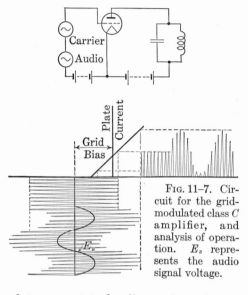

FIG. 11–7. Circuit for the grid-modulated class C amplifier, and analysis of operation. E_s represents the audio signal voltage.

The variations in grid potential when the carrier and audio-frequency voltages are impressed simultaneously are shown in Fig. 11–7. These changes in grid potential will cause the plate current to be distorted as shown. As in previous instances, this current will contain, among other values, the carrier and the two side bands. These will cause a large voltage drop across the tuned parallel circuit as explained in the preceding section, and this voltage is impressed on the antenna.

When operated so that the grid is always negative and draws no current, negligible power is taken from the carrier-frequency and the audio-frequency amplifiers. All the power in the modulated wave, including that due to the presence of the side bands, comes from the plate supply of the class C tube. The plate efficiency and power output are lower than for the plate-modulated class C amplifier system. Two tubes are sometimes used in a push-pull connection for modulation in low-power transmitters.[15] Note that with this push-pull scheme the *carrier* is not eliminated as in the push-pull system to be described on page 325. With present receivers the carrier must be transmitted for broadcast purposes, although its transmission is not necessary in order to convey a program (pages 337 and 357).

When the grid-modulated class C amplifier is operated so that the grid draws current, then both the carrier-frequency and the audiofrequency amplifiers must supply power.   This power is supplied only to the grid circuit, however, and the modulating audio frequency *does not* supply the power to generate the side bands as in the plate-modulated scheme.   The efficiency of a grid-modulated amplifier is lower than the plate-modulated amplifier, and hence the former is best suited only for low-power transmitters [15] where high efficiency is not so important.

103. The Van der Bijl System of Modulation.—This system, named after its inventor, was developed early in the history of vacuum tubes.[13] It has been widely used in carrier telephone systems [16, 17] where simplicity and reliability are more important than high efficiency.   In this modulator the desired distortion and modulation occur *in the plate circuit* due to the nonlinear relation between plate current and grid voltage.   Owing to the fact that this system well illustrates the theory of modulation, it will be treated in considerable detail.

The circuit is arranged as in Fig. 11–8, and the operation is as follows: Assume that the audiofrequency sinusoidal signal A is to modulate the carrier-frequency signal B. These two frequencies are impressed simultaneously on the grid of the tube, which is biased so that operation is on the nonlinear part of the grid voltage-plate current curve as indicated in Fig. 11–9.   The relative magnitudes of the two components are adjusted

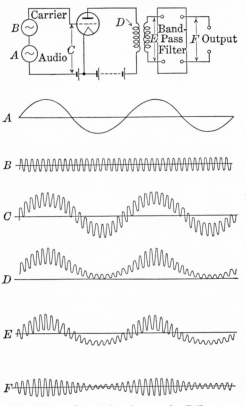

Fig. 11–8.   Circuit for the van der Bijl system of modulation, and analysis of currents and voltages in various parts of the circuit.

to the values shown. The combined action of the carrier and audio frequencies will cause the potential of the grid to vary as indicated by *C* of Fig. 11–8, and as in Fig. 11–9.

If the bias were such that the grid-voltage variations were on the linear portion of the grid voltage-plate current curve, *amplification alone would occur*, and the plate current would be a replica of the grid-voltage variations. Since the high negative grid bias shifts the operation to the non-linear portion, the plate current is distorted as indicated by Fig. 11–9, and also by curve *D* of Fig. 11–8. This distorted curve

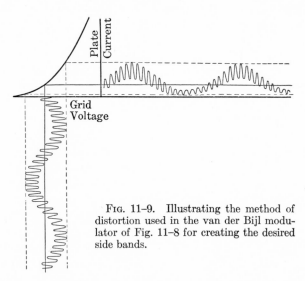

Fig. 11–9. Illustrating the method of distortion used in the van der Bijl modulator of Fig. 11–8 for creating the desired side bands.

will contain a large number of frequency components, among which are the audio frequency, the carrier frequency, and the upper and lower side bands. It will also contain a direct-current component.

After the plate current *D* of Fig. 11–8 passes through the output transformer, the voltage induced in the secondary will vary as shown by curve *E*. On the output side of the band-pass filter,[3, 4] which is inserted to remove the audio-frequency and the higher-frequency components (page 325) the wave shape would be as shown by curve *F*. This is the familiar "amplitude modulated" wave (page 307) and *contains the carrier and the upper and lower side bands.*

With this system a low value of load resistance should be placed in the plate circuit so that the dynamic curve of Fig. 11–9 will not approach a straight line (page 127). Since the grid is always negative, negligible carrier-frequency and audio-frequency power is required from the driving amplifiers. The efficiency of this system is low, but this is not of great importance in wire carrier-telephone installations where it is used. This method is sometimes referred to [9, 10] as a modulated amplifier. Although amplification does take place, the primary function is to *distort the wave and produce modulation*.

Analysis of Van der Bijl System.—Over the *lower curved portion* of the grid voltage-plate current curve of Fig. 11–9, the plate current may be represented by the following power series:

$$I_p = ae_g + be_g{}^2 + \cdots. \qquad (11\text{–}5)$$

For a practical explanation of modulation all terms of this series higher than those given by equation (11–5) may be neglected.

If the instantaneous value of the carrier-frequency voltage is $E_1 \sin \omega_1 t$, and that of the audio-frequency or voice-frequency voltage is $E_2 \sin \omega_2 t$, then the instantaneous grid potential will be

$$e_g = E_1 \sin \omega_1 t + E_2 \sin \omega_2 t. \qquad (11\text{–}6)$$

Substituting this value of instantaneous grid potential in equation (11–5), we find that the instantaneous plate current is equal to

$$i_p = aE_1 \sin \omega_1 t + aE_2 \sin \omega_2 t + bE_1{}^2 \sin^2 \omega_1 t + bE_2{}^2 \sin^2 \omega_2 t \\ + 2bE_1 E_2 \sin \omega_1 t \sin \omega_2 t. \qquad (11\text{–}7)$$

This equation can be expanded by the relation

$$\sin \omega_1 t \sin \omega_2 t = \left[\frac{1}{2} \cos (\omega_1 - \omega_2)t - \frac{1}{2} \cos (\omega_1 + \omega_2)t \right]. \qquad (11\text{–}8)$$

After these substitutions are made, equation (11–7) becomes

$$i_p = aE_1 \sin \omega_1 t + aE_2 \sin \omega_2 t + bE_1{}^2 \left(\frac{1}{2} - \frac{1}{2} \cos 2\omega_1 t \right) \\ + bE_2{}^2 \left(\frac{1}{2} - \frac{1}{2} \cos 2\omega_2 t \right) + 2bE_1 E_2 \\ \times \left[\frac{1}{2} \cos (\omega_1 - \omega_2)t - \frac{1}{2} \cos (\omega_1 + \omega_2)t \right]. \qquad (11\text{–}9)$$

Performing the indicated multiplications and dropping all constant terms (since only the alternating components are of present interest) gives the relation

$$i_p = aE_1 \sin \omega_1 t + aE_2 \sin \omega_2 t - \frac{bE_1{}^2}{2} \cos 2\omega_1 t - \frac{bE_2{}^2}{2} \cos 2\omega_2 t \\ + bE_1 E_2 \cos (\omega_1 - \omega_2)t - bE_1 E_2 \cos (\omega_1 + \omega_2)t. \qquad (11\text{–}10)$$

Remembering that the frequency of the carrier is $f_1 = \omega_1/2\pi$, and that the audio frequency is $f_2 = \omega_2/2\pi$, the following alternating components are found to exist (along with other components) in the output; that is, in curve E of Fig. 11–8:

1. The **audio frequency,** f_2, represented by the second term.
2. Twice the **carrier frequency,** $2f_1$, represented by the third term.
3. Twice the **audio frequency,** $2f_2$, represented by the fourth term.
4. The **carrier frequency,** f_1, represented by the first term.
5. The **lower side band,** $f_1 - f_2$, represented by the fifth term.
6. The **upper side band,** $f_1 + f_2$, represented by the last term.

As previously explained on page 323, the band-pass filter would remove all but the last three frequencies, giving the so-called amplitude modulated wave of curve F, Fig. 11–8. For commercial carrier-telephone service, in which the voice range is from about 250–2750 cycles, if the carrier frequency is assumed to be 20,000 cycles, then these three frequency components will be $f_1 = 20,000$ cycles; $f_1 - f_2 = 17,250$ to 19,750 cycles; and $f_1 + f_2 = 20,250$ to 22,750 cycles. In carrier telephony [4] these frequencies as shown by Fig. 11–9F *are not all transmitted.* Since only one side band is necessary for conveying the intelligence, there is nothing to be gained by transmitting a wider band. Thus, in one system only *one side band is transmitted,* and the carrier is supplied for the demodulation at the distant end by a local oscillator. If a 20,000-cycle carrier were modulated by a sinusoidal wave of 1000 cycles, then only a 19,000-cycle *or* 21,000-cycle wave would be transmitted.

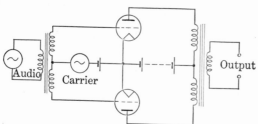

Fig. 11–10. A balanced modulator arranged for suppressing the carrier as in a carrier-telephone system.

104. Balanced Modulators.—As explained in the preceding section, in a widely used system of carrier telephony, only one side band is transmitted. The other frequencies must, therefore, be removed by some means. Band-pass filters will accomplish this, theoretically, at least. The difficulty lies in the fact that a margin of only 250 cycles lies between the carrier to be suppressed and the side band to be transmitted and that the amplitude of the carrier is much greater than that of the side band. Special filters of the quartz crystal type [18] would probably be necessary for such sharp discrimination.

It is possible, however, to suppress *the carrier* in the modulator circuit if the **balanced modulator** of Fig. 11–10 is employed. Then, the filter will not need to be so sharp in its cut-off characteristics, since it need only discriminate between the two side bands, and crystal filters need not be employed.   For each individual tube, modulation will occur as in the van der Bijl system of the preceding section.   Thus, the two side bands will exist (with other products of modulation) in the output of the transformer.

The carrier frequency is suppressed in the following manner: As Fig. 11–10 shows, the carrier-frequency voltage is impressed on the two grids in phase.   That is, for the positive half cycle of the carrier, *both* grids are driven more positive; for the negative half cycle, *both* grids are driven more negative.   Thus, the plate-current changes which occur for *carrier-frequency* variations will be the same for each tube, and will be *balanced out in the primary of the output transformer*.

105. Grid–Circuit Modulation.—As previously mentioned (page 314) vacuum-tube modulators may be classified as *plate-circuit* modulators or as *grid-circuit* modulators.   All of the types which previously have been considered may be classified as plate-circuit modulators; grid-circuit modulators will be considered in this section.   The material largely will be summarized from the work [12] of Peterson and Keith.

Referring to Fig. 5–14 it is seen that the grid voltage-grid current curve is non-linear.   Over the lower part of the grid-current curve equation (11–5) and the accompanying derivations, showing how the side bands are generated, apply.   It is apparent that this non-linear grid-current characteristic can be used to produce modulation *in the grid circuit*, just as the non-linear part of the plate-current curve can be used to produce modulation *in the plate circuit*.

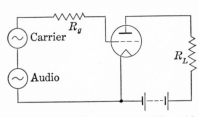

A simplified circuit of a grid-circuit or grid-current modulator is shown in Fig. 11–11.   The tube may be operated with no bias, or with the bias either *slightly* positive or *slightly* negative, depending on conditions.   The carrier and audio voltages are impressed on the grid with a resistor R_g of about 1,000,000 ohms in series.   The load resistor R_L has about the same magnitude as the plate resistance of the tube.   The grid bias and plate voltages are so selected that distortion occurs *in the grid circuit*, and amplification occurs *in the plate circuit*.

FIG. 11–11.   Circuit arranged for grid-circuit modulation. The unwanted components would be suppressed by filters or by a tuned parallel anti-resonant circuit.

With these adjustments, the operation is described [12] somewhat as follows: The resultant potential, due to the combined action of the carrier-frequency and the audio-frequency voltages, will be somewhat as shown by curve C of Fig. 11–8. With the bias at about zero value, so long as the grid-potential variations maintain the grid negative, no grid current flows; but, when the grid is driven positive by the combined action of the carrier and the audio signals, grid current flows and a *voltage drop occurs* across the high resistance R_g. Thus, when grid current flows and a voltage drop occurs across R_g, the voltage actually impressed *on the grid* is distorted, and contains the desired (and also undesired) products of modulation; that is, the side bands.

With proper adjustments, modulation occurs in the *grid circuit*, and amplification in the *plate circuit*. With this ideal arrangement, the efficiency of the system is made very high. Filters in the output are used to suppress the undesired frequency components. Although this system of grid-circuit modulation presents certain apparent advantages it has not received extensive commercial application. One disadvantage is that current is drawn by the grid so that power is taken from the audio and carrier amplifiers. They must both have good voltage regulation.

Suppressor-Grid Modulation.—This system [14] is extensively used in low-power radio-telephone transmitters such as are employed by many amateurs. A suppressor-grid voltage-amplifying pentode, as distinguished from the power-output pentode, is used. In the former tube the shielding effect of the screen grid is very good, and self oscillations of the tube are prevented without the use of neutralizing circuits.

The circuit is arranged as in Fig. 11–12. Both the suppressor grid and the control grid are made negative, and the carrier wave and the modulating audio wave are introduced as indicated.

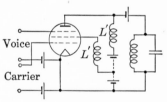

Fig. 11–12. Suppressor-grid modulation using a pentode.

The electron current flowing to the plate is affected by both these voltages, and the desired side bands are generated. The radio-frequency choke coils L' offer high impedance to the radio-frequency components, which accordingly flow through the tuned anti-resonant circuit L–C. A high voltage will exist across this circuit for the carrier and the side bands, and this voltage is impressed on the antenna.

The suppressor grid may be driven positive on modulation peaks and hence take power from the audio-frequency amplifier driving it. This amplifier must have good voltage regulation. Modulation of 100 per cent can be obtained with very little signal distortion if the modulator is well designed.

106. Miscellaneous Systems of Modulation.—These are very extensive, and no attempt will be made to record them in detail. Any device in which a component of the output wave is proportional to the *product* of two input waves will cause modulation.[3]

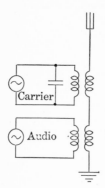

A simple arrangement for modulating a carrier wave is shown in Fig. 11–13. This is sometimes classified as **absorption modulation.** From another viewpoint, it is sometimes classified as **impedance modulation.** This system has very definite power-handling limitations, and also causes undesired frequency modulation.

A very interesting historical record of the many and varied systems of modulation will be found in Reference 19.

Copper-Oxide Modulators.—The electronic principles of the copper-oxide rectifiers were discussed on page 47. The electrical characteristics were shown in Fig. 7–19, page 196, where its uses as a rectifier were treated. From this figure it is evident that the resistance of the copper-oxide disk (or disks) varies widely with changes in the magnitude and polarity of the applied voltages. Thus the descriptive term **Varistor** is often applied to these units, particularly where they are used primarily to introduce

FIG. 11–13. A simple (but unsatisfactory) method of modulation.

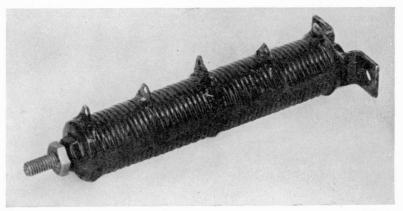

A Varistor extensively used in modern carrier telephone systems for modulation and demodulation. (Courtesy Western Electric Co.)

a variable-control element into a circuit. The resistance of a Varistor varies with the dimensions of the disks and with other factors. Those used for modulators and demodulators have curves the same shape as in Fig. 7–19, but maximum and minimum resistance values of about 40,000 ohms and 30 ohms respectively.

This control feature can be accomplished somewhat as follows: A comparatively large impressed voltage (or current), which may be controlled in magnitude, fixes the point of operation on the copper-oxide Varistor characteristic curve much the same as a grid-bias voltage fixes the point of operation on the characteristic curve of a vacuum tube. Then, the resistance (or impedance to be general) which the device offers to a smaller voltage, such as a speech signal, is readily controllable.

This principle is now used in carrier-telephone systems.[20] In these, copper-oxide Varistors, instead of vacuum tubes, are used for modulation and demodulation with excellent results. They are not used to any great extent in radio. One reason is that the capacitance between disks interferes with their operation at frequencies above several hundred thousand cycles per second.

Very little has been published[21] giving the detailed principles of operation. In one article the theory was described as a switching action.[22] More exactly, the Varistor units are arranged in a bridge circuit, the impressed carrier voltage is used to control the imped-ance of the path offered the

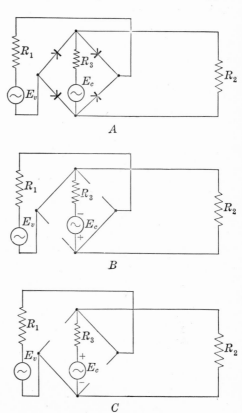

A

B

C

FIG. 11–14. In A is shown a simplified circuit of a copper-oxide bridge modulator. In B and C are shown the equivalent circuits with the polarities of the carrier voltage E_c as indicated. These equivalent circuits are based on the rectifier characteristics of Fig. 7–19, page 196. When the copper is positive and the oxide negative, the resistance is very high, and when the polarity is reversed, the resistance drops to a low value. For the special units used for modulation and demodulation (see page 328) in carrier telephone circuits, these variations may be from a maximum of about 40,000 ohms to a minimum of about 30 ohms.

voice frequencies, and as in the other types of modulation, the side bands desired to transmit the intelligence are created by a process of distortion.

Several systems of modulation with these Varistors have been perfected for use under different circuit requirements. Among these, one system suppresses the carrier frequency; another suppresses both the carrier and the voice; and a third suppresses the voice and transmits the carrier and the side bands. Only this latter system will be discussed, it being shown schematically in Fig. 11–14.

As previously mentioned, the carrier-frequency voltage is used to control the resistance of the path offered to the voice frequencies. Thus, referring to Fig. 7–19, page 196, when the polarity of the carrier frequency is as shown in Fig. 11–14B, the path offered the voice frequencies by the bridge circuit is, in effect, as indicated. When the polarity of the carrier is reversed during the next half cycle, the path offered the voice frequencies is as shown in Fig. 11–14C. Note that the path of the current through R_2 has been reversed. Of course Fig. 11–14C represents an exaggerated condition, because the resistance of the copper-oxide Varistor does not rise directly to infinity nor drop directly to zero, but in telephone circuits, which are of low impedance, this assumption is justified for an approximate analysis which will give results satisfactory for most purposes.

The current flowing through resistor R_2 represents the modulated output current flowing into the line for transmission to the distant station. This current is determined by the **transfer impedance** [1] between the source of voice-frequency voltage E_v and the load resistor R_2. It is in reality this transfer impedance which is controlled by the carrier frequency impressed on the bridge circuit. If it is assumed that the bridge circuit varies as indicated by B and C of Fig. 11–14, then, the transfer impedance between the source of audio voltage E_v and the load resistor R_2 varies as a rectangular wave between equal maximum positive and negative values.

The *maximum* value of the transfer impedance may be found as follows: The transfer impedance $Z_t = E_v/I_2$, where I_2 is the current through the resistor R_2 which represents the line (or load) to which modulated energy is to be fed. Thus, using either Fig. 11–14B or C, and assuming that the bridge elements are either of zero or infinite resistance, an expression for the current I_2 through R_2 is written, and when this is divided into E_v, the transfer impedance becomes

$$Z_t = \frac{(R_1R_2 + R_2R_3 + R_1R_3)}{R_3}. \tag{11–11}$$

For solving mathematically, it is more convenient to write the expression for the transfer admittance and use this instead of the transfer impedance. The transfer admittance merely is the reciprocal of the transfer impedance, and also varies between equal positive and negative maximum values in accordance with the impressed carrier frequency.

The equation for a rectangular recurring wave is

$$y = \frac{4Y}{\pi} \left(\sin \omega t + \frac{1}{3} \sin 3\omega t + \frac{1}{5} \sin 5\omega t + \cdots \right), \qquad (11\text{--}12)$$

where y is the instantaneous value and Y is the maximum value. For representing the variations in the admittance of the circuit, Y is the maximum value as explained in the preceding paragraph, and ωt becomes $\omega_c t$, and $\omega_c = 2\pi f_c$ where f_c is the carrier frequency. It is, therefore, possible to write an expression for the admittance of the circuit at any instant, as this circuit is varied at the carrier frequency rate.

The instantaneous expression for the voice frequency is

$$e_v = E_v \sin \omega_v t, \qquad (11\text{--}13)$$

where $\omega_v = 2\pi f_v$, and f_v is the voice frequency. When the expressions for the varying transfer admittance and the voice frequency voltage are multiplied, an equation is obtained for the instantaneous current through the load circuit R_2. In this equation will be found the upper and lower side band terms. These side bands have been created in the circuit by a process of distortion due to the varying admittance.

The use of copper-oxide Varistors for modulation and demodulation in carrier-telephone systems, and the generation of the carrier frequencies by magnetic means [23] mark a change of considerable importance in electrical communication. Formerly, both these functions were performed by vacuum tubes. The use of these Varistors in radio has, however, been limited by their capacitance and by their low power-handling ability.

Frequency Modulation.—All the methods of modulation previously considered in this chapter are defined as *amplitude modulation*, although it should be remembered that the process involves the *creation of new frequencies*. That is, the audio-frequency intelligence is translated to a new band of frequencies, created in the process of modulation.

It is possible to transmit intelligence electrically by *varying the frequency* [24] and maintaining the amplitude constant. This is termed **frequency modulation** and is the second of the three possible types of modulation discussed on page 310. Frequency modulation is not used in commercial systems and will be but briefly discussed.   A complete frequency-modulated transmitting and receiving radio system has been developed by Armstrong and described by him in a recent article [25] in which is listed the available literature on the subject.   An excellent discussion [10] is given by Terman from which the following is summarized:

When a sinusoidal audio-frequency signal is used to *frequency* modulate a carrier-frequency wave, the resultant wave would appear as follows: The *extent* (that is, the limits) of the frequency variation is determined by the *amplitude* of the audio-frequency signal.   The *number of times* per second the frequency is changed between these limits is determined by the *frequency* of the modulated wave.

To clarify these statements, assume that a 500-cycle audio frequency is used to frequency modulate a 1,000,000-cycle carrier.   This *could* be done by varying the transmitted frequency between 1,000,010 and 999,990 cycles 500 times per second.   If the amplitude of the audio wave were doubled, then the transmitted frequency would vary between 1,000,020 and 999,980 cycles 500 times per second.   For a 1000-cycle audio signal, the wave would vary 1000 times per second. One of the simplest methods of producing frequency modulation is to *vary the capacitance* of the tuned parallel circuit of the carrier-frequency oscillator at an audio-frequency rate.

An excellent summary of frequency modulation, giving many of the advantages and disadvantages, will be found in Reference 26.   The method of receiving these signals will be discussed on page 355.

Phase Modulation.—With this modulation process, the audio-frequency intelligence to be transmitted is made to vary the *phase* instead of the frequency of the carrier wave.[10, 24]   The amplitude remains constant.   No satisfactory means has been devised for demodulating phase-modulated waves.

The importance of phase modulation is that phase modulation (and also frequency modulation) often occur as unwanted by-products of *amplitude* modulation.   This adds undesired additional frequency components to the modulated wave, and these may result in distortion at the radio receiving set.[10]   Frequency modulation was common in the plate-modulated oscillator system (page 314).   This was because in these oscillators, the carrier frequency generated depended to some extent on the plate voltage, and this was caused to vary at an audio-frequency rate to effect the amplitude modulation.

107. Beat-Frequency Oscillators.—These were not considered in Chapter 10 because they involve the principle of modulation.   In this device two vacuum-tube circuits oscillate at slightly different frequencies; for example 100,000 and 101,000 cycles. These two voltages simultaneously are impressed on a *vacuum-tube modulator*, and sum and difference frequencies are created by the modulating or distorting process. The output of the modulator is connected to a low-pass filter which passes the lower side band. In the instance here considered this would be a 1000-cycle wave.

The words *vacuum-tube modulator* are stressed because it is often stated that the two frequencies are "beat together and the beat frequency is extracted by the detector tube." Such statements are meaningless, because merely "beating" two waves or "mixing them together" *does not create a new frequency* unless the process of modulation (distortion) is involved. This principle cannot be overstressed because it is seldom clearly understood and is the cause of much confusion.

The beat-frequency oscillator is an excellent device. Since the frequencies generated by the two oscillators are high, small coils and condensers can be used. Furthermore, since the frequency of one oscillator only need be changed, and this variation need be only a small per cent to cover the entire audio range, the frequency control is very simple. In most instances it is only necessary to vary the setting of an air condenser in one oscillating circuit. The frequency range can be made continuously variable, an important factor in many testing circuits. Also, the output voltage can be made substantially constant over the entire range.

REFERENCES

1. American Institute of Electrical Engineers. *Definitions of Electrical Terms.*
2. Institute of Radio Engineers. *Reports of the Standards Committee.*
3. Everitt, W. L. *Communication Engineering.* McGraw-Hill Book Co.
4. Albert, A. L. *Electrical Communication.* John Wiley & Sons.
5. Strieby, M. E. *A million-cycle telephone system.* Electrical Engineering, Jan., 1937, Vol. 56, No. 1.
6. Snow, W. B. *Audible frequency ranges of music, speech, and voice.* Jl. of the Acoustical Society of America, July, 1931, Vol. 3.
7. Pender, H., and McIlwain, K. *Electrical Engineers' Handbook.* Vol. 5, Electric Communication and Electronics. John Wiley & Sons.
8. Mathes, R. C., and Wright, S. B. *The "Compandor"—an aid against radio static.* Electrical Engineering, June, 1934, Vol. 53, No. 6.
9. Glasgow, R. S. *Principles of Radio Engineering.* McGraw-Hill Book Co.
10. Terman, F. E. *Radio Engineering.* McGraw-Hill Book Co.
11. Eastman, A. V. *Fundamentals of Vacuum Tubes.* McGraw-Hill Book Co.
12. Peterson, E., and Keith, C. R. *Grid current modulation.* Bell System Tech. Journal, Jan., 1928, Vol. 7, No. 1.

13. Van der Bijl, H. J. *The Thermionic Vacuum Tube and Its Applications.* McGraw-Hill Book Co.

14. American Radio Relay League. *The Radio Amateur's Handbook.*

15. Kishpaugh, A. W. *A low-power broadcast transmitter.* Bell Laboratories Record, Oct., 1932, Vol. 11, No. 2.

16. Colpitts, E. H., and Blackwell, O. B. *Carrier current telephony and telegraphy.* Trans. A.I.E.E., 1921, Vol. 40.

17. Affel, H. A., Demarest, C. S., and Green, C. W. *Carrier systems on long distance telephone lines.* Bell System Tech. Journal, July, 1928, Vol. 7, No. 3.

18. Mason, W. P. *Electrical wave filters employing quartz crystals as elements.* Bell System Tech. Journal, July, 1934, Vol. 13, No. 4.

19. Blake, G. G. *History of Radio Telegraphy and Telephony.* Chapman & Hall.

20. Chesnut, R. W., Ilgenfritz, L. M., and Kenner, A. *Cable Carrier-Telephone Terminals.* Electrical Engineering, May, 1938, Vol. 57, No. 5.

21. Hellmann, R. K. *The Modulator Bridge.* Electronics, March, 1938.

22. Blessing, E. C. *Modulation in the G–1 carrier system.* Bell Laboratories Record, March, 1937, Vol. 15, No. 7.

23. Peterson, E., Manley, J. M., and Wrathall, L. R. *Magnetic generation of a group of harmonics* Electrical Engineering, Aug., 1937, Vol. 56, No. 8.

24. Roder, Hans. *Amplitude, phase, and frequency modulation.* Proc. I.R.E., Dec., 1931, Vol. 19, No. 12.

25. Armstrong, E. H. *A method of reducing disturbances in radio signaling by a system of frequency modulation.* Proc. I.R.E., May, 1936, Vol. 24, No. 5.

26. *Phase-frequency modulation.* Electronics, November, 1935.

SUGGESTED ASSIGNMENTS

1. Prove the statement on page 313 regarding the power output for 100 per cent modulation, and the power on modulation peaks.
2. Explain the method of designing a modulator of the plate-modulated class C amplifier type. Illustrate with numerical calculations.
3. Explain why the modulating efficiency of the grid-modulated class C amplifier is lower than that of the plate-modulated class C amplifier.
4. Prepare a list of the various systems of modulation which have been either suggested or used.
5. Explain why it appears possible, with frequency-modulated signals, to obtain a higher signal-to-noise ratio.
6. Prove the statement, made on page 328, that any device in which a component of the output wave is proportional to the product of two input waves will cause modulation.

CHAPTER 12

DEMODULATORS

The preceding chapter was devoted to a study of modulation, a process by which the low-frequency audio signals are translated to higher-frequency bands for transmission over wires or through space to the distant receiving station. This chapter will consider the methods used at the receiving station for returning these translated signals to their original bands of low frequencies. This process is termed **demodulation**.

Demodulation is defined [1] as "the process whereby a wave resulting from modulation is so operated upon that a wave is obtained having substantially the characteristics of the original modulating wave." Demodulation is also defined [2] as "a term applied to the process of modulation when carried out in such a manner as to recover the original signal. In radio reception the term **detection** is commonly used for this process."

As this definition states, the term *detection* is commonly used in radio; *demodulation* is more widely used in wire transmission. Detection is defined [2] as "any process of operation on a modulated signal wave to obtain the signal imparted to it in the modulation process." The terms "rectification" and "rectifier" are often used in radio instead of detection and detectors. This usage is often misleading since it veils the true nature of the process of demodulation. In this connection, the standards [2] state that "in the reception of radio signals the term detector is preferred to rectifier."

In the following pages, only the terms demodulation and detection will be employed.

108. The Demodulation Process.—As was previously shown, a high-frequency carrier wave is modulated by the low-frequency audio signal voltage so that the intelligence may be translated to the high-frequency side bands. Then, these high-frequency bands conveying the intelligence can be *radiated effectively* from antennas, and *many messages* can be transmitted simultaneously through space or over the same wires. Demodulation is necessary to translate the intelligence back to the original audio-frequency band.

From this discussion it should *not* be inferred that demodulation is a process the reverse of, and therefore different from, modulation.

335

It is true that modulation translates the audio-frequency signals to a high-frequency band, and that the process of demodulation returns the signals to their original low-frequency band. Nevertheless, there are good reasons for assuming that *modulation and demodulation are merely different aspects of the same fundamental process* as will now be shown. This is indicated by the second definition of demodulation given in the preceding section.

In the process of *modulation*, new frequencies are created. Thus, if a 1000-cycle signal wave modulates a 20,000-cycle carrier wave, the upper side band of 21,000 cycles, and the lower side band of 19,000 cycles would be created. Now suppose that a 20,000-cycle carrier wave is modulated with a 19,000-cycle wave. An upper side band of 39,000 cycles, and a *lower side band of 1000 cycles will be created*. This is the original modulating frequency.

Suppose that this process is now applied to an actual audio-frequency speech signal varying from 250 to 2750 cycles per second for commercial carrier-frequency telephony. If a 20,000-cycle carrier is modulated, the audio frequencies will be translated to the upper side band of 20,250 to 22,750 cycles, and to the lower side band of 17,250 to 19,750 cycles. Of course other frequency bands are also created by the modulating or *distorting* process, but these are undesired and accordingly have been disregarded.

Suppose that all these spurious frequencies and the upper side band are suppressed, and that *only* the carrier and the lower side band are transmitted to the distant receiving station. Now suppose that at this point the 20,000-cycle carrier is "modulated" with the 17,250 to 19,750 cycle lower side band. In the distorted output, upper and lower side bands again will be created, together with unwanted frequencies. The upper side band will be a band of from 37,250 to 39,750 cycles, and the lower side band will be a band of from 250 to 2750 cycles. Thus, by the same fundamental process of modulation (or distortion), the intelligence is returned to the original *audible* frequencies.

From the preceding discussion, and from the definition given,[2] it is apparent that there is ample justification for considering modulation and demodulation (or detection) as the same fundamental processes. Thus, in a sense, there is no good reason for a separate treatment of demodulation. Such a treatment will be given, however, because certain of the systems extensively used for demodulation are not used for modulation. For instance, in radio, modulation often occurs at relatively high power levels, but demodulation occurs at low power levels.

109. Carrier and Side Band Suppression.—As has been stressed, after modulation the side bands, and *not* the carrier, contain the intelligence.   Furthermore, *each* side band is complete within itself, each containing the complete intelligence.   It is, therefore, possible to suppress all other frequencies in the modulated wave, *transmit only one side band*, and convey the message or program with complete satisfaction.   Such systems now will be discussed.   For a more complete treatment, Reference 3 should be consulted.

In the original type *A* carrier-telephone system [3] used commercially by the Bell System, the carrier was suppressed by the balanced-modulator system of Fig. 11–10 and *only one side band* was transmitted. The carrier frequency was supplied at the receiving end by an interesting harmonic producer (a vacuum tube operated so that it distorted) driven by a master oscillator transmitting a control frequency *throughout the entire system*.   From the preceding section it is apparent that a wave of the carrier frequency and at *least* one side band are necessary for demodulation.

In the type *B* carrier-telephone system,[3] *both the carrier and one side band* were transmitted.   Hence, no signal from a master oscillator need be transmitted throughout the system, and the harmonic producers were not necessary.

In the type *C* carrier-telephone system,[4] *only one side band* is transmitted.   The carrier frequency for demodulation is generated at each receiving point by a separate or local oscillator.   No master oscillator is required because more stable circuits are now available than when the first systems were designed.   The type *C* system is widely used today.

The discussions just given apply to carrier-telephone systems; however, carrier and side band suppression is also used in radio-telephone transmission systems such as are employed in transoceanic work. Thus, the original long-wave transatlantic radio-telephone system[5] transmitted *only one side band*, the carrier wave being supplied for demodulation by local oscillators.   With such an arrangement, a narrower frequency band is used than when the carrier and both side bands are employed.   Also, the power capacity of the expensive final amplifiers may be less because *the carrier* (which conveys no intelligence) and *one side band* are suppressed; all the power output is *useful* power.

In the first short-wave transatlantic systems,[6] the carrier and both side bands were transmitted.   One reason was because stable short-wave oscillators were difficult to construct for such high frequencies. In the later short-wave telephone systems,[7] the carrier is largely suppressed, only a small amount being transmitted for frequency-control purposes.

In no case is the carrier suppressed and the *two* side bands transmitted. If this were done, the carrier would need to be supplied for demodulation at *exactly* the correct *frequency* and *phase*. This would be impracticable. If only *one* side band is transmitted, then the phase relations are of no importance, and the frequency of the supplied carrier may vary slightly from the correct value [7, 8] without creating objectionable distortion.

110. Systems of Demodulation.—As has been pointed out, the process of demodulation or detection is, from a fundamental viewpoint, the same as the process of modulation. The details of the various systems of demodulation are somewhat different, however.

It should be expected that the systems of demodulation are classified much as for modulation, and this is true. Thus, for a triode, *modulation* was shown to occur in either the grid or the plate circuit. Similarly, systems of demodulation may be classified on this same basis. In the triode, demodulation may be caused by the non-linear grid voltage-grid current characteristic, or the non-linear grid voltage-plate current curve. As for modulators, any system of classification depends on the point of view.

The diode or two-electrode tube is not used as a modulator, but in recent years it has become widely used as a demodulator or detector. Its demodulating action is often referred to as one of rectification although this viewpoint is not entirely advisable (page 335).

If the true nature of rectification is understood, then regarding demodulation as a rectification process is not misleading. Thus, it was shown on page 178 that rectification of a 60-cycle power wave *is a process of distortion* in which a direct-current component and various alternating components are caused to exist in the rectified wave. Similarly, rectification (demodulation) of the modulated carrier wave (containing the side bands) results in *distortion* and in the creation of new components, among which is the *desired audio frequency*. This statement is true *no matter what system is used*, whether it be with crystals, copper-oxide rectifiers, diodes, or triodes. Furthermore, it is true for *all* types of *vacuum tube* demodulation. In *all* systems the desired audio-frequency component is *created* by making the demodulator distort the impressed wave containing the carrier and one or more side bands.

111. Detection with Crystals.—Many methods [9] have been used for demodulating or detecting radio-frequency signals. Early in the art, crystal detectors were employed. Both natural and artificial mineral crystals were used. Their operation depended on the fact that the current-voltage characteristic curve was asymmetrical (that is, non-symmetrical). The familiar galena crystal with a fine, light, "cat-whisker" contact is an example.

The current-voltage characteristic curve of a crystal used as a radio detector is shown in Fig. 12–1. If a radio-frequency voltage containing the carrier and the two side bands is impressed on the crystal, the current which flows will be distorted, and new frequencies will be created. Among these will be the desired audio-frequency component which can be separated from the undesired frequencies and used to operate a telephone receiver. Such systems of demodulation are quite limited in application and there seems no reason to give them further consideration.

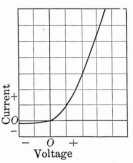

FIG. 12–1. Characteristics of a crystal detector.

Copper-Oxide Demodulators.—Starting on page 328, modulation by copper-oxide Varistors was discussed in considerable detail. As has been previously stressed, modulation and demodulation may be regarded as the same fundamental process of distortion and frequency translation. This viewpoint is particularly applicable to carrier-telephone systems, where modulating and demodulating equipment is so closely alike. It is, therefore, unnecessary to consider further demodulation by copper-oxide means, the theory as previously given for modulators applying to demodulators as well.

In some of the carrier systems the *same* copper-oxide Varistor serves both as a modulator and as a demodulator at the terminal. Where this dual function is performed, the device is known as a **Modem** unit. Although some attempts have been made (see Proc. I. R. E., Oct., 1932) to use copper-oxide units for radio detection, they have not achieved wide use for this purpose.

112. Diode Detection.—The principle of the two-electrode thermionic vacuum tube or diode was discovered by Edison in 1883, but it was not until 1904, when Fleming used it as a detector, that it became of importance. The diode was soon supplanted by the triode for demodulation, and was not used for this purpose for many years. It is, however, now widely used as a detector in modern radio-broadcast receiving sets. Although the diode does not amplify when used as a detector, and although it takes power from the source driving it, the distortion resulting from its use is generally lower than with other demodulators. Furthermore, automatic volume-control voltages may be obtained from diode detectors (page 343).

The circuit of the diode detector [10] is illustrated by Fig. 12–2. The modulated radio-frequency signal E_{rf} containing the carrier and

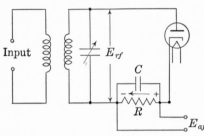

the side bands is impressed as indicated. If the condenser C has a capacitance of about 0.0001 microfarad, the reactance to radio frequencies will be low. The resistor R is often 0.5 megohm. The characteristic curve for a typical diode is as shown in Fig. 12–3. It will be observed that this curve is similar to that for a crystal. Thus,

Fig. 12–2. Simplified circuit of a diode detector.

when the modulated radio-frequency signal is impressed on the tube, the plate current will be distorted.

In this distorted current exist three components of special interest. *First*, there will be radio-frequency components; *second*, audio-frequency components; and *third*, a rectified or direct component. The radio-frequency components readily will pass through the condenser C, and negligible radio-frequency voltage will exist across R. Another way of interpreting the use of the condenser C is to say it causes negligible radio-frequency drop and hence the entire voltage E_{rf} is impressed across the tube. The drop across R will therefore be a direct voltage on which is superimposed the alternating audio-frequency component. This audio voltage E_{af} is the desired product of demodulation, and it is amplified in an audio-frequency amplifier and then used to drive the loud speaker.

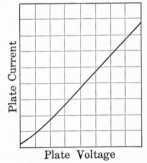

Fig. 12–3. Approximate shape of a diode characteristic curve.

Triodes may be used for diode detection in circuits similar to Fig. 12–2. There are two possible arrangements; in the *first*, the control grid is connected directly to the plate, giving the characteristics of a two-electrode tube. In the *second*, the cathode and plate are connected. This second method has the advantage of the plate acting as an internal shield since the cathode is at ground potential.

The circuit of Fig. 12–2 is of a **half-wave diode detector.** The diode tubes ordinarily employed are usually constructed with *two* anodes or plates. Thus, **full-wave diode detection** is possible. This offers certain possibilities such as requiring (theoretically) no radio-frequency filtering in the output circuit, because the carrier-frequency components, which are no longer needed, can be balanced out in the full-wave detector.

In practice, however, the advantages of full-wave detection usually do not justify the additional circuit complications.[11] Since this system is not so widely used as the half-wave type, it will not be further discussed. The two plates previously mentioned are often tied together for half-wave detection. Or, one plate may be used for a detector and the other for automatic volume-control purposes.[11] The tubes usually employed are of the multi-electrode type. These contain a diode unit, and either a triode, a tetrode, or a pentode unit in the same envelope. The diode portion is used for demodulation, and the other part for amplification of the demodulated audio-frequency signal.

113. Automatic Volume Control.—Although the *power radiated* from the antenna of a radio transmitter may be held at a *constant average value* (of course, it varies instantaneously due to modulation peaks caused by variations in the speech or program currents), the voltage induced in the antenna of a receiving set is not constant. This induced voltage will be found to change due to variations in the space transmission paths from the transmitting to the receiving antenna. The term *paths* was used because a received signal may be composed of two components which have traveled different paths from the transmitter to the receiver. One is the **ground-wave component,** and the other the **sky-wave component** (or components).

The first of these has traveled directly along the surface of the earth; the second has traveled upward from the transmitting antenna and has been reflected back to the surface of the earth from the ionized Kennelly-Heaviside layer (or layers) in the upper atmosphere. The paths traveled are different, and hence the phase relations of the two received components are not the same. Furthermore, variations in the ionized layer cause changes in the reflected component. This combined action of the ground and sky waves is to cause fluctuations in the strength of the radio-frequency voltage induced in the antenna, resulting in continual fluctuations in the received message or program. This is called **fading.**

Circuits which automatically control the amplification of the received signal have been developed. These **automatic volume–control circuits** (a.v.c.) maintain the strength of the demodulated signal at an approximately constant value. Although such circuits can control the volume, they do not compensate for distortion which often accompanies fading.

Automatic volume-control circuits are of two general types: *first,* those employing a separate volume-control tube, and *second,* those in which the diode detector also acts as a volume-control tube. One of the important reasons for using diode detectors is that they are so well suited for automatic volume control.

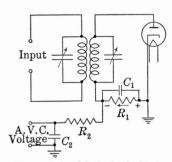

FIG. 12–4. Method of obtaining an automatic volume-control voltage using a separate volume-control tube.

Circuits.—A circuit [11] of the first type is shown in Fig. 12–4. The purpose of this tube and the associated circuit is to provide a direct voltage which will *increase* when a strong radio-frequency signal voltage is induced in the antenna, and which will *decrease* when the signal fades and the induced voltage becomes less.

This direct voltage is then used as a bias for the variable-mu or super-control radio-frequency and intermediate-frequency amplifier tubes (page 172). When a strong signal is received a high bias will be put on the grids of these tubes, and the point of operation of each tube will be shifted to the portion of the curve (Fig. 6–31) where the amplification is low. When a weak voltage is received the point of operation will be shifted back to the region where the amplification is high. In this way, variations in the modulated carrier voltage impressed on the detector tube are largely prevented, and the message or program, as reproduced by the loud speaker, will not fade as variations in the space transmission paths occur.

By the rectifying action of the diode of Fig. 12–4, a *direct-current* component, proportional to the strength of the received signal, will flow through the resistor R_1. Radio-frequency (or intermediate frequency, page 358) and audio-frequency variations also will exist across R_1. It is desired only to use the relatively slow variations (due to fading) of the voltage drop across R_1 for biasing the super-control tubes. This bias voltage is taken off as indicated. Because of the high resistance of R_2, the condenser C_2 can charge and discharge only at a very slow rate. The automatic volume control bias voltage will accordingly follow only the variations due to fading, and the radio-frequency and audio-frequency components will be effectively filtered and prevented from reaching the grids of the radio-frequency amplifier tubes.

In the circuit of Fig. 12–4 a bias is applied to the grids as soon as a signal is received. This would immediately lower the gain on the radio-frequency and intermediate-frequency amplifiers. It may be desired to keep the gain of these as high as possible for the weak signals, however, and this is done with **delayed automatic volume-control circuits.**[11]

Detection and Automatic Volume Control.—As mentioned on page 342, in some systems the *detector* tube also supplies the automatic volume-control biasing voltage. One such circuit, using a duplex-diode triode tube is shown in Fig. 12–5. As explained on page 340, the condenser C_1 offers a low-impedance path for the radio-frequency components. The rectified plate current of the diode unit will flow (conventional direction)

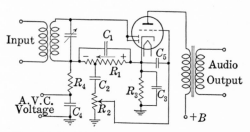

Fig. 12–5. Method of obtaining an automatic volume-control voltage from the diode detector tube.

through the resistor R_1 as indicated. This rectified pulsating current will contain a direct-current component and an audio-frequency component, and will also fluctuate, rather slowly, due to fading.

A voltage for the grid of the triode unit is tapped off where desired. The condenser C_2 permits alternating current only to flow and hence impresses only the audio-frequency voltage variations on the grid of the triode amplifier. The variable voltage divider R_2 serves as a *manual* volume control. The grid of the triode amplifying unit is biased by the self-biasing resistor and condenser arrangement in the cathode circuit (page 202). The condenser C_5 is to by-pass radio-frequency currents to the cathode and thus prevent their further amplification. For duplex-diode tetrodes and pentodes, resistance coupling, instead of transformer coupling, would be used.

As previously stated, the voltage drop across R_1 also varies with the received signal strength. Thus, when there is little fading, the signal will be strong, the rectified current will increase, and the point of contact of R_1 and R_4 will be *more* negative. When fading is bad, this point will be *less* negative. As explained in the preceding section, these variations are relatively slow (compared to the audio-frequency components) and cause the relatively large condenser C_4 slowly to charge and discharge through R_4. The voltage across this condenser provides the automatic volume-control bias voltage for the variable-mu or super-control radio-frequency and intermediate-frequency amplifier tubes.

As previously stated, this is a **self-biased circuit.** It is also possible to have the bias furnished by the diode itself as in the **diode-biased circuit.** This system is not suited for *combined* demodulation and automatic volume-control purposes.[11]

Attention is called to the fact that in all the circuits which have been considered the automatic volume-control voltages are applied to the radio-frequency or intermediate-frequency tubes (or to both) and not to the audio-frequency amplifying tubes. It is desired that the control systems *hold constant* the radio-frequency or intermediate-frequency voltage impressed on the demodulator tube. The dual wording radio frequency and intermediate frequency (page 358) has been necessary because of the wide variety of circuits used. Reference 11 is especially recommended to those desiring additional information. Excellent discussions will also be found in References 8, 12, and 13, which also give extensive listings of the literature available on the subject.

114. Triode Plate-Circuit Square-Law Detection.—With this system, demodulation occurs *in the plate circuit* because the modulated radio-frequency signal is impressed on the non-linear portion of the grid-voltage plate-current curve. This distorts the impressed signal and thus the desired audio-frequency voltage exists in the output. The output is proportional to the *square* of the impressed voltage, hence the name. It has been selected as the first type of triode detection to be explained because it so well illustrates the process and parallels the explanation of modulation given on page 322. This system is also called **weak-signal plate detection.**

The circuit of Fig. 12–6, chosen to illustrate plate-circuit square-law detection, is that employed in a carrier-telephone system. In this particular circuit both the carrier and one side band are suppressed. In this instance, assume that at the sending end a 1000-cycle sine wave is being used to modulate a 20,000-cycle carrier, and that only the upper side band is transmitted. This will be a sinusoidal 21,000-cycle impulse as shown by curve *A*.

As the circuit shows, and as was explained on page 336, the carrier illustrated by *B* of Fig. 12–6 must be introduced for demodulation. When this is done, the alternating potential of the grid will be as shown by *C* which represents the conventional "amplitude-modulated" wave. The tube is so biased that operation is on the curved part of the plate current-grid voltage curve of Fig. 12–7. The plate current accordingly will vary as curve *D*, and this current will contain, along with other frequencies, the desired audio-frequency component.   This plate current D will induce a voltage E in the secondary of the output transformer.   The low-pass filter suppresses all components but the desired audio component F which flows to the receiver.

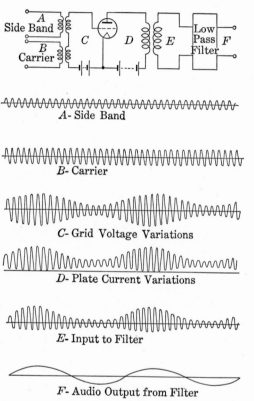

A- Side Band

B- Carrier

C- Grid Voltage Variations

D- Plate Current Variations

E- Input to Filter

F- Audio Output from Filter

Fig. 12–6.   Illustrating plate-circuit square-law detection.

Analysis of Plate-Circuit Square-Law Detection.—As was mentioned on page 324, over the *lower curved portion* of the grid voltage-plate current curve of Fig. 12–7, the plate current may approximately be represented by the power series

$$I_p = ae_g + be_g^2 + \cdots. \tag{12–1}$$

Thus, for the condition of Fig. 12–7 this equation applies, provided that the *strength* of the impressed signals *is low*.   This being the case, plate-circuit square-law detection or *demodulation* can be explained as for modulation on page 324.

Thus, if f_1 represents the carrier, and f_2 the voice, then the upper side band $(f_1 + f_2)$ and the carrier f_1 are simultaneously impressed as voltages on the grid of the tube of Fig. 12–6. If the substitutions and

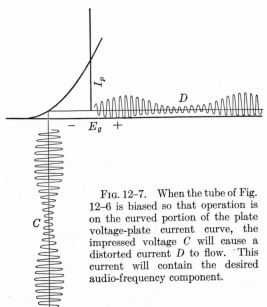

FIG. 12–7. When the tube of Fig. 12–6 is biased so that operation is on the curved portion of the plate voltage-plate current curve, the impressed voltage C will cause a distorted current D to flow. This current will contain the desired audio-frequency component.

expansions are made as on page 324, then it will be found that a component $(f_1 + f_2) - f_1$ exists in the output. This is the desired audio component. Although in this analysis a single-frequency was used to represent the audio-frequency band, the principles apply to the practical problem.

This method of weak signal demodulation has been widely used in carrier-telephone systems [3, 4] operating over land lines. The method is simple and reliable in operation, well adapted for commercial telephone operation. Furthermore, in telephone circuits the voltages and power levels are not so high as in radio-receiving sets where loud speakers must be operated. With this method, amplification as well as demodulation of the signal occurs. (Amplification does not occur in *diodes*, but this is no longer objectionable in radio because of the high voltage gains which can be readily obtained from pentodes.)

With any type of square-law detection much distortion occurs. In telephone systems greater distortion can be tolerated than in the reception of radio programs. Square-law detection is not suited for demodulation in modern radio-receiving sets which must handle 100 per cent modulation. It can be shown that with square-law detection

25 per cent second-harmonic distortion will result for a completely-modulated signal such as would be radiated from a modern broadcast transmitter on modulation peaks.

115. Triode Plate-Circuit Linear Detection.—With this system, the grid of the detector tube is biased about to cut-off, so that the plate current is substantially zero when no signal is applied to the grid. The distortion and resulting demodulation occur *in the plate circuit.* It is apparent that its operation is closely that of a class *B* amplifier. The grid should not be driven positive unless the preceding amplifier can supply, with good regulation, the required power when grid current flows in the detector tube.

This method of detection is known as **power detection,** and also as **linear plate detection.**   Much *larger* radio-frequency or intermediate-frequency voltages for demodulation are impressed on the grid of the tube in this system than for the square-law detector just considered, and a greater output results.   This accounts for the term *power* detection.   The output of this detector is proportional to the magnitude of the impressed signal (instead of the square); hence, the term *linear* detection.   The *sensitivity* of linear detectors is accordingly less than that of square-law detectors, but the distortion is very much less on the highly-modulated signals now in use to increase the effective service area of a broadcast station.   As previously mentioned, high sensitivity is no longer so important because of the high-gain pentodes available for voltage amplification.

An arrangement for plate-circuit linear detection using a triode is shown in Fig. 12–8.   The high negative grid bias is obtained from the

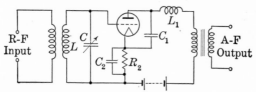

Fig. 12–8.   Circuit for triode plate-circuit linear detection.

self-biasing arrangement $R_2 - C_2$ in the cathode circuit.   The radio-frequency choke coil L_1 and the condenser C_1 form a high-frequency filter, allowing only low-frequency components to pass through the transformer in the plate circuit.   The modulated carrier signal of radio frequency is impressed on the circuit $L - C$.   This wave is distorted in the detector circuit owing to its non-symmetrical grid voltage-plate current characteristics (see next paragraph), and the desired audio-frequency component is created in this demodulation process.

This audio-frequency plate-current component induces an audio-frequency voltage in the output circuit.

As in much vacuum-tube work, a mathematical analysis of plate-circuit linear detection is somewhat difficult and not entirely necessary, a graphical and experimental study being a more practicable approach. The diagram of Fig. 12–9 can be used to study this method of demodulating the signal containing the carrier and the side bands. Curve *A* is the input signal voltage, and *B* is the distorted plate current con-

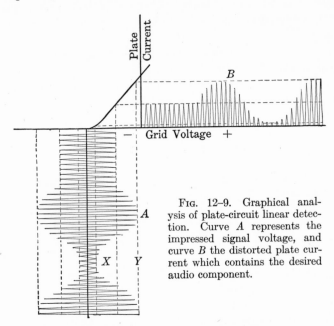

Fig. 12–9. Graphical analysis of plate-circuit linear detection. Curve *A* represents the impressed signal voltage, and curve *B* the distorted plate current which contains the desired audio component.

taining the demodulated audio component. If the degree of modulation is such that the *envelope* of the radio-frequency signal lies between the limits *x* and *y*, operation will be over the *linear* part of the dynamic curve and little distortion of the *audio* component will result. When modulation approaches 100 per cent, however, then considerable audio distortion will be produced because the lower end of the curve is *not* linear. This method is, therefore, best suited for demodulation of *large signals* with somewhat *less than 100 per cent* modulation. The advantage of an automatic volume control to hold the impressed signal voltage at a large value is apparent.

Pentodes and tetrodes are also used as linear plate-circuit detectors. Although they are more sensitive, they may produce greater distortion than triodes. The method of demodulation discussed in this section is fully covered by Ballantine in Reference 14.   Much design data will be found in References 8 and 15.

116. Triode Grid-Circuit Square-Law Detection.—With this system, demodulation occurs *in the grid circuit*. Adjustments are made so that grid current flows, and so that distortion is caused by the non-linear *grid voltage-grid current* characteristic. Owing to this distortion, demodulation occurs and the desired audio-frequency component is created. This audio signal is then impressed between the grid and cathode, and is amplified in the plate circuit. The term **square-law detection** is applied because operation is over the non-linear portion, and the output is proportional to the *square* of the impressed voltage. Various other names such as **grid leak-condenser method** and **grid-current detection** also are applied.

A circuit for grid-circuit, square-law detection is shown in Fig. 12–10. The grid resistor R_g or **grid leak** is usually several million

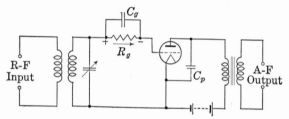

Fig. 12–10.   Circuit for grid-current square-law detection.

ohms, and the grid condenser C_g about 250 micromicrofarads. No *external* battery or other method is used to bias the grid of the tube. The grid return is connected directly to the cathode in separate-heater tubes, or to the positive terminal in filament-type tubes.

As was shown on page 125, grid current flows in a triode even when the *grid is slightly negative*, due to the initial velocity of the electrons as they are thrown off by the heated cathode. A positive potential on the plate accelerates the electrons in the space-charge region, and will increase this current. Thus, referring to Fig. 12–11, with *no radiofrequency signal* on the grid, the grid potential will *be less* than indicated by the value for point *x*. The *conventional* direction of this current is from the grid to the cathode; therefore an *IR* drop is caused across the grid resistor R_g and the *grid is made negative*.

When an *unmodulated* radio-frequency carrier signal is received, some rectification will occur and the grid current will increase. This will make the grid more negative, and will determine the point of operation *x* on the grid voltage-grid current curve of Fig. 12–11.

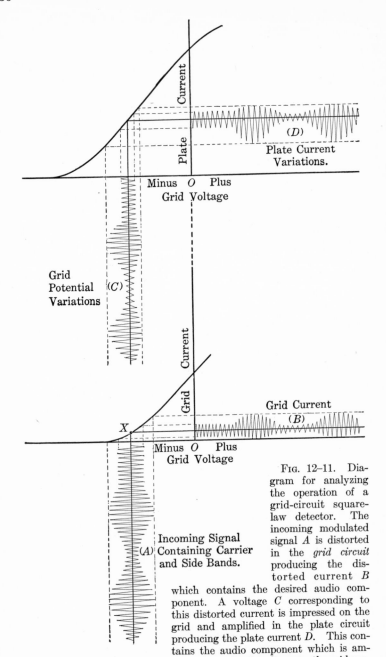

F$_{IG}$. 12–11. Diagram for analyzing the operation of a grid-circuit square-law detector. The incoming modulated signal A is distorted in the *grid circuit* producing the distorted current B which contains the desired audio component. A voltage C corresponding to this distorted current is impressed on the grid and amplified in the plate circuit producing the plate current D. This contains the audio component which is amplified and then drives the loud speaker. In this diagram, the grid current would be in microamperes and the plate current in milliamperes.

When the received signal A is *modulated*, then the resulting grid current will be distorted as indicated by curve B. In this distorted current will exist radio-frequency components and the *desired audio-frequency component*. As for square-law plate-circuit detection, an expression such as equation 11–5, page 324, can be used to analyze this process of demodulation.

It is now necessary to explain the function of the grid condenser of Fig. 12–10. If the condenser C_g did not shunt the resistor R_g, then most of the radio-frequency *voltage* induced in the secondary of the radio-frequency transformer would be lost in forcing the radio-frequency current through the high resistor R_g. Nevertheless, a distorted current would flow and *some* demodulation would occur; the process would be very inefficient, however. With a condenser C_g (which has in comparison a *low* reactance to the radio-frequency components, but a *high* reactance to the desired audio-frequency components) connected across the grid circuit resistor R_g of Fig. 12–10, the following operation occurs.

The desired *audio-frequency* component causes a large voltage drop across the circuit composed of the condenser C_g and the resistor R_g in parallel, but the radio-frequency components do not. This means that in addition to the instantaneous potential variations of the grid caused by the *impressed modulated carrier* (composed of the carrier and the two side bands), the grid potential will also vary with *the desired audio-frequency component*. This audio signal has been "generated" in the grid circuit due to the non-linear grid voltage-grid current curve. Other undesirable components also are generated (equation 11–10). The condenser C_g offers a high impedance to the desired audio component, but not to the high frequencies; [15] the audio component is, accordingly, amplified.

Thus, the potential of the grid will vary somewhat as in curve C of Fig. 12–11, in a manner determined by the audio frequency and the modulated carrier components. These variations will be amplified by the tube.* The corresponding plate current variations will be as in D. Note in particular that the *direction* of the voltage drop across the parallel circuit $C_g - R_g$ is such that increases in *grid* current cause *decreases* in plate current. The high-frequency components are by-passed by the condenser C_p in the plate circuit, and the desired audio-frequency current induces a voltage in the secondary of the transformer for audio-frequency amplification.

---

* It appears that since the condenser C_g does not offer a load impedance to the high-frequency distortion components generated in the grid circuit, the grid-voltage variations C should not vary *exactly* as the grid-current B; this apparently has not been experimentally determined.

From this analysis it appears that the purpose of the condenser is as follows: *First*, to provide a *low-impedance path for the radio frequencies* so that a large percentage of the received signal reaches the grid, and *second* to offer a *high impedance to the audio-frequency component* of the distorted grid current so that an audio-frequency voltage also will be impressed on the grid. The purpose of the resistor is to bias the tube. Obviously, the tube could not be operated with a "free" grid as would result if only the condenser C_g were present. It is important to note that power is taken by the grid circuit.

As with the plate-circuit square-law detector, distortion is excessive when the received radio signals are highly modulated as with modern broadcast transmitters. Thus, this type detection is not widely used, although prior to about 1930 it was almost the universal method. It has been extensively studied by Terman, and Reference 16 especially is recommended to those interested in further studying the subject. Much valuable information also will be found in References 8, 15, and 17.

117. Triode Grid-Circuit Linear Detection.—In the detector just considered, *weak* signals were impressed on the non-linear portion of the grid voltage-grid current curve. The grid current which flowed was distorted and contained the desired audio-frequency component, thus effecting the demodulation process. The output was proportional to the *square* of the input voltage, hence the term square-law detection.

In the **grid-circuit** or **grid-current linear detector,** now to be considered, a *much larger* radio-frequency signal voltage is impressed on the grid, five volts or more being common. The circuit operates as a *linear* detector, the demodulated audio-frequency component being proportional to the *magnitude* of the impressed radio signal. This is also called **grid-leak power detection.** Linear detection is not so sensitive as square-law detection, but in general less distortion is produced.

The circuit for grid-circuit linear detector is almost the same as for the square-law detector of Fig. 12–10. The essential difference is that *first*, the grid resistor is smaller, being only about 1/4 megohm instead of several megohms; *second*, the grid condenser is smaller, being about 100 micromicrofarads; and *third*, the voltage impressed is much larger as mentioned in the preceding paragraph. Since the circuits are substantially the same, it should be expected that the operation of the two methods of detection would be similar, and this is true.

Referring to Fig. 12–12 the operation of the grid-circuit linear detector may be explained as follows: With *no* radio-frequency signal

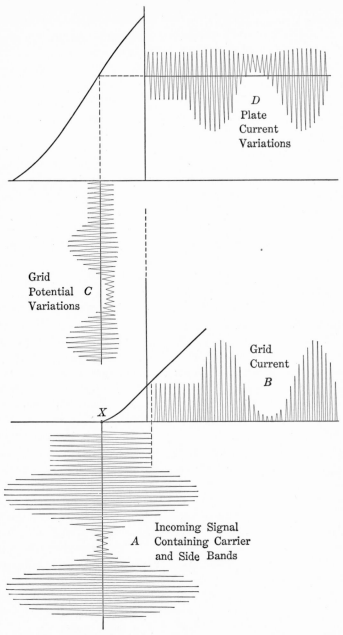

Fig. 12–12.   Diagram for analyzing the operation of a grid-circuit linear detector.   The grid-current values would be measured in microamperes and the plate-
current values would be in milliamperes.

on the grid, some direct current would flow (as explained in the preceding section). This will bias the grid negatively. If now an *unmodulated carrier* is being received, this carrier will be rectified (or distorted) and the direct current flowing in the grid circuit will be increased, thus biasing the tube more negatively to some point x.

When the signal *is modulated*, the voltage impressed on the circuit for demodulation will be as indicated by A. This will cause a grid current B to flow. This *distorted* grid current contains many components, among which are the following: a *direct-current* component; *radio-frequency* components; and the desired *audio-frequency* component. The direct-current component will flow through the grid resistor and will cause the tube to be biased the desired amount. Although this grid resistor is smaller than for square-law detection, the current is much higher because the impressed signal is larger, and thus the tube is biased to the point where *grid current* flows only during the positive half cycles. The condenser C_g will offer a low impedance to the radio-frequency components, and hence but little radio-frequency voltage drop will occur across the circuit composed of R_g and C_g in parallel. A high impedance will be offered the audio component, however, and thus a *large* audio-frequency voltage drop will exist across the R_g–C_g combination.

As a result of this combined action, the potential of the grid *before* and *after* modulation is as indicated. These potential variations of the grid will be amplified and the plate current will flow as indicated by D. The high-frequency components will be by-passed by the condenser C_p, and the desired audio-frequency current will flow through the primary of the transformer inducing an audio voltage (to be further amplified) in the secondary. As is apparent, the plate circuit of the tube, for both square law and linear detection, functions merely as an amplifier.

Attention is directed to the peculiar shape of the grid potential variations shown by curve C of Fig. 12–12. This can be explained [16] on the basis of the instantaneous and average potential values of the charge on the grid condenser. Or, this grid voltage can be considered as composed of a direct-voltage value upon which are superimposed alternating-voltage components. This method [15] is very helpful.

As previously explained, the grid condenser C_g allows almost the entire signal voltage composed of the carrier and the side bands to reach the grid. A distorted grid current, containing the desired audio-frequency components, flows. This current also contains other alternating terms as well. The grid condenser C_g in parallel with the grid resistor R_g offers a high impedance to the desired audio component.   There is *no load impedance* in the circuit for the various high-frequency components which are generated by distortion in the grid circuit.   Thus, the grid potential as shown by curve C largely consists of the carrier and the side bands (to which the tuned input circuit offers high impedance) and the desired audio-frequency component voltage which is produced across $C_g - R_g$.

The action of the grid-circuit linear detector also can be explained in a manner *similar* to the grid-circuit *modulator* of page 326.   Thus, during the *negative* half cycles *no grid current flows*, and the signal voltage impressed *on the grid* is substantially that induced in the secondary of the input coil.   During *positive* half cycles *grid current flows*, there is a voltage drop across the grid resistor-grid condenser combination, and the voltage impressed *on the grid* drops.   Thus, the potential *of the grid* varies somewhat as shown by curve C of Fig. 12–12.

118. Further Classification of Detectors.—Now that the action of vacuum-tube detectors has been explained, a classification [15] made by Everitt will be given.   This classification is of considerable importance.

Class 1.   Driving-Point Impedance Detectors.—The distortion produced and thus the detector action depends on the *non-linear* relation between the voltage applied across a pair of terminals and the current through the *same* terminals.   An external *linear impedance,* such as a resistor and condenser in parallel, must be connected in series with the non-linear element.   The desired demodulated component causes a voltage drop across this impedance, and this voltage is then amplified.   Examples of this type detector are the crystal, the copper oxide rectifier, the diode, and the grid-circuit detector.

Class 2.   Transfer-Impedance Detectors.—The distortion produced and thus the detector action depends on the *non-linear* relation between the voltage applied to one circuit and the current which flows through an impedance connected in another circuit.   An example is the plate-circuit detector in which the signal voltage to be demodulated is applied to a highly-biased grid circuit and a distorted current (containing the desired components) flows through an impedance connected in the load circuit.

119. Detection of Frequency-Modulated Waves.—Methods of transmitting intelligence by frequency-modulated signals were discussed on page 331.   To receive such signals, two steps are necessary. *First,* the *frequency-modulated* impulses must be converted to *amplitude-modulated* signals; *second,* these must be demodulated by ordinary methods and the original audio-frequency component produced.   Two methods [18] of converting from frequency-modulated to amplitude-modulated signals have been devised.　Only one system will be here discussed.

The principles involved in the detection of frequency-modulated waves are essentially as follows: In these waves, the *frequency* of the output from the antenna is varying between maximum and minimum values at a *rate* depending on the frequency of the wave to be transmitted.　For the 500-cycle audio signal considered on page 332, the *frequency* of the received signal would vary between maximum and minimum values 500 times per second.　For a given *degree* of modulation, the maximum value *could be* 1,000,020 and the minimum value 999,980 cycles per second.　The problem is to convert these *frequency* variations to voltage *amplitude* variations, so that the resulting amplitude-modulated wave can be demodulated by the ordinary methods as previously explained in this chapter.

To accomplish this, the frequency-modulated wave is passed through a single *series-resonant* circuit which is made resonant to the center of the band transmitted; that is, to 1,000,000 cycles per second for the conditions on page 332.　The *magnitude* of the current through the resonant circuit is *held constant*.　Then for *no* (frequency) modulation, the *combined* voltage across the *inductance* and *capacitance* in the series resonant circuit will be zero.　But, when the received signal is *frequency* modulated, and the constant (magnitude) current through the resonant circuit varies as previously explained, a resultant voltage *will exist* across the inductance and capacitance.　The *magnitude* of this resultant voltage will be determined by the frequency limits of the waves (1,000,020 to 999,980 cycles) and the *frequency* by the rate (500 cycles) at which the (constant) current through the resonant circuit changes.

By this means, an *amplitude-modulated* wave containing the desired frequency components is created from the *frequency-modulated* wave which was transmitted and received.　This wave is then demodulated to give the desired audio-frequency message or program components. The interesting details of these processes and the circuits used are given in Reference 18.

120. Speech Inversion.—One of the important requirements of any system of communication is *secrecy*, and this must be possible with radio as well as with wire systems.　Of course, with telegraph messages, codes can be, and are, extensively used, but this method of obtaining secrecy is not well suited to speech transmission.　It is apparent that if ordinary broadcast methods were used in transmitting transoceanic radio-telephone conversations, the lack of secrecy would render the system almost valueless.

Secrecy methods of several types [13] have been developed; these include a **frequency inverting** or **speech scrambling process** which will now be considered. Although the details may differ with various systems,[8, 15, 16] the process is somewhat as follows: Suppose that a 50,000-cycle wave is modulated with a 3000-cycle wave, and that the *lower side band only* is selected with a filter. The output of the filter will be a 47,000-cycle impulse. Now suppose this 47,000-cycle wave and a 42,000-cycle wave are impressed on a modulator and the *lower* side band *only* is selected by a filter. The output of this second filter will be a 5000-cycle wave. By the same process, if the original 50,000-cycle wave is modulated by 200 cycles, the output of the *second* filter will be a 7800-cycle impulse.

To apply this to an audio-frequency wave, assume that the 50,000-cycle wave is modulated by the voice which is considered in this instance to contain frequency components from 200 to 3000 cycles. By the double-modulation system just described, the low-frequency components of 200 cycles will be high-frequency components of 7800 cycles, and the high-frequency components of 3000 cycles will become the low-frequency components of 5000 cycles in the *output of the second filter*. In this wave the speech is *inverted* or *scrambled*, and the conversation is unintelligible except to those equipped with special apparatus for re-inverting the frequencies.

The frequencies just considered would be suited for secrecy operation over wire lines; for radio transmission the inverted band would need to exist at higher frequencies for effective radiation. It is apparent that the system could be adjusted at intervals so that the frequency bands would be changed and reception rendered even more difficult. For making reception still more difficult, the inverted frequencies could be divided into several groups and each of these could be transmitted at different wavelengths.

121. Radio Receiving Sets.—*Tuned Radio-Frequency Amplifier (TRF)*.—To illustrate the application of certain of the principles discussed in the preceding chapters, a tuned radio-frequency set for broadcast reception will be considered. The superheterodyne will be discussed below. The tuned radio-frequency set is not so extensively used as formerly.

A block diagram of a typical tuned radio-frequency set is shown in Fig. 12–13. The name is derived from the fact that the *selectivity* of the set depends on the tuned voltage amplifiers indicated. This part of the radio-receiving set is often a three-stage transformer-coupled radio-frequency amplifier using suppressor-grid voltage-amplifying pentodes. Its purpose is to amplify the weak signal voltage, composed of the carrier and the two side bands, until it is sufficient for demodulation in the so-called detector.

In a typical receiving set, a duplex-diode triode would probably be used, with demodulation and automatic volume control being accomplished in the diode portion, and audio-frequency voltage amplification

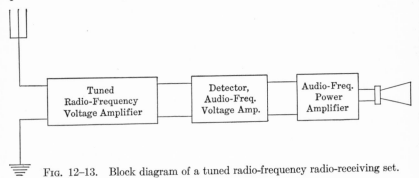

Fig. 12–13.   Block diagram of a tuned radio-frequency radio-receiving set.

in the triode unit.   This amplified audio-frequency voltage is then used to drive the audio-frequency power amplifier, the output of which in turn drives the loud speaker.

Superheterodyne Sets.—This is also called a **double-detection receiving set,** but neither this term nor "superheterodyne" is very descriptive of the principle of operation.   This set has largely supplanted the tuned radio-frequency receiver previously considered. The reasons for this will be made clear after the operation of the superheterodyne has been explained.

A block diagram of the circuit arrangement is given in Fig. **12–14.** In most of the better sets, at least one tuned radio-frequency voltage-amplifying stage is connected to the antenna.   This stage increases the sensitivity and selectivity and otherwise improves operation, especially in suppressing **image frequencies.**[13, 15]

The purpose of the so-called first detector is to translate the received radio-frequency signal, consisting of the carrier and the two side bands, to a lower or **intermediate frequency.**   The reasons for this will be discussed later.   This translation of the radio-frequency signal to an intermediate-frequency signal is accomplished as follows: Suppose that the radio-frequency signal being received is a 1,000,000-cycle carrier, the upper side band of 1,000,100 to 1,005,000 cycles, and the lower side band of 995,000 to 999,900 cycles.   This voltage, occupying a frequency band of from 995,000 to 1,005,000 cycles, is used to *modulate* a frequency (from the local oscillator) of 1,465,000 cycles per second in the so-called "first detector."   By this *distortion* process, sum and difference frequencies or side bands are created just as in any other type of modulation.   Among these is the *lower side band* which is called the *intermediate frequency*.   The so-called pentagrid converter [11] is often used in modern broadcast receiving sets; this tube acts as a combined local oscillator and modulation tube.

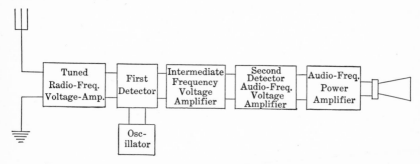

FIG. 12–14.   Block diagram of a superheterodyne radio-receiving set.

This intermediate frequency will be a 465,000-cycle impulse when the received radio-frequency signal is *not* modulated.   When it *is* being modulated by an audio-frequency program varying from (for example) 100 to 5000 cycles, the intermediate-frequencies will cover a band of from 460,000 cycles to 470,000 cycles.   This band is the same width and contains the same audio-frequency "intelligence components" as the original radio-frequency wave received by the antenna. This fact can be proved by assuming that the 1,465,000-cycle wave is modulated separately by each of the originally received side bands. Of course, many other frequencies are also produced by the modulation or distortion process, but these are largely suppressed.

The intermediate-frequency amplifier is a sharply-tuned transformer-coupled, radio-frequency voltage amplifier.   Although the tuning is relatively sharp as stated, it must be broad enough to pass the band from 460,000 to 470,000 cycles.   The frequency for which the amplifier of Fig. 12–14 is tuned is assumed to be 465,000 cycles. This is common practice in modern receivers, although other frequencies are used.[13]   The output of the intermediate-frequency amplifier is impressed on the so-called second detector.   This is usually a duplex-diode triode which demodulates (by diode action) the intermediate frequency signal, creating the desired audio-frequency component.   This tube also supplies the automatic volume-control voltages.

The demodulated audio-frequency voltage component is amplified in the triode portion of the duplex-diode triode and then impressed on the power amplifier. This power stage then drives the loud speaker reproducing the program.

The superheterodyne has many advantages over the tuned-radio frequency receiving set; several of these will now be discussed. *First,* in the tuned radio-frequency set the *selectivity* depends on the tuning of the radio-frequency stages, and these must be variable over a wide frequency range. It is difficult to obtain uniform and high amplification characteristics over a wide frequency band. In the superheterodyne, the intermediate-frequency amplifier, in which much of the voltage gain is obtained, is *permanently* adjusted to a fixed value; that is, no adjustments are made by the operator although it may be necessary to realign these stages at intervals. *All* radio-frequency signals to be received are translated to the intermediate-frequency band. The desired signal is selected by varying *both* the tuned-radio frequency stage and the *frequency of the local oscillator.*

A *second* and important advantage of the superheterodyne in increasing selectivity is demonstrated by the following illustration. Suppose that it is desired to receive a broadcast station on a carrier of 1,500,000 cycles. The local oscillator would be adjusted to 1,965,000 cycles, as previously explained, to translate the radio-frequency signal to an intermediate-frequency signal of 465,000 cycles. Now suppose that the antenna connected to the set is also intercepting a signal from an *unwanted* station operating on a carrier of 1,510,000 cycles. The tuned radio-frequency voltage amplifying *stage* of Fig. 12–14 would pass some of this unwanted signal because the difference between the two is *less than one per cent.* This unwanted signal would modulate the signal from the local oscillator and produce a frequency of 455,000 cycles per second. Under these conditions, the difference between the *desired* intermediate frequency of 465,000 cycles and the unwanted "intermediate frequency" is about 2.2 per cent, giving greater selectivity. This improvement becomes quite large where lower intermediate frequencies are used, or when the superheterodyne is used for short-wave reception.

REFERENCES

1. American Institute of Electrical Engineers. *Definitions of Electrical Terms.*
2. Institute of Radio Engineers. *Report of the Standards Committee.*
3. Colpitts, E. H., and Blackwell, O. B. *Carrier current telephony and telegraphy.* Trans. A.I.E.E., 1921, Vol. 40.
4. Affel, H. A., Demarest, C. S., and Green, C. W. *Carrier systems for long distance telephone lines.* Bell System Tech. Journal, July, 1928, Vol. 7, No. 3.

5. Bown, Ralph. *Transatlantic radio telephony*. Bell System Tech. Journal, April, 1927, Vol. 6, No. 2.
6. Oswald, A. A. *Transoceanic telephone service: Short-wave equipment*. Trans. A.I.E.E., 1930, Vol. 49.
7. Polkinghorn, F. A., and Schlaack, N. F. *A single side band short-wave system for transatlantic telephony*. Proc. I.R.E., July, 1935, Vol. 23, No. 7.
8. Glasgow, R. S. *Principles of Radio Engineering*. McGraw-Hill Book Co.
9. Blake, G. G. *History of Radio Telegraphy and Telephony*. Chapman and Hall.
10. Kilgour, C. E., and Glessner, J. M. *Diode detection analysis*. Proc. I.R.E., July, 1933, Vol. 21, No. 7.
11. R.C.A. Manufacturing Co. *Receiving Tube Manual*.
12. Pender, H., and McIlwain, K. *Electrical Engineers' Handbook*. Vol. 5. Electric Communication and Electronics. John Wiley & Sons.
13. Henney, K. *Radio Engineers Handbook*. McGraw-Hill Book Co.
14. Ballantine, S. *Detection at high signal voltages*. Proc. I.R.E., July, 1929, Vol. 17, No. 7.
15. Everitt, W. L. *Communication Engineering*. McGraw-Hill Book Co.
16. Terman, F. E. *Radio Engineering*. McGraw-Hill Book Co.
17. McIlwain, K., and Brainerd, J. G. *High-Frequency Alternating Currents*. John Wiley & Sons.
18. Armstrong, E. H. *A method of reducing disturbances in radio signaling by a method of frequency modulation*. Proc. I.R.E., May, 1936, Vol. 24, No. 5.

SUGGESTED ASSIGNMENTS

1. Referring to page 312, compare the amplifier capacities required for radiating the carrier and two side bands, and for radiating only one side band.
2. Refer to Fig. 12–2, and to the rectification theory given on page 178. From a tube manual obtain the constants and tube data given, and assuming a value of *unmodulated* carrier impressed on the tube, calculate the biasing voltage available across resistor R.
3. Fully explain the theoretical considerations involved in the last paragraph of Section 109 ending on page 338.
4. On page 341 it is stated that the advantages gained by full-wave detection usually do not justify the added circuit complications. Explain why this is true.
5. Diagram and explain the operation of a delayed automatic volume-control circuit.
6. Following in general the method used on page 324, derive the equations necessary to show that the desired audio component exists in the output of a plate-circuit square-law detector.
7. Prove that 25 per cent distortion exists when a completely-modulated signal is demodulated with a square-law detector.
8. Explain how the tuned radio-frequency stage of a superheterodyne radio receiver acts to suppress image frequencies.

CHAPTER 13

PHOTOELECTRIC DEVICES AND CIRCUITS

It was shown in Chapter 2 that visible light (and other electromagnetic radiations) had at least three effects when it fell on certain metals. *First*, by a *photoemissive* effect, electrons are liberated from metals; *second*, by a *photovoltaic* effect, radiations cause a difference of potential to exist between two terminals of a correctly constructed cell; *third*, by a *photoconductive* effect, light shining on certain metallic substances causes the resistance of these substances to vary.

The various theories underlying these photoelectric phenomena were considered in Chapter 2. It is recommended that these be fully understood before proceeding. Although the exact natures of these phenomena are obscure, an understanding of the accepted viewpoints is necessary.

This chapter will be devoted to a consideration of the characteristics of the various photoelectric devices, and to the uses of these devices in electric circuits.

122. Phototubes.—A **phototube** is defined [1] as a "vacuum tube in which one of the electrodes is irradiated for the purpose of causing electron emission." The radiation liberates the electrons by a photoemissive effect. By some process, the exact nature of which is obscure, the radiant energy of the light (or other radiation) imparts energy to a few of the electrons of the metal so that these are able to escape through the surface forces of the metal to the region outside.

The essential elements of a phototube are an evacuated glass bulb containing an electron-emitting *cathode* and a positive electron-collecting *anode*. These electrodes may be, and have been, arranged in a variety of ways. The electron-emitting light-sensitive material may be on a small electrode at the center of the bulb (central-cathode type), or the electron-collecting anode may be at the center (central-anode type). The characteristics of these two types are different.[2] The latter type is most widely used today.

The bulb may be highly evacuated or may contain gas. Thus, phototubes may be of the high vacuum or the gas type. The **high-vacuum phototube** is defined [1] as one which is "evacuated to such a degree that its electrical characteristics are essentially unaffected by gaseous ionization." A **gas phototube** [1] is one "in which the pressure of the contained gas or vapor is such as to affect substantially the electrical characteristics of the tube."

High-Vacuum Phototubes.—In many modern phototubes the light-sensitive material is a caesium-oxygen-silver layer formed on a cylindrically shaped metal electrode. The anode is a wire or rod at the center. The entire arrangement, showing a top view of the phototube, and a circuit for studying its characteristics, are shown in Fig. 13–1. It is assumed that the intensity of the light striking the phototube is variable. The anode voltage can be changed, and the resulting current as indicated by the galvanometer (or preferably a sensitive microammeter) can be measured. With this arrangement curves such as are shown in Fig. 13–2 can be readily obtained.

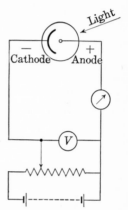

FIG. 13–1. Simple circuit for studying a *high-vacuum* phototube.

The energy in the visible light (or other radiation) striking the light-sensitive layer causes electrons to be emitted. Some of these are just able to escape from the surface of the composite metallic layer, but others have considerable initial velocities when they are emitted. These liberated electrons are influenced by the electric field existing between the cathode and anode, this field being *largely* due to the positive potential *on the anode.*

These two qualifying statements require further explanation. Disposing of the last one first, since any phototube may be (and gas phototubes should be) operated with high resistances in the anode circuit, a correction due to the IR drop across this resistance often needs to be applied to determine the exact anode potential.

Regarding the strength of the electric field within a phototube, it will be of interest to refer to Fig. 4–5 for a thermionic vacuum tube having two electrodes. For low voltages, the current flowing to the plate or anode is limited by the space charge. At the higher voltages, however, the current is limited by emission from the filament. Although it is recognized that the shapes of the electrodes are vastly different in thermionic tubes and in phototubes (in the former the cathode is small and the anode is large, but in the latter the reverse is true), it is conceivable that a space-charge effect also exists in phototubes.

In considering space charge and its effect in phototubes, it should be remembered that many of the photoelectrons have very low initial velocities when they are emitted, and that they are speeded to high velocities by the positive electric field from the anode.   Thus, for a *given current* to flow to the anode and on around the wire circuit, many more electrons per second must be passing a given point near the emit-

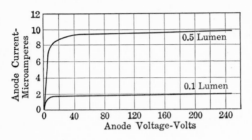

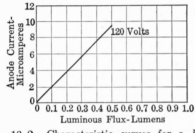

Fig. 13–2.   Characteristic curves for a *high-vacuum* phototube.   (Data from Reference 8.)

ting cathode than are passing a point near the electron-collecting anode. This phenomenon was ably used [3] by McArthur in explaining space-charge effects in thermionic tubes. It shows clearly that in the vicinity of the emitting surface the electron density must exceed greatly that in other parts of the tube. This concentration of electrons is the space charge, and the influence of the resulting negative electric field is the space-charge effect. It seems reasonable to expect such an effect in phototubes as well as thermionic tubes, even if to only a minor degree.

Returning to Fig. 13–2 it is apparent that the output of a phototube is greater if the light intensity striking the photo-sensitive material is increased.   The curves also show that the tube soon becomes saturated, after which the current to the anode is limited (for given conditions) by the photo-emission.   The lower curve of Fig. 13–2 is of extreme importance.   It clearly indicates that the current output of a phototube varies *directly* with the luminous flux from the light source.   It is this important characteristic which makes possible the use of the phototube as a distortionless (essentially) transducer [4] in sound motion pictures, television, and many other applications.

Gas Phototubes.—In many instances the physical construction of these phototubes is essentially the same as the vacuum type just considered.   An exception to this statement is the fact that in the vacuum phototube, which has a very high internal resistance, the anode connection is made at the *top* of the tube instead of the base so that leakage may be minimized.   In making the gas phototube, after the evacuating process a small amount of some inert gas (such as argon at a pressure of about 150 microns) is admitted.

The function of the gas in this type phototube is as follows: The electrons emitted from the light-sensitive cathode are drawn to the positive anode. If the voltage is sufficient, the electrons may attain a velocity sufficient to cause ionization by collision when they strike neutral gas atoms. As a result of this ionization, additional electrons are produced, and these in turn flow on to the positive anode. Some of these liberated electrons will also cause ionization by collision thus further increasing the current through the tube for a given light intensity.

Massive, slow-moving, positive ions are also produced by the ionization process. These move toward the negative cathode, thus increasing the current flow. They further increase the current by knocking electrons out of the cathode surface.[5] In view of the discussion on space charge in the preceding paragraphs, and the discussion of space-charge effects in gas thermionic tubes (page 84), it is conceivable that a similar space-charge reducing influence is also exerted by positive ions in gas phototubes.

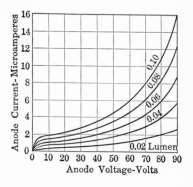

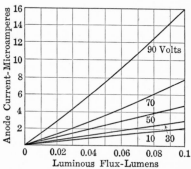

Fig. 13–3. Characteristic curves for a gas-type phototube. (Data from Reference 5.)

Thus, the effect of the inert gas introduced into a phototube is to increase the sensitivity by an ionizing process. Since this will become cumulative and large currents may flow, a gas phototube should always *be operated with a protective current-limiting resistor in the anode circuit,* unless, of course, other control provisions are made.

Curves illustrating the characteristics of a gas phototube are shown in Fig. 13–3. As is evident, after ionization occurs the current increases rapidly and would reach a value which would damage the tube if a protective resistor were not used. The lower curves of Fig. 13–3 indicate that for the gas phototube (as well as the vacuum type) the output current is substantially *directly* proportional to the luminous flux from the light source. This characteristic is of great importance.

123. Photometric Definitions.—Before proceeding with the discussion of phototubes, it is advisable to define certain photometric terms by quotations from Reference 4.

Light.—This is defined as "radiant energy evaluated according to its capacity to produce visual sensation."

Luminous Flux.—This is defined as "the time rate of flow of light." The unit is the **lumen.**

Lumen.—This is equal to the "flux through unit solid angle (steradian) from a uniform point source of one candle, or to the flux on a unit surface all points of which are at unit distance from a uniform point source of one candle." Assuming that the lamp is a point source, the luminous flux F in lumens falling on the *projected* cathode area (sometimes called the window area) is

$$F = \frac{AC}{d^2}, \tag{13-1}$$

where A is the projected area (not the *entire* area, because the cathode is cylindrical), C is the luminous intensity [4] or candle power of the source, and d is the distance (in the same system of measurement as A) from the source to the cathode. These relations are shown in Fig. 13-4.

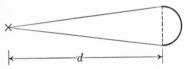

Fig. 13-4. Illustrating the terms of equation 1. The projected area of the phototube is indicated by the dotted line.

It is also of interest to point out that reflection of light by the curved cathode causes certain rays of light to be reflected back to the light-sensitive surface where they again liberate electrons. This increases the effectiveness of the radiant light energy.

Phototube Definitions.—These are given in Reference 1, from which certain terms will be selected and defined by quotations.

Static Sensitivity.—This is the "quotient of the direct anode current by the incident radiant flux of constant value."

Dynamic Sensitivity.—This is the "quotient of the alternating component of anode current by the alternating component of incident radiant flux."

Luminous Sensitivity.—This is the "quotient of the anode current by the incident luminous flux."

Conductance of a Phototube.—This is the ratio of the current through a phototube at a specified radiant flux to the voltage at its terminals. Mathematically,

$$s_p = \frac{I}{E}, \tag{13-2}$$

where s_p is the conductance in mhos, when I is the current in amperes, and E is the anode voltage in volts.

Resistance of a Phototube.—This is the reciprocal of the conductance.

Gas Amplification Factor.—This is the "factor of increase in the sensitivity of a gas phototube due solely to the ionization of the contained gas."

124. Comparisons of Vacuum and Gas Phototubes.—For comparative purposes the characteristics of a vacuum and of a gas phototube are plotted in Fig. 13–5. These data are from Figs. 13–2 and 13–3 at luminous flux (also called light flux) values of 0.1 lumen.

These data are for identical phototubes with the exception that one contains argon gas at a pressure of 150 microns and the other is a vacuum type with the anode lead brought out the top to increase the insulation resistance.

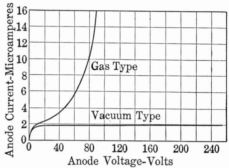

FIG. 13–5. Characteristics of vacuum type and gas type phototubes at 0.1 lumen. (Data from Figs. 13–2 and 13–3.)

These curves show that the characteristics are (almost) identical until ionization by collision occurs in the gas tube. They also indicate (as do Figs. 13–2 and 13–3) that the operating voltage needed on gas tubes is considerably less than for the vacuum type. The gas amplification ratio of a typical phototube is less than 10.

Vacuum phototubes are especially suited for circuits for precise measurements of illumination, such as will be explained in later sections. In general it can be stated that the vacuum phototube, although not so sensitive as the gas type, is more stable in operation and constant in calibration. It is not likely to be damaged by drawing high instantaneous currents, while the gas tube should always be operated with a current-limiting resistor in the anode circuit.

125. Testing Phototubes.—Various tests for phototubes are listed in Reference 1; these include current-voltage characteristics, current-illumination characteristics, current-wavelength (spectral) characteristics, frequency response characteristics, gas amplification tests, and others. Only the first two tests will be included, the details largely being from the reference given.

For determining the current-voltage characteristic the illumination is held constant, the voltage is varied, and the current is observed.

For the current-illumination tests the voltage is held constant, the luminous flux is varied, and the current measured. To make these measurements a calibrated light source, a photometer box, and an electrical circuit are necessary.

The type of light source to be selected depends on the nature of the light-sensitive cathode and the purpose for which the phototube is to be used. For example, if the phototube is to be used in sound motion picture reproduction, where the light source is a lamp with a tungsten filament, it should be tested with such a lamp and with the filament at the same operating temperature. But, if the phototube is designed to measure ultra-violet radiation, it should be tested with an ultra-violet light source. In regard to the tungsten-filament lamp, its candle power should be measured carefully by photometric methods (see any standard book on illumination). In selecting this lamp certain precautions [1] should be considered. In using it to test a phototube, the current should be measured accurately because a one per cent variation in current may cause a *six per cent* variation in the light flux.

The photometer box should exclude all extraneous light, and all interior parts should be painted a dull black so that light will not be reflected. One or more masks should be arranged to insure that the only light striking the cathode comes directly (and not by reflection) from the calibrated lamp. This lamp may be mounted on a carriage so that d of equation 1 may be varied.

The test circuit is as shown in Fig. 13–6. The protective resistor R may be omitted so that corrections for the voltage drop across it are

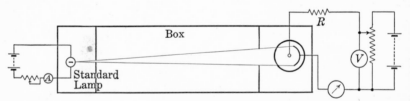

Fig. 13–6. Arrangement for studying a phototube. Either the lamp or the phototube may be moved in the light-tight box. The phototube current is measured with the indicating galvanometer or microammeter.

not necessary. If this is done, care must be taken to prevent damaging gas phototubes. It may be desired to make the resistor R equal to the load resistance which will be used with the phototube in the actual circuit.

With the arrangement of Fig. 13–6 the curves of Figs. 13–2, 13–3, and 13–5 may be obtained. For any location of the calibrated lamp, the luminous flux in lumens is given by equation (13–1).

126. The Caesium-Oxygen-Silver Cathode.—These cathodes, with composite instead of pure metal light-sensitive surfaces, are now extensively used in phototubes of both the vacuum and gas types for purposes where either ordinary incandescent lamps or daylight furnish the illumination.   The preparation of these cathodes is so interesting, and so well illustrates electronic technique, that it will be explained in some detail.   Of course, the various methods differ somewhat in practice; this explanation is summarized from Reference 6.

The cathode itself is a cylindrical section of silver.   The composite layer of light-sensitive material is formed after the phototube is connected to the evacuating system.   After a thorough pumping, with all metallic parts at a high temperature to free occluded gases, pure oxygen is admitted and the silver cathode is oxidized by a glow discharge produced between the cathode and anode.   An exact amount of oxygen is combined with the silver.

The correct amount of caesium is then formed on the cathode.   A pellet containing caesium chromate, chromic oxide, and powdered aluminum, which was placed in the tube, is heated by a high-frequency induction furnace and the caesium is evaporated by the resulting chemical reaction and is condensed on the glass walls of the tube.   It is then necessary to transfer the caesium from the walls to the cathode. This is accomplished by placing the phototube in a stream of hot air. This heats the glass without a corresponding rise in temperature of the cathode.   The caesium is evaporated from the glass walls and con-

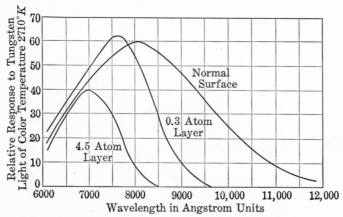

FIG. 13–7.   Illustrating the effect on the photoelectric sensitivity of various thicknesses of the outer layer of caesium.   (From Reference 6.)

denses on the cooler cathode, where it combines with the silver oxide. The tube is then sealed from the exhaust pump if a vacuum phototube is desired, or the correct amount of gas is introduced for the gas type.

The process is so controlled, and the quantities of caesium and oxygen so adjusted, that after the reactions occur there is a surface layer of caesium approximately one atom thick. The effect of the thickness of this layer on the output of the phototube is indicated by Fig. 13–7.

Current-Wavelength Characteristics.[1]—The direct-current output of a phototube at various wavelengths of luminous flux (the **spectral sensitivity**) is an important characteristic. This characteristic depends on at least two factors; first, the nature of the light-sensitive cathode surface, and second, the light-transmitting nature of the enclosing bulb.

The characteristics of phototubes with two different types of light-sensitive cathodes are shown in Fig. **13**–8. The potassium-hydride

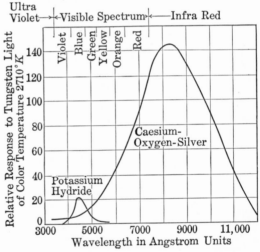

Fig. 13–8.   Relative response of an old type potassium-hydride phototube as compared with the caesium-oxygen-silver phototube. (From Reference 6.)

layer was used in early phototubes. The wavelength in Angstrom units (10^{-10} meters) and the visible spectrum are both shown. Phototubes are commercially available with cathodes other than the caesium-oxygen-silver type, and with bulbs of special glass or of quartz; and these phototubes are most sensitive to other than visible light. Ordinary glass will largely absorb ultra-violet radiation.

The current-wavelength characteristics are apparently determined almost entirely by the cathode surface and the transmission qualities of the glass. Whether the tube is of the vacuum type or contains an inert gas apparently has little effect on the spectral characteristics, at least from the commercial standpoint.

127. Phototube Applications.—Although these tubes have been commercially available only a few years, they have been used in a variety of ways. It is not the purpose of the following pages even to attempt to summarize these applications, but rather to classify them and to consider the basic principles involved. The various practical developments of phototubes and their applications have been reported in the various journals, and have been summarized [7] and explained by Henney who also gives detailed lists of references to the literature on the subject.

Broadly considering the uses of phototubes, three classifications can be made. *First*, phototubes are used to open or close relays and control mechanical operations when light beams falling upon their cathodes are interrupted or restored. *Second*, phototubes are used as transducers [4] to cause electrical currents to vary in accordance with light-beam variations such as those in sound motion picture reproduction and similar applications. *Third*, phototubes are used to measure light intensities and for related purposes. The fundamental principles of these various systems will be considered in this order in the following pages.

Relay Operations.—Suppose that it is desired that a phototube close a relay and operate a counter every time a box on a conveyer belt passes between a light source and a phototube. Examination of Figs. **13–2** and **13–3** will indicate the impracticability of attempting to build a relay for commercial purposes which could be operated *directly* by the phototube which could at best change the relay current only a few microamperes. Thermionic-vacuum tubes are therefore

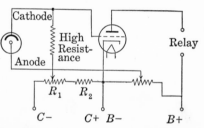

Fig. 13–9.   Circuit for operating a relay from a phototube.

used with phototubes to increase the current change available for relay operation.

A circuit for performing the functions of the preceding paragraph is shown in Fig. **13–9**. With the phototube *out* of the circuit, the grid bias on the thermionic vacuum amplifier tube is determined by the voltage drop across R_1 and R_2. With the phototube *in* the circuit, but *with the light beam intercepted*, a current will flow through the phototube because of residual room illumination, and this current will cause an opposing voltage drop across R_1 and R_2 *reducing* the grid bias on the amplifier tube and allowing a *larger* plate current to flow.   When the light beam *is not intercepted*, the phototube current will greatly increase thus reducing the grid-bias voltage considerably, and causing the plate current of the amplifier tube to increase greatly.   This will operate the counter.

The design of such a circuit is very simple.   The phototube currents with residual illumination, and with the light beam shining on the cathode, must be known.   From these values the grid-bias voltage variations can be calculated.   Also, the current on which the counter relay (or other relay device) will *close* and the current on which it will *open* must be known.   An amplifier tube is then selected which will furnish these currents at these available bias voltages.   In case much power is needed to operate the counter or other device, a sensitive relay controlling a local source of power, such as a battery, for operating the larger device can be used.   Gas phototubes are widely used in the circuit just considered.

Sound Reproduction.—In the reproduction of sound on films, a constant light beam is directed onto the sound track on the edge of the moving film.   The light which passes through and falls on the cathode of the phototube will, accordingly, vary in intensity as does the recorded speech and music variations on the edge of the film.   The corresponding phototube current is, therefore, a very faithful reproduction of the original sounds recorded in the studios.   For sound reproduction in the theater the weak phototube output must first be amplified to a high level and then used for driving the loud speakers.

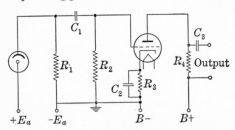

Fig. 13–10.   Circuit for reproducing sound on films.   Phototube and first amplifying stage shown.   The phototube anode voltage is connected at E_a.

The first stage of amplification is (and some of the following stages may be) usually resistance-capacitance coupled.   The final stages are usually transformer-coupled class A amplifiers.   A circuit of a typical amplifier is shown in Fig. **13**–10. Since this type amplifier was fully treated in a previous chapter (page 217), no further explanation is necessary at this point.   Gas phototubes are now extensively used in sound motion picture reproduction.

Matching Measurements.—An interesting circuit for matching brightness, color, turbidity, and other qualities is shown in Fig. **13–11**. This diagram and the following discussion is based on Reference 8 in which further details can be found.   High vacuum phototubes are used in this circuit because they are better suited to precise measurements than are the gas type.

In this matching circuit, one phototube receives light from the lamp or from (by reflection from, or transmission through) the material to be studied.   The other phototube receives light directly from a standard lamp, or material.   A very slight difference between the standard and the unknown can be determined.

The two phototubes are in series and so *must* pass the same current. If the two tubes are identical, and if the circuit is properly adjusted, the voltage across each tube will be the same *for the same illumination*.   If the illumination is *different* in any respect, then the voltage across each tube will *not* be the same. This will cause the bias on the thermionic vacuum tube to change, and the microammeter reading to vary.

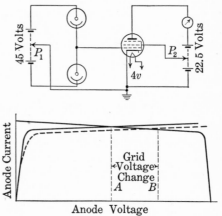

This action, and the high degree of sensitivity obtainable, are indicated by the curves of Fig. **13–11**. The characteristic curve of one phototube has been plotted reversed.   A small change in the illumination of one tube causes a large voltage change

Fig. 13–11.   A very sensitive circuit for color matching.   With equal illumination the grid bias voltage will be at A.   For unequal values it shifts to B.   The dotted curve is for slightly less illumination on one phototube. Type 917 high-vacuum phototubes and a type 38 amplifier tube are recommended. (Adapted from Reference 8.)

to be applied to the control grid of the suppressor-grid pentode amplifying tube.   This will cause a large change in the plate current.

According to the data given in Reference 8, the battery voltages and other data are as indicated.   Because of the high resistance in the grid circuit of the amplifying tube, this tube is operated at reduced heater and plate voltages.   The leakage resistance of the phototubes is kept high by cleaning the glass with alcohol, and if necessary by mounting them in containers with phosphorous pentoxide.   For high precision and constancy of calibration, a *vacuum* phototube should be operated at a low potential of about 20 volts.   Higher anode voltages may cause ionization of any residual gas, and the currents resulting from this may cause the characteristics to vary.

Telephotograph Systems.—Various systems [9, 10] have been devised for transmitting photographs and similar recordings by electrical means.   The transmission path may be a wire line or a radio circuit. One system [11] was installed for commercial operation in 1925, but has been replaced by an improved method.[12]

In the conventional telephotograph system a beam of light passes over each portion of the film and the light passing through the film at a given instant depends on the density of the film at that point.   This light beam falls on a phototube, and the electrical output will correspond to the characteristic of the film at that point.   These electrical impulses are transmitted to the distant station where they are used to operate a **light valve** [12] which exposes a photographic film in such a manner that, when completed, it is a reproduction of the film at the sending station.

Conventional phototubes are used in most of the telephotograph systems, and need no further consideration.

128. Phototubes in Television.—A system of **television** requires that light impulses be changed to electrical signals; this is done by phototubes.   There are three fundamental systems employed for this: First, the **Nipkow disk;** second, the **Farnsworth image dissector;** and third, the **Zworykin Iconoscope.**   The first system uses phototubes of the conventional form, or substantially so; the second and third systems use special phototubes, and these will be treated in separate sections.

The general features of television scanning [9, 10] are familiar.   The strength of the light beam striking the cathode of the phototube, or phototubes, at a given instant varies in accordance with the light reflected by the portion of the image being scanned at that instant.

The phototubes usually employed with the scanning-disk systems are, as was mentioned, of the conventional type (at least from the electronic standpoint, although they may differ in construction) and need no further consideration.   Although the scanning-disk method may be replaced in commercial systems (when completely developed) by the methods to be considered in the following sections, *two-way* television,[13] and television *in colors,*[14] were possible with it.   This last system used a very interesting arrangement of phototubes sensitive to different colors, color filters, and special reproducing equipment.

The Farnsworth Image Dissector.—In the scanning disk arrangement just discussed, a beam of light passes across each element of the object, and the light reflected at each instant from the object controls the output of one or more phototubes. In the Farnsworth image dissector system the reflected light from each element of the scene (in other words, the **optical image**) *simultaneously* falls on the special phototube shown in Fig. 13–12, reproduced from Reference 15.

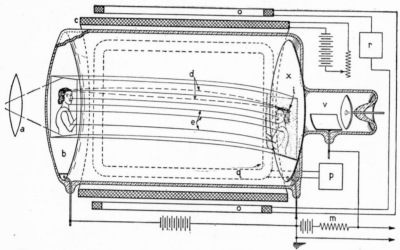

FIG. 13–12.   Diagram of the Farnsworth image dissector used in television.
(From Reference 15.)

On the inside of the end of the phototube on which the light falls is a translucent light-sensitive film or **photoelectric screen** b, as it is often called. At *each point* on this film electrons are emitted in proportion to the light striking it at *that point*. That is, the optical image focused on the end of the tube *is transformed into an image of electrons*, and these electrons are attracted to the opposite end of the tube by the *positive* plate x.

Each electron must maintain its place in the electron pattern of flow progressing to the plate x. The *constant* magnetic field produced *parallel to the axis of the tube* by coil c prevents the electrons from following the distorted paths d, and causes them to take the parallel paths e.

In order for the optical image to be transmitted electrically, electrical impulses proportional to each element of the image must be available. A small square hole exists in the center of the positive plate or anode x. By magnetic means, the *entire* electronic image pattern is *progressively* moved back and forth from top to bottom across this hole. Thus, the number of electrons passing through this hole (due to their kinetic energy) *at each instant* is proportional to the number of electrons in the electronic image *at that instant*. In this way, electrical impulses, corresponding to each *element* of the optical image, are obtained.

The magnetic shifting of the *entire* electronic image is accomplished by the two coils o and q, placed at right angles. These coils are supplied with alternating sweep currents by the so-called "sawtooth" oscillators r and p. The frequencies of these oscillators are such that the electronic image is correctly moved (or scanned) across the square hole at the center of the positive plate or anode x.

The number of electrons passing through the hole at a given instant is very small, and very great amplification is required. Farnsworth has developed[15] an interesting **electron multiplier** which is located immediately behind the plate x. This multiplier is a secondary-emission system (page 43), so arranged that the electrical output of the complete image-dissector tube is much greater than would be that due to the electrons passing through the square hole in the plate x. This amplified output is further increased in vacuum-tube amplifiers (page 206) until it has been raised to a level sufficient for transmission.

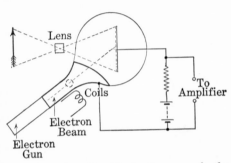

FIG. 13–13. Simplified diagram of the Iconoscope. Details of electron gun omitted. Two deflecting coils at right angles are placed as shown. (See Reference 16 for greater detail.)

The Iconoscope.—A diagram of the Iconoscope[16] invented by Zworykin is given in Fig. 13–13. It is in reality an interesting combination of a phototube and the *electron gun* portion of a cathode-ray tube (page 388).

The phototube portion consists of a photo-sensitive cathode formed on a layer of insulating material such as mica. The opposite side of this sheet of mica is coated with a conducting layer forming a **signal plate**. The light-sensitive material on the front of the plate *is not a continuous layer*. Instead, it is a **light-sensitive mosaic** composed of a large number of isolated and insulated light-sensitive spots or globules on the mica sheet. Each of these globules forms, with the signal plate, a minute condenser.

The electron gun is focused on this mosaic. By a system of deflecting coils carrying "sawtooth" alternating sweep currents the beam of the gun can be moved across the mosaic from top to bottom, and the mosaic can be "scanned" by shooting at it a stream of electrons. The electrical connections are made as indicated, and the operation is as follows:

Light from the image is focused on the light-sensitive mosaic cathode by an optical system. In this manner, the light striking *each* small light-sensitive spot or insulated globule is proportional to the light reflected from the corresponding part of the object to be televised. Each globule will emit electrons in proportion to the strength of the light striking it. These negative electrons are attracted to the walls (which are at ground potential and hence less negative than the cathode) of the lower part of the envelope. By this action, *each*

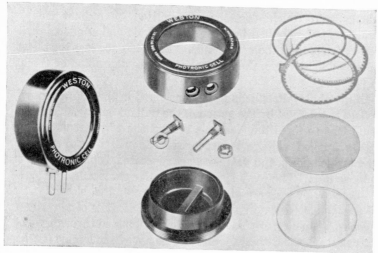

Assembled view and component parts of a commercial photovoltaic cell of the iron-selenium type. (Courtesy Weston Electrical Instrument Corp.)

globule (which is insulated from the other globules, *and from the signal plate*) assumes a *positive* charge in proportion to the strength of the light striking it. The optical image is therefore established as a corresponding "electrical potential image" on the cathode by charging the minute condensers formed by the globules and the signal plate.

The function of the electron gun is to shoot a constant stream of negative electrons against this cathode and to discharge *individually* each small condenser or group of condensers. This is accomplished by sweeping the electron beam (of the correct size) across the mosaic as previously explained. As the beam passes in turn over each globule (or groups of globules), the deficiency of electrons is supplied by the beam, and the small condenser formed between the globules and the signal plate is suddenly discharged. This gives an instantaneous electrical impulse to the vacuum-tube amplifier corresponding in magnitude to the light reflected from a given point on the object or scene to be transmitted.

It is not the purpose of this discussion to give the relative merits of the Farnsworth image dissector and the Iconoscope of Zworykin. Both have advantages and disadvantages, and both have proved quite successful in trials and demonstrations which have been made. At present it appears that both these methods will be used in television transmission to convert from optical to electrical impulses.

129. Photovoltaic Cells.—The phototubes considered in the preceding pages are photoemissive devices containing a light-sensitive cathode from which electrons are emitted by radiant energy. A voltage must be applied between the cathode and anode to draw the electrons on around the wire circuit. Thus, in one sense the phototube is merely a light valve, the internal resistance depending on the luminous flux.

In the **photovoltaic cells** to be considered in the following sections, a *voltage is generated* by the action of the radiant energy. This voltage is sufficient to force the electrons around the wire circuit and no externally applied voltage is necessary. As will be shown later the *current* which flows, and *not the voltage* generated, is proportional to the luminous flux. These are also called **barrier photocells.**

Photovoltaic cells are of two general types: *first*, electrolytic cells; and *second*, electronic cells. The first type consists of two electrodes immersed in an electrolyte. A window is provided through which the light can reach the cathode. Since these have been largely superseded by the electronic (or dry) type cell, they will not be further discussed.

There are two forms of the electronic photovoltaic cell of commercial importance in this country. The *first* is the iron-selenium **Photronic cell,** and the second the copper-oxide **Photox cell.** The theory of operation was discussed on page 47. The copper-oxide cell consists essentially of an oxidized layer formed on a copper disk. A semitransparent metallic layer or a grid (through which the light can reach the oxidized layer) covers the copper oxide. When radiant energy strikes the copper-oxide layer, electrons are forced into the copper disk and on around the wire circuit. This is equivalent to saying that the semitransparent layer or the grid is made *positive* and the copper is made *negative* by the energy of the radiation (Fig. 2–12). These also are called **cuprous-oxide cells;** however, the term copper-oxide seems to be in more general use at present as was explained in the footnote on page 48.

The Photronic iron-selenium cell [18] is constructed in the same general manner as the copper-oxide type just discussed.   An iron disk is coated with a selenium compound and this in turn with a semitrans-

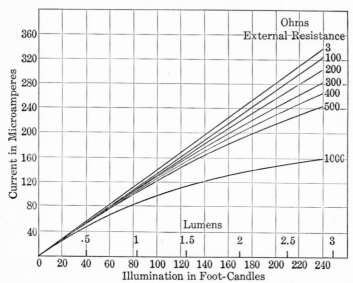

FIG. 13–14.   Effect of external resistance on current output of the photronic cell. Light source—tungsten lamp at 3000° K.   (From Reference 18.)

parent metallic coating.   This cell should not be confused with the conventional selenium cell to be described on page 382.

Photronic Cell Characteristics.—The spectral characteristics of this iron-selenium photovoltaic cell are shown by Fig. 2–13.   These and the other characteristics as well seem to be quite permanent, the cells operating without apparent chemical or physical change.

As was mentioned in the preceding section, although these cells generate a voltage which forces a current around the wire circuit, *the current* and not the voltage *is proportional to the luminous flux* striking the light-sensitive electrode.

This statement of proportionality applies *only to external loads of* low resistance as illustrated by Fig. **13**–14.

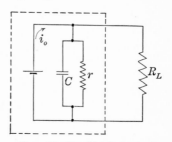

FIG. 13–15.   Equivalent circuit for a photovoltaic cell connected to a load of resistance R_L.

These curves may be explained [18, 19] by reference to the equivalent circuit, Fig. 13–15, of the Photronic cell.   The condenser shown is of importance only when the cell is being used with a variable light source.

For constant illumination, it may be omitted.   This circuit applies to all photovoltaic cells of the electronic type including, therefore, the copper-oxide Photox cell.

The current generated by the cell is represented by the fictitious battery at the left of Fig. 13–15.   This current is *exactly* proportional to the intensity of the luminous flux striking the light-sensitive layer.   As explained on page 49, part of this generated current flows within the cell and never reaches the external circuit. Thus the *internal* resistance is represented by *r in parallel* with the current source.   This value of the internal parallel resistance r is not constant, but varies *with the illumination* and *with the external resistance* as indicated by Fig. 13–16.

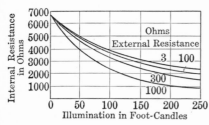

FIG. 13–16.   Internal resistance of the Photronic cell for varying conditions of illumination and external resistance.   (Light source and reference same as Fig. 13–14.)

As this figure shows, the internal resistance of the Photronic cell is high.   Thus, to have a large percentage of the total generated current flow to an external circuit, *the resistance of the external load must be low.* Referring to Fig. 13–14, *for an external load resistance of 3 ohms*, the output current is directly proportional to the luminous flux in lumens.

For loads of higher resistance, the output current is not directly proportional to the lumens as indicated by the 1000-ohm curve.

The open-circuit voltage between the output terminals of the Photronic cell is *not* directly proportional to the luminous flux, *except* at very low intensities where the relationship is almost linear.   This is illustrated by Fig. 13–17.   Temperature has some effect on the output of this photocell as explained in Reference 18.

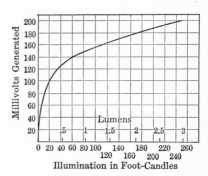

FIG. 13–17.   Voltage output of the Photronic cell.   (Light source and reference same as Fig. 13–14.)

Photox Cell Characteristics.—The spectral characteristics of the copper-oxide Photox photovoltaic cell are shown by Fig. 2–13.   The close agreement of these characteristics with those of the human eye is interesting.

In the copper-oxide Photox cell, the *current generated* (and not the output voltage) is directly proportional to the luminous flux striking the oxide surface. In this and its other characteristics it is like the iron-selenium type previously considered. The equivalent circuit of Fig. 13–15, and the accompanying theory regarding the effect of the external load resistance on the current output, also apply to the copper-oxide cell. These characteristics are as shown in Fig. 13–18. It will be noted that these curves are plotted in foot candles instead of lumens. A foot-candle is defined[4] as the "illumination on a surface one square foot in area on which there is a uniformly distributed flux of one lumen."

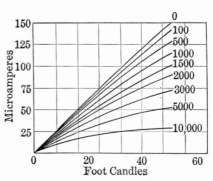

FIG. 13–18. Relation between illumination in foot candles and output of a copper-oxide Photox cell for various external load resistances in ohms as shown on the curves. (From Reference 17.)

As for the iron-selenium cell, only at low illumination intensities does the output *voltage* approach a direct proportionality with the illumination. These relations are shown in Fig. 13–19.

Photovoltaic Cell Connections.—With a *phototube*, a *high* series resistance may be used in the external circuit and a rather large voltage change is produced across this resistance. For example, if the current is 10 microamperes when a beam of light shines on a *phototube*, and 4 microamperes when the beam is interrupted, a change of 30 volts would be produced across a 5-megohm resistor connected in the anode circuit. Such a large drop can be readily made to change the grid bias on a thermionic-vacuum tube and thus cause a large plate-current change for relay operation. In other words, *phototubes* are well adapted to operation with thermionic-tube amplifiers which will amplify the changes in electrical output.

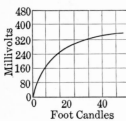

FIG. 13–19. Relation between open-circuit output voltage and illumination for the copper-oxide Photox cell. (From Reference 17.)

With *photovoltaic cells only low voltage changes are available* at the output terminals with large variations in illumination as is indicated by Figs. 13–17 and 13–19. Also, if the output current is to be directly proportional to the luminous flux striking the cell, low load resistances must be used as shown by Figs. 13–14 and 13–18. But, as these characteristics show, the output current is quite large for a photocell as compared with a phototube. The *phototube* is, therefore, best suited for operating directly voltage-driven circuits, and the *photovoltaic cell* is best suited for operating directly current-driven devices such as relays.

For operating relays and similar circuits, photovoltaic cells should be connected in *parallel* if larger current changes are desired. Since the internal resistance of such cells is high, they work best in this manner. Another interesting fact is that, with a number of cells in parallel, if some are dark the resistances of these become quite high (Fig. 13–16) and they do not take appreciable current from the illuminated cells and hence do not reduce the available output current from the combination.

Of course if several photovoltaic cells are connected in series their output voltages will add. As Fig. 13–19 indicates, however, even when no current is drawn the voltage available is very low. Light interrupters, operating at about 60 interruptions per second, are sometimes used to change the output of a photocell to an alternating current so that the output may be readily amplified by a thermionic tube amplifier.

Photovoltaic Cell Uses.—These cells, represented commercially by the Photronic and the Photox cells, are extensively used for two types of service. *First,* in conjunction with a sensitive microammeter they are used for such purposes as measuring illumination intensity, and *second,* they are used to operate sensitive relays when the illumination changes or when a beam of light is interrupted. Sensitive relays are available which will operate directly on the cell output.

This first classification will include illumination indicators, color-matching devices, smoke indicators, and density controls. Such uses will be found described in References 7, 10, 17, 18, and 19. The fact that these cells *require no sources of voltage* adapts them for many uses for which phototubes are not suited.

130. Photoconductive Cells.—These cells are merely resistance elements, the resistance of which becomes less when the cell is illuminated. The theories regarding this phenomenon were presented on page 50. These cells are often called **selenium bridges.** Compared to the phototube and the photovoltaic cell, they are of little commercial importance.

Such cells are usually made by applying a thin layer of selenium to two conductors which are parallel and insulated from each other except for the conducting selenium. In one cell the selenium is formed entirely in a vacuum and the cell contained within an evacuated bulb, to which has been admitted dry inert gas.[7] This cell is very stable in operation and the time lag and other undesired effects are eliminated.

Selenium cells may be used to operate sensitive relays without amplification, or they may be used to vary the bias on thermionic tubes and thus control larger outputs. It should be mentioned that modern selenium cells constructed in accordance with approved vacuum-tube manufacturing methods are very satisfactory devices. In all probability, had such technique been known and used at an earlier date, the selenium cell would have been well established in industry today.

REFERENCES

1. Institute of Radio Engineers. *Reports of the Standards Committee.*
2. Ives, H. E. *The alkali metal photoelectric cell.* The Bell System Technical Journal, April, 1926, Vol. 5, No. 2.
3. McArthur, E. D. *Electronics and Electron Tubes.* John Wiley & Sons.
4. American Institute of Electrical Engineers. *Definitions of Electrical Terms.*
5. R.C.A. Manufacturing Co. Pamphlet describing the type 918 phototube.
6. Kelley, M. J. *The caesium-oxygen-silver photoelectric cell.* Bell Laboratories Record, Oct., 1933, Vol. 7, No. 2. See also Bell System Technical Journal, July, 1932, Vol. 11, No. 3.
7. Henney, K. *Electron Tubes in Industry.* McGraw-Hill Book Co.
8. R.C.A. Manufacturing Co. Pamphlet describing the type 917 phototube.
9. Henney, K. *Radio Engineering Handbook.* McGraw-Hill Book Co.
10. Pender, H., and McIlwain, K. *Electrical Engineers' Handbook.* Vol. 5. Communication and Electronics. John Wiley & Sons.
11. Ives, H. E., Horton, J. W., Parker, R. D., and Clark, A. B. *The transmission of pictures over telephone lines.* Bell System Technical Journal, April, 1925, Vol. 4, No. 2.
12. Reynolds, F. W. *A new telephotograph system.* Electrical Engineering, Sept., 1936, Vol. 55, No. 9.
13. *Two-way television: A group of three papers on television.* Bell System Technical Journal, July, 1930, Vol. 9, No. 3.
14. Ives, H. E., and Johnsrud, A. L. *Television in colors by a beam scanning method.* Journal of the Optical Society of America, Jan., 1930, Vol. 20.
15. Brolly, A. H. *Television by electronic methods.* Electrical Engineering, Aug., 1934, Vol. 53, No. 8.
16. Zworykin, V. K. *The iconoscope—A modern version of the electric eye.* Proceedings of the Institute of Radio Engineers, Jan., 1934, Vol. 22, No. 1.
17. Westinghouse Electric and Mfg. Co. *Industrial Electronic Tubes.* Course No. 25.
18. Weston Electrical Instrument Corporation. *The Photronic Photoelectric Cell.* Monograph B–8.

19. Lamb, A. H.   *Applications of a photoelectric cell.*   Electrical Engineering, Nov., 1935, Vol. 54, No. 11.

SUGGESTED ASSIGNMENTS

1. Explain why the characteristics of the central-anode and the central-cathode phototubes are different.   Why have central-anode tubes become standard?
2. As shown in Fig. 13–5, the characteristics of the high-vacuum and the gas phototube (which are otherwise identical) are the same until ionization by collision occurs.   Are they *exactly* the same up to this point?   Explain why.
3. Determine the approximate gas amplification for the phototube of Fig. 13–3.
4. A phototube gives 3 microamperes through 5 megohms with 90 volts on the anode when it is in room illumination with a beam of light interrupted, and gives 10 microamperes when the light beam directed toward it is not interrupted.   The relay it is to operate closes on 12 milliamperes and opens on 4 milliamperes.   Design a *complete* circuit so that the relay will be closed when the light beam is interrupted.
5. Prepare a comprehensive list of the practical applications of phototubes and photovoltaic cells in industry.

CHAPTER 14

CATHODE-RAY TUBES AND MEASURING DEVICES

The vacuum tube has revolutionized the technique of electrical measurements. Studies of electrical phenomena which formerly were extremely difficult, if not impossible to perform, are now accomplished with the aid of vacuum tubes and electronic equipment. Perhaps this is one of the most important reasons for the rapid progress of electronic engineering; without reliable measurements little true progress can be made.

Among the electronic devices extensively used in electrical measurements are thermionic vacuum tubes, phototubes, photovoltaic cells, and cathode-ray tubes. The first three of these have been considered in the preceding chapters. This chapter will present the theory of cathode-ray tubes, and then will consider their application, and the application of other electronic devices, to circuits for electrical measurements.

In addition to its extensive use for electrical measurements, the cathode-ray tube has other important applications, perhaps the most outstanding of which is as the image-reproducing device of a television receiving set. This use also will be considered in this chapter.

The great utility of the cathode-ray tube is due to the fact that the beam of electrons or cathode ray, flowing from the cathode to a fluorescent screen, possesses so little inertia that the beam can be deflected at a very rapid rate, thus making possible the observing of high-frequency and transient phenomena. Furthermore, negligible power is required to deflect the cathode-ray beam, and hence studies of weak signals can be made because no power is required and the circuit conditions are not disturbed by the presence of the measuring equipment. Other important features of the cathode-ray tube will be emphasized in the following pages.

The beam of negative electrons constituting the cathode ray can be deflected by a magnetic field or by an electric field. When this beam strikes a spot on the fluorescent screen, visible light is given off. As the beam is deflected by the current or voltage to be studied, the trace made by the spot makes observable the current or voltage variations. If the spot is moved over the fluorescent screen at a rapid rate, an entire area on the screen will glow. Thus, if the instantaneous values

385

can be varied at different points, a television image can be "painted" on the fluorescent screen by the rapidly moving spot.

The use of the cathode ray in measurements was suggested [1] by Hess in 1894. The modern cathode-ray tube is based on a device de-

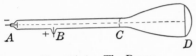

veloped [1] by Braun in 1897. A diagram of his tube is shown in Fig. 14–1. It consisted essentially of a *cold* cathode A (as distinguished from the thermionic cathode now almost universally used), a *positive*

FIG. 14–1.   The Braun cathode-ray tube.

anode B, a beam-forming diaphragm C and a fluorescent screen D. The tube contained air at low pressure.

An electrostatic generating machine (described in most physics texts) was used to supply a high voltage between electrodes A and B. The positive potential of B drew electrons (due to natural ionization, page 13) to it, and these were accelerated sufficiently to cause ionization by collision with gas atoms of the residual air. The positive ions were attracted to the negative cathode and a cold-electrode discharge (page 16) was established.

Owing to the high velocities reached (the potential from the electrostatic generator being 50,000 volts or more) the electrons were carried beyond positive electrode B, and some passed through the hole in C and to the zinc sulphide fluorescent screen used by Braun at D. Since these electrons traveled at high velocities, their mutual repulsion (they are individual negative charges) did not cause the beam to spread appreciably.

The cathode ray striking the fluorescent screen of the Braun tube could be deflected magnetically by coils placed to the right of the diaphragm C, or electrically by placing the tube in an electric field such as is produced between the plates of a high-voltage condenser. This tube almost immediately found application in the communication and in the power fields. Much information on these early developments will be found in References 1 and 2 which also list many articles on this subject.

A development of much importance was made by Wehnelt in 1905 when he produced a thermionic cathode-ray tube with a heated, lime-coated filament. This tube could be operated from low-voltage 220 volt power circuits.[1] A diagram of this tube, showing two deflecting plates to which the voltage to be studied is connected, is given in Fig. 14–2.

Another contribution of importance was made by Dufour in 1914. In his tube no fluorescent screen was used; instead, a photographic plate was placed *within* the tube, and the electron beam impinged directly on this plate. In this way, records of rapidly changing phenomena could be readily made. It had previously been necessary to place the photographic plate near the fluorescent screen, and expose the plate by the weak light from the screen. For the satisfactory photographing of a rapidly occurring electrical phenomenon many repetitions of the phenomenon were often required.

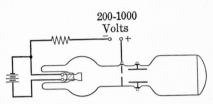

FIG. 14–2. The Wehnelt cathode-ray tube obtained the electrons by thermal emission. (From Reference 1.)

To summarize, there have been developed three general classes [1] of cathode-ray tubes: *First*, tubes resembling the original develpoment of Braun, of which there may still be some in limited use; *second*, thermionic cathode-ray tubes based on the contribution of Wehnelt; and *third*, the Dufour cathode-ray tube in which the plate (or films) are placed directly in the path of the electron beam. The first tube needs no further consideration and the following discussion will be confined to the last two types.

In the past few years, the thermionic-type cathode-ray tube was generally used for low-voltage studies, particularly in the communication field. The Dufour type was extensively used for studying lightning and other high-voltage phenomena. Recently,[2] the *thermionic* tube has been adapted to this field, and, because of its relative simplicity, will probably replace the Dufour tube for most *routine* high-voltage measurements.

131. Thermionic Cathode-Ray Tubes.—In these tubes the electrons are supplied by a heated filament, usually of the oxide-coated type. High voltages need *not* be used between the cathode and anode, and thus the electrons do *not* reach extremely high velocities as in the cold-cathode tube. If the electrons are moving slowly as they proceed to the fluorescent screen, they are *easily deflected*. Thus, the thermionic-type cathode-ray tube is *sensitive*, and is well suited to measurements in low voltage communication circuits.

The first thermionic cathode-ray tube to be introduced commercially was probably the one described [3] by Johnson. These tubes were gas-filled, quite sensitive, and required anode voltages of only a few hundred volts to give the electrons the necessary velocity. This low anode voltage was important because at the time the tube was introduced, satisfactory vacuum-tube rectifiers were not readily available, and radio *B* batteries were used almost exclusively.

As electronic technique developed, and as vacuum-tube rectifiers were perfected, thermionic cathode-ray tubes operating at higher anode voltages became practicable.   At first, these were largely confined to communication and low-voltage power circuit studies; but, as previously mentioned, they are now used for lightning and other high-voltage investigations.

Summarizing, there are *three* types of *thermionic* cathode-ray tubes: *first,* the low-voltage gas-filled tube; *second,* the medium-voltage high-vacuum tube; and *third,* the newly developed high-voltage high-vacuum type.   The first two tubes will now be discussed.   The last type will not be treated until after the Dufour high-voltage type, because a discussion of its application and advantages best follows a study of those of the older tube.

Low-Voltage Tube.—As previously mentioned this tube was designed to operate at low anode potentials of several hundred volts obtainable from ordinary radio *B* batteries.   The tube contained gas to focus the beam as will be explained later.   Since this tube is no longer commercially available its consideration would not be justified if it were not for the fundamental electronic principles involved.   These will be summarized [1, 3] in the following paragraphs.

A diagram of the **electron gun** is shown in Fig. 14–3.   The source of electrons is the oxide-coated cathode *C*.   This is in the shape of a helix and is mounted coaxially with the hole in the disk *D* and with the positive anode *A*.   The diameter of the helix is larger than the size of the hole in *D* so that the oxide-coated *wires are not in a direct line with* the opening.   This was done to reduce the bombarding effect of the positive ions arising from the argon gas in the tube.

Although the entire electron-gun structure is enclosed in a small glass tube, as is apparent from Fig. 14–3, and although the dimensions of

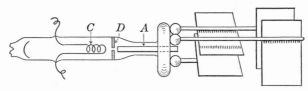

FIG. 14–3.   Diagram of an electron gun.   (From Reference 1.)

the tube [1] are "less than the mean free path of electrons in the gas so that no appreciable ionization can build up" there is *some* ionization in the space between the cathode and anode.   For this reason, some positive ions are produced *within* this small tube, and these massive ions are attracted by the negative cathode.   If this oxide-coated filamentary cathode were exposed to the direct bombardment of these positive ions, the active material would soon be knocked off and the cathode ruined in several hours.   By means of the special construction, which places the coated wires out of the direct path, the life was extended to several hundred hours.

In operation, the electrons emitted by the heated cathode are drawn to the positive anode A which is a metal tube or barrel having an opening about one millimeter in diameter.   Many of the electrons pass through this tube and, owing to their velocities, proceed as a somewhat divergent ray or beam through the deflecting plates of Fig. 14–3 and to the fluorescent screen.   The beam diverges because the electrons initially do not all leave the tube with parallel paths, and because in this low-voltage tube their velocities are relatively low and their time of flight correspondingly long.   They therefore have time to spread, by mutual repulsion, since each electron has a negative charge.

Argon gas at a pressure of about 0.01 millimeter is contained in the cathode ray tube (not merely in the small glass tube confining the electron gun elements from which it would be well if all gas could be excluded).   This gas performs *two* important functions.   *First*, the positive ions produced by ionization neutralize negative ions which tend to accumulate on the walls of the tube.   This prevents the formation of high negative charges on the walls of the tube.   It is apparent that such charges would cause an unwanted deflection of the electron beam.   *Second*, the gas focuses the electron beam as now will be explained.

As the electrons constituting the cathode ray or beam proceed toward the fluorescent screen, they strike neutral gas atoms and ionize them by collision, producing additional electrons and massive positive ions.   The positive ion receives little acceleration from the impact, and is displaced but little from the original position of the atom.   The original electron, and the one produced by ionization, are shot out of the path.   As a result of this action, there is a column of positive ions down the length of the beam with electrons constituting a negative space charge surrounding it.   A radial electric field is produced in this way, and outer electrons of the cathode beam are forced inward toward the center of the beam by the action of this field.   This focuses the beam.

For a given tube with a certain gas and pressure, the focusing of the spot on the fluorescent screen is determined by the *temperature of the cathode* for the following reasons: The tube is operated in a saturated condition so that increasing the cathode heating current increases the beam current.   Increasing the beam current increases the ionization and hence the focusing effect.   Decreasing the beam current decreases the ionization and causes less focusing effect.   Thus, the focusing can be readily controlled by varying the cathode heating current.

Medium-Voltage Tube.—As has been explained, the original thermionic cathode-ray tubes contained gas at a low pressure for focusing the beam.   This was necessary because the tubes were operated with only 200 to 400 volts on the anode, and this small voltage gave low electron velocities in the beam and consequently considerable time for spreading.   There is another serious objection to low electron velocities: The kinetic energy of an electron striking the fluorescent screen is low, and hence the spot on the screen is not brilliant.   The fact that even with good design the positive ions bombard the hot cathode, at least to some extent, is also a limitation of gas tubes.

If *high-vacuum* tubes operating at *medium* voltages of from about 1000 to 2000 volts are used, certain of the undesired features of the gas tube can be avoided.   The higher voltage makes a focusing gas unnecessary, and in addition, the higher electron velocities (together with better fluorescent screens) give a brilliant trace, readily visible at considerable distances even with the room illuminated.   Photographs of the path traced by the fluorescent spot are easily made with ordinary cameras.[4]

These medium voltages are dangerous, but this can be cared for by proper construction.   Such voltages are readily obtainable from ordinary thermionic-tube rectifiers, so that high-voltage batteries are not necessary.   The absence of the gas requires, in many of these tubes, that the inside of the glass envelope be coated with a conducting layer to prevent the formation of undesirable charges on the glass.   In some tubes,[4] this layer is the high-voltage anode.

There is another important advantage of the high electron velocities. In the very sensitive *low-velocity gas tubes*, the beam is deflected by the magnetic field of the earth.   This requires that in the laboratory counteracting fields be provided by large electromagnets or other means, or that extreme precautions be taken to shield the tube.   With the higher-velocity tubes, the beam is less easily deflected, counteracting fields seldom are required, and simple shielding precautions are satisfactory.

Diagrams of two medium-voltage, high-vacuum, cathode-ray tubes are shown in Fig. 14–4.   These tubes are identical except that the upper one is arranged for (electrostatic) deflection by an electric field, and the lower one for deflection by magnetic fields.   That is, the upper one is arranged for observing *voltage* phenomena, and the lower one for *current* phenomena.   The magnetic cores shown in the deflecting coils of the lower figure are not always necessary, and in fact would be objectionable at high frequencies.

In this type tube the oxide-coated *cathode C* is indirectly heated by a separate heater using alternating-current supplied from the power transformer, usually at 2.5 volts.   Surrounding the cathode C is the *control grid* G_1.   This is *not* a mesh in the usual sense, but contains a single hole; it is often designated as *grid No. 1*.   The next electrode is a

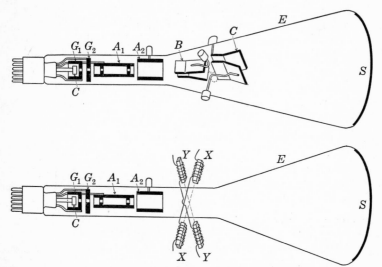

FIG. 14–4.   Arrangements of the electrodes in medium-voltage high-vacuum cathode-ray tubes.   The upper tube uses an electric field and the lower a magnetic field for deflecting the beam.   (From Reference 4.)

positive accelerating grid, G_2, often designated as *grid No. 2*.   The electron beam then enters *positive anode No. 1*, designated as A_1, and then passes through *positive anode No. 2*, called A_2.   The beam then passes between the deflecting plates or the deflecting coils and to the fluorescent screen.   In certain forms of the cathode-ray tube of Fig. 4, the accelerating grid G_2 *is omitted*.   Electrodes C, G_1, G_2, A_1, and A_2 constitute the electron gun.

132. Theory of the Electron Gun.—The design of the electron gun [5] is based on the new branch of science known as **electron optics.**[6]   Just as optical lenses are placed in the path of light rays to focus them on a surface, so are electron lenses (electrodes) placed in the path of the cathode ray (beam of electrons) to focus this negative ray on the fluorescent screen of a tube.

It will not be possible to include in detail the application of the principles of electron optics to the design of an electron gun.   The subject is new and the action of the various electronic lenses requires a specialized treatment.   Suffice it to say, therefore, that the paths of the electrons constituting the cathode ray will be influenced *at any point* by the *direction and magnitude of the electric field* at that point. Since electrodes A_1 and A_2 are at different positive potentials an electric field will exist between them.   Thus, it is possible to have electrodes so shaped geometrically, and at such potentials electrically, that the electric field will cause a focusing of the cathode ray at any desired point.

The two illustrations of Fig. **14–5** are included to demonstrate these phenomena.   The tube chosen is like the upper diagram of Fig. **14–4**

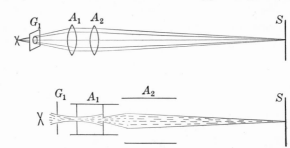

FIG. 14–5.   In the upper figure the amount of *light* from the source at x is controlled by the shutter and focused by lenses A_1 and A_2 to a point on the screen S. In the lower figure, the number of electrons from the cathode at x is controlled by the negative grid G_1 and focused by electrodes A_1 and A_2 to a point on the fluorescent screen S.   This focusing is due to the electric field between anodes A_1 and A_2 (which is at the higher potential).

except that it does *not* contain an accelerating grid G_2.   The control-grid G_1 limits the flow of electrons just as does the light shutter G_1 in the optical analogy.   This grid is located in a region of low electron velocity, is always biased negatively, and since it controls the *number* of electrons in the beam, it can be used to vary the *intensity* of the fluorescent spot.

The *focusing* of the beam on the fluorescent screen is determined by the *ratio* of the positive voltages on anodes A_1 and A_2.   This is because electric lines of force will extend between two bodies not at the same potential.   The number of these lines and their distribution (that is, the shape of the field) depends on the ratio of the voltages impressed. By applying various ratios the resulting electric fields caused by these two electrodes can be made to focus the cathode ray on the fluorescent screen.   Of course, it is also the function of the positive anodes A_1 and A_2 to give the electrons in the beam the required acceleration toward the screen.

A cathode-ray tube with *two* electron guns has been described,[7] and recent advertising material * has announced cathode-ray tubes with *three* electron guns in the same glass envelope and focussed on the *same* fluorescent screen.   With such tubes available, *simultaneous* observations of *three* electric phenomena can be made, a very desirable feature. One of the serious limitations of past cathode-ray oscillographic studies has been the fact that simultaneous observations have been difficult. They have been possible, however, if rapid switching arrangements [8] are provided for connecting first one, and then the other phenomenon to the deflecting plates.   It appears possible that the development of these multi-gun cathode-ray tubes will prove revolutionary in the field of oscillography.

133. Cathode-Ray Tube Connections.—The connections for a typical cathode-ray tube are shown in Fig. 14–6.   Note that this tube

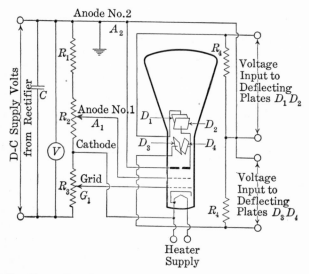

FIG. 14–6.   Connections for a typical cathode-ray tube.   (From Reference 4.)

does *not* contain the accelerating grid G_2 of Fig. 14–4.   This diagram and circuits for other tubes will be found in Reference 4.

As indicated, the direct-current supply is obtained from a thermionic-tube rectifier.[4]   By the voltage-dividing arrangement, the correct voltages are obtained for operation.   By varying the setting of R_3 the potential of the control grid G_1 is changed.   In this way, the number of electrons in the beam, and hence the *intensity* of the spot (for specified conditions) on the fluorescent screen, is varied.   The *focusing*

* Western Electric Co.

of the spot is controlled by varying R_2 which changes the potential on anode A_1 with respect to anode A_2.

The effect of the control grid G_1 in regulating the electron flow to anode A_2 is indicated by Fig. **14–7.** If the negative potential of the grid is sufficient, the beam current can be entirely cut off just as in the ordinary vacuum tube.

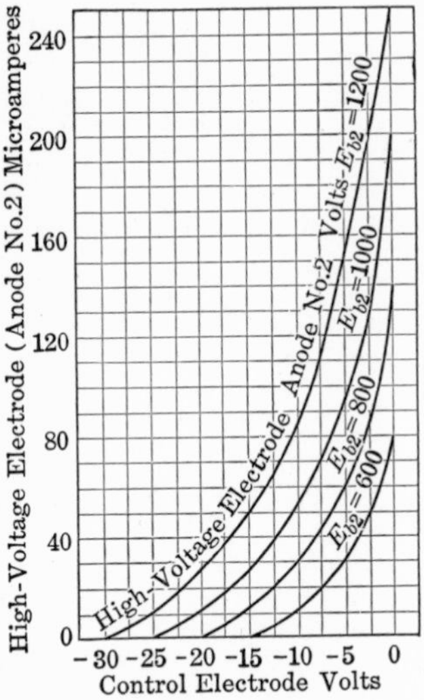

The input to the deflecting plates is impressed as indicated, the resistors R_4 largely determining the input impedance to the cathode-ray tube. It is apparent that the tube is a voltage-operated device. When it is desired to study the wave shape of currents, these may be passed through deflecting coils, or the voltage drop across low resistors carrying the currents may be impressed on the tube. This last method usually is more satisfactory in communication work.

It is well to stress the fact that potentials of over 1000 volts are used in these tubes, and that *safety precautions should be taken.*

FIG. 14–7. Illustrating the effect of the control-grid voltage G_1 on the beam current of a cathode-ray tube. The potential of A_1 was adjusted for focus. (From Reference 4.)

134. Electrical Characteristics of the Cathode-Ray Tube.—In Fig. 14–7 the effect of the control grid in regulating the electron beam and thus the *intensity* of the fluorescent spot is indicated. There are several other important characteristics which now will be considered.

For example, as inferred in the preceding paragraph the intensity of the spot on the fluorescent screen depends on two factors; *first,* the number of electrons in the beam as determined by the potential of the control grid G_1; and *second,* the final velocity of the electrons determined (for given conditions) by the positive potential of anode A_2. These relations are shown by Fig. **14–8.** As should be expected, at higher voltages the increased velocities result in a greater emission of light from the fluorescent spot.

Another characteristic of importance is the spectral distribution of the light radiated by the fluorescent screen. This is indicated by Fig. **14–9** which should be compared with the curve of Fig. **2–13**, showing the sensitivity of the human eye. These characteristics are determined largely by the nature of the fluorescent material [4] used.

The time of persistence is important.   For the visual observation of recurrent phenomena a fluorescent material which will continue to radiate visible light for a short time after the pattern has been traced is desirable.   But for some purposes, such as photographing phenomena with motion-pic-ture cameras, a long time of persistence would cause blur-ring of the reproduced image. These characteristics are illus-trated, for a typical fluores-cent material, by Fig. 14–10. Long persistence screens are available, when their use is desired.

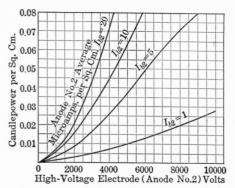

Fig. 14–8.   For given beam currents in a cathode-ray tube the light emitted by the fluorescent screen depends on the voltage of anode No. 2.   (From Reference 4.)

When a transient phe-nomenon, instead of a steady-state recurring variation is being observed, the "speed" of the transient is an important factor in determining the brilliancy of the image on the fluorescent screen.   If the transient occurs very quickly, the beam will follow the variations satisfactorily, but the beam will move across the screen so rap-idly that insufficient electrons will strike at given points along the path to cause a plainly visible image.   This is an important con-sideration in the use of the high-voltage cathode-ray tube to be con-sidered on page 404.

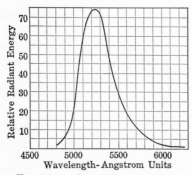

Fig. 14–9.   Spectral energy charac-teristics of the fluorescent screen widely used in a cathode-ray tube.   One Ang-strom unit = 10^{-8} centimeter.   (From Reference 4.)

Deflections of the Ray.—The cathode ray consists of a beam of electrons in rapid flight to the fluorescent screen, which as has been explained, can be deflected either by an electric or by a mag-netic field.   An analysis [1] of this action, applying to both types of fields, has been made by Johnson.   His explanation for *electric* (or elec-trostatic) deflection will be summarized in the following paragraphs.

In passing from the negative cathode to the positive anode A_2 of Fig. 14–4, the electrons are accelerated by the potential difference through which they "fall." The kinetic energy $1/2\ mv^2$ which they have when they *pass the anode* must equal the work eV done on the electrons. That is,

$$\tfrac{1}{2}mv^2 = eV, \qquad (14\text{--}1)$$

where m is the mass, v is the velocity, and e is the charge on an electron, and V is the voltage between the cathode and anode. Thus, the velocity becomes

$$v = \left(2\,\frac{e}{m}\,V \right)^{1/2} \qquad (14\text{--}2)$$

The ratio of e/m is quite accurately known to be 5.3×10^{17} statcoulombs per gram (page 2); also, one volt equals $1/300$ statvolts. On this basis,

$$v = 5.95 \times 10^7 V^{1/2}. \qquad (14\text{--}3)$$

That is, v is the velocity in centimeters per second of the electrons from the gun, when V is expressed in volts.

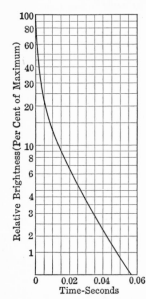

FIG. 14–10. Time of persistence of the fluorescent screen widely used for visual observation in cathode-ray tubes. (From Reference 4.)

The actual bending of the ray is illustrated by Fig. 14–11. The voltage V' to be studied is impressed between the two deflecting plates spaced d centimeters apart. The voltage gradient (assuming a uniform field) is, therefore, V'/d volts per centimeter. The electrons traveling along the tube with velocity v will be acted on by a force tending to deflect them as they pass through the electric field due to the voltage to be studied which is impressed between the two plates.

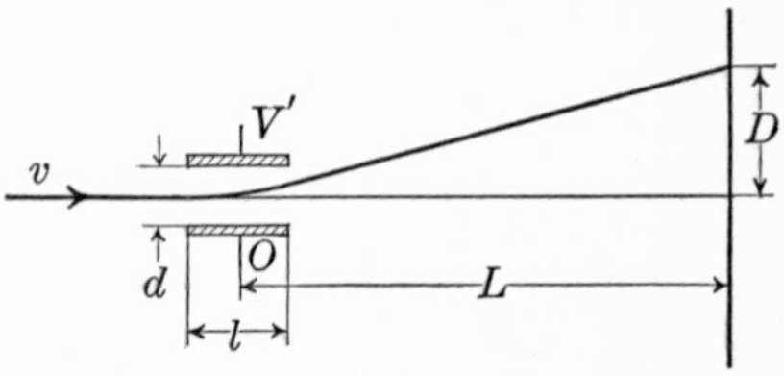

This deflecting force acting on an electron is proportional to the magnitude of the electronic charge e, and to the field strength V'/d. Since in general,

FIG. 14–11. Diagram for studying the deflection of the electron ray or beam in a cathode-ray tube. (From Reference 1.)

force equals the product of mass and acceleration, it can be written that the acceleration is

$$a = \frac{eV'}{md}. \qquad (14\text{--}4)$$

The deflecting acceleration which an electron experiences begins when the electron enters the field between the two plates and continues until it leaves the field; that is, it acts for the distance l, and continues for a time equal to this distance divided by the velocity v. Since the velocity at right angles to the original path equals the product of the acceleration as given by equation (14–4) and the time through which it acts (the time to pass between the plates), the transverse velocity, or velocity at right angles, is

$$v' = at = \frac{eV'l}{mdv}. \qquad (14\text{–}5)$$

After deflection, the electron beam progresses in a straight line to the fluorescent screen where the spot is deflected a distance D from

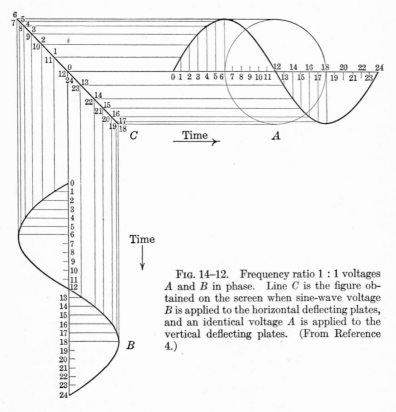

FIG. 14–12. Frequency ratio 1 : 1 voltages A and B in phase. Line C is the figure obtained on the screen when sine-wave voltage B is applied to the horizontal deflecting plates, and an identical voltage A is applied to the vertical deflecting plates. (From Reference 4.)

the center of the tube. An expression for this deflection in terms of the tube dimensions, the cathode-anode voltage V, and the deflecting voltage V' can be derived.

Patterns.—In the conventional tube there are two sets of deflecting plates ordinarily referred to as the **vertical deflecting plates** and the **horizontal deflecting plates.** The deflection of the cathode ray or beam, and the resulting trace on the fluorescent screen, is controlled by the voltages impressed on these plates.

Thus, if an alternating voltage is impressed on the *horizontal* deflecting plates (which is the pair in the *vertical* plane) of the tube of Fig. **14**–6, page 393, the beam will trace a straight *horizontal* line. If an alternating voltage is impressed on the *vertical* deflecting plates (which lie in the horizontal plane), the beam will trace a *vertical* line.

Now suppose that *equal* alternating voltages which are *in phase* and which have the *same* frequency are impressed on *each* set of plates. This is shown by Fig. **14**–12 in which *A* represents the voltage on the *vertical* plates and *B* that on the *horizontal* set. There are now *two* forces acting on the beam, and the trace *C* on the screen will be produced by the *resultant* force. By projecting corresponding points from these two curves, the figure *C* on the screen is proved to be a *straight line* inclined at an angle of 45 degrees.

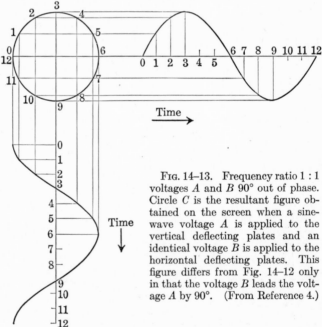

Fig. 14–13. Frequency ratio 1 : 1 voltages *A* and *B* 90° out of phase. Circle *C* is the resultant figure obtained on the screen when a sine-wave voltage *A* is applied to the vertical deflecting plates and an identical voltage *B* is applied to the horizontal deflecting plates. This figure differs from Fig. 14–12 only in that the voltage *B* leads the voltage *A* by 90°. (From Reference 4.)

The conditions of the preceding paragraph were for equal in-phase voltages of the same frequency. If the two voltages are now equal in magnitude and frequency, but 90 degrees out of phase as in Fig.

14–13, a projection will show that the resulting wave trace C will be a *circle*. The possibilities of the cathode-ray tube as a phase-measuring device are apparent.

The voltages impressed on a cathode-ray tube may differ in magnitude, frequency, or phase. It is possible, therefore, to have patterns of almost any conceivable type on the fluorescent screen. Such traces are called **Lissajou's figures,** after an experimenter. These figures are given in Reference 4 which also contains an explanation of their interpretation and the original sources (such as Reference 9) from which they were obtained.

135. The Cathode-Ray Oscilloscope.—When two alternating voltages which are (more or less) sinusoidal are placed on the two sets of deflecting plates, the trace observed is the resultant of their characteristics. For most work, it is desired to observe directly the characteristics of an *individual* current or voltage wave. The **cathode-ray oscilloscope** has been developed for this purpose. This device is also called an oscillograph, but strictly speaking, it is an *oscilloscope* when used to observe phenomena visually and an *oscillograph* when used photographically.

Suppose that a sinusoidal voltage to be observed is impressed across the vertical deflecting plates. As previously mentioned, this will result in a straight vertical line being traced on the fluorescent screen. Now suppose that the vertical plates are disconnected and that a "saw-tooth" wave is impressed on the horizontal deflecting plates. The horizontal force acting on the beam will deflect the beam slowly across the tube as the voltage gradually increases, but will sweep the beam back *very quickly* as the saw-tooth wave rapidly dies to zero.

If now the sinusoidal alternating voltage is again connected to the vertical plates and the saw-tooth sweeping voltage simultaneously is connected to the horizontal plates, the sinusoidal voltage which formerly merely caused a vertical line on the screen now will be "stretched out" and will appear as a sinusoidal trace (or otherwise if the first voltage is not sinusoidal) on the fluorescent screen. A point-by-point analysis of this action is shown in Fig. 14–14.

The saw-tooth wave is usually generated by **sweep-circuit oscillators** [4] employing grid-controlled gas-filled thermionic vacuum tubes considered on page 133. By varying the frequency of the sweep-circuit oscillator, waves of very high frequency can be made to appear on the screen for study. The sweep-circuit oscillator can be synchronized [4] or "locked in" with the voltage to be viewed so that the figure on the screen will remain stationary. As mentioned early in this chapter, the figures on the modern fluorescent screen can be photographed [4] without difficulty.

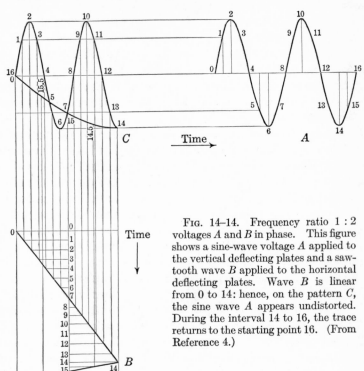

FIG. 14–14. Frequency ratio 1 : 2 voltages A and B in phase. This figure shows a sine-wave voltage A applied to the vertical deflecting plates and a saw-tooth wave B applied to the horizontal deflecting plates. Wave B is linear from 0 to 14: hence, on the pattern C, the sine wave A appears undistorted. During the interval 14 to 16, the trace returns to the starting point 16. (From Reference 4.)

136. Measurements with Cathode-Ray Tubes.—This versatile device has been adapted to a wide variety of measurements. It will be possible to discuss only a few of these very briefly, and to give references containing additional information.

Voltage Measurements.—The unknown voltage to be measured is impressed on one pair of deflecting plates, and the resulting deflection compared with that caused by a known voltage. A sweep voltage may or may not be used.

Current Measurements.—The current to be measured can be passed through a resistor and the voltage drop applied to one set of plates. The deflection (either with or without a sweep applied) is observed on the screen. A cross-section background for the screen is advantageous but not necessary. The deflection can be compared with that produced by a known current; or, if the tube has been calibrated in volts and the resistance is known, the current can be calculated.

Power Measurements.—Fig. **14**–12 shows that the pattern of the cathode ray is a straight line when two *in-phase* voltages of the same magnitude and frequency are impressed simultaneously on the two sets of deflecting plates; but as Fig. **14**–13 shows, the figure is a circle when the two voltages are *90 degrees out of phase*. Since power is equal to the product $EI \cos \theta$, from the area of the figure the power taken by any circuit can be determined.[10, 11]

Phase Measurements.—Since the phase relation causes the figure on the screen to shift from a straight line to a circle, phase angles can be determined [11] with a cathode-ray tube.

Frequency Measurements.—This is one of the widest uses of the cathode-ray tube. An analysis of this subject is given by Reference 9, and is summarized in References 4 and 11.

Hysteresis Measurements.—The hysteresis loss per cycle in a magnetic material is proportional to the area of the hysteresis loop for that material. The hysteresis loop can be reproduced [12] by a cathode-ray tube and the power loss determined.

Vacuum-Tube Characteristics.—The cathode-ray tube can be used to study both the static and dynamic characteristics of vacuum tubes, and to study their uses in amplifiers.[13]

Modulation Measurements.—There are at least two ways [4, 11] of studying the output of a modulator to determine the percentage modulation and to insure that it does not exceed 100 per cent. The **trapezoidal method** employes an audio-frequency sweep on one set of plates and the modulated signal voltage on the other. The **modulated-envelope method** uses a saw-tooth sweep on one set of plates and the modulated signal on the other. With the first method a trapezoidal figure is observed, but with the second the modulated signal itself is reproduced on the fluorescent screen.

137. Cathode-Ray Tubes for Television.—In the early television systems a rotating scanning disk in front of a neon tube (or other gas tube) was used to reproduce the image. The intensity of the radiation of the neon tube varied at each instant as the light reflected from each spot of the image or scene being televised. In this way the image was reproduced. Imperfect as this system was, it is significant to note that mechanical reproducers were used in two-way television. Also, images in color were transmitted. (See references on page 383.)

The cathode-ray tube has largely supplanted the mechanical reproducer in television receiving sets.[14, 15] *Three* types of tubes are used,[15] classified on the basis of the method of concentrating or focusing the electron beam. These employ (1) electrostatic concentration, (2) magnetic concentration, and (3) gas concentration. An example of the first type is the **Kinescope** of Zworykin; the **Oscillite** of Farnsworth is an example of the second type. The method of focusing the first type was considered on page 392. In the second, a coil carrying direct current is placed over the tube and coaxially with it. The field thus produced concentrates the electrons into a beam.[15]

In reproducing television images by cathode-ray tubes, the beam is deflected, either by plates as in the Kinescope or by coils as in the Oscillite, so that the beam progresses over the fluorescent screen just as the image is being scanned at the transmitting station. As this is done, the *intensity* of the beam is varied by the output of the transmitting station. This is accomplished by properly impressing the received signal on the *control grid* of the cathode-ray reproducing tube. Since the potential of this grid controls the number of electrons in the beam, it also will control the intensity of the spot on the fluorescent screen.

Since the cathode ray or beam moves in exact synchronism with the scanning beam (or what corresponds to it) at the distant station, and since the intensity of the beam as it strikes the fluorescent screen varies at each instant just as the reflected light varies at each spot on the image being televised, the distant image is reproduced on the fluorescent screen. Of course elaborate synchronizing controls and other features are necessary, but these and other details are being satisfactorily solved. In the television receivers the fluorescent screen is viewed directly, by a mirror reflecting system, or through lenses. Many articles covering the subject of television will be found in recent journals.

138. Cathode-Ray Oscillograph.—*Dufour Tube.*—This device, in a widely used form, is shown in Fig. 14–15. It consists essentially of a cold cathode C and an anode A, with a voltage of about 50,000 to 60,000 volts applied between these two electrodes. An opening O serves to concentrate the electron beam which then passes through the deflecting plates D and strikes the photographic plate or film at S *directly*. The electrodes are mounted in a glass tube at the top, and this tube is sealed to the metal container E. A viewing window for observing the film is provided on one side. The metal container may be opened for inserting the plates or films. This necessitates the continuous use of an evacuating system. In most instances a mechanical arrangement is provided so that films may be changed without opening the tube until several films are exposed.

When the anode A is made positive with respect to the cathode C, some of the free electrons in the residual gas within the tube are drawn rapidly toward the anode, and ionization by collision with residual gas atoms results. A beam, which passes through the opening *O,* is formed, and this beam or ray exposes the photographic film by impinging on it. There is less spreading of the beam because of the high velocities attained at the voltages used. Some Dufour tubes use magnetic and some use electric fields to further concentrate the beam; others have no concentrating provisions.

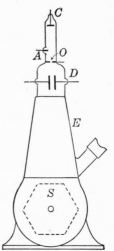

As was mentioned previously, one of the factors limiting the frequency range of the tube with fluorescent screens is the high speed with which the electron beam moves across the screen. If the speed is too great, the illumination becomes very low. With the Dufour tube, since the electrons themselves strike the film, even very high beam speeds produce good exposures. Thus, experimenters have obtained recording speeds of 60,000 kilometers per second, or one-fifth the velocity of light.[2]

Fig. 14–15. The Dufour high-voltage cathode-ray oscillograph. (From Reference 16.)

The Dufour oscillograph has been, and is, extensively used in high-voltage investigations. It is well suited for the photographic study of transients of very short time duration. By its use, a study of the transient nature of high-voltage lightning discharges has been possible. Such surges may last only a few microseconds.

The literature on the use of this tube is very extensive. Those interested in high-voltage studies with this oscillograph will find many articles listed in Reference 2.

The Lenard Tube.—It is apparent that the necessity for inserting the film *into the tube* itself seriously complicates the operation of an oscillograph tube. Evacuating troubles caused by air leaks and other difficulties arise. Thus an attempt was made to shoot the electron beam *out of the tube* into the air and to have the electrons impinge on a photographic film *outside of the tube.*

As is well known, a beam of high-velocity electrons will pass through a thin metal foil, such as aluminum, without excessive attenuation, and without damage to the aluminum. Apparently, many of the high-velocity electrons find inter-atomic paths through the foil. Of course it is necessary that the foil hold air from the tube, and thus the foil must be backed by a strong grid to stand the pressure of the air. This tube and its use are described in articles in the bibliography of Reference 2.

High voltages of about 75,000 volts were used on this tube to obtain very high electron velocities.[16] It has never achieved wide application as an oscillograph tube, however, probably largely because of the limitations due to the window. The tube does offer future possibilities as a device for supplying high-velocity electrons directly into the outside air.

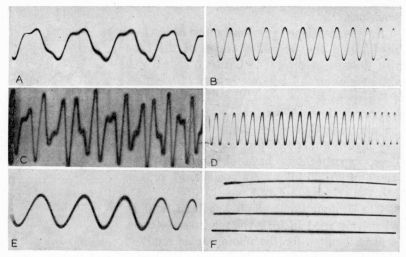

Fig. 14–16. Oscillograms made with a high-voltage thermionic cathode-ray tube. A to E, 100,000, 500,000, 500,000, 2,000,000 and 2,000,000 cycles per second respectively; F, direct-current calibration. (From Reference 2.)

Thermionic Tube.—In the past, when very short transient impulses were photographed, the film was placed inside the tube as in the Dufour oscillograph. The obvious complications of this method brought about attempts to use the Lenard tube. This was followed by other studies [2] and finally to the use of a *thermionic* high-vacuum cathode-ray tube of the general type discussed on page 390, and as described by Zworykin [17] and Metcalf.[18]

The thermionic cathode-ray tube uses a voltage as high as 15,000 volts between the cathode and anode and hence gives the electrons in the beam quite high velocities. The sensitivity is about 500 volts per inch. That is, a voltage of 500 volts between deflecting plates will deflect the spot on the fluorescent screen about one inch.

The adopting [2] of a thermionic cathode-ray tube with a fluorescent screen and the photographing of phenomena on this screen with a camera has been made possible by a number of factors which will be summarized. *First*, as mentioned in the preceding section *high-voltage* thermionic cathode-ray tubes with high electron velocities are now available; also, the spectral sensitivity of the fluorescent screen has been made suitable for photographic purposes. *Second*, better cameras and more sensitive films now are available. *Third*, an examination [2] of the requirements of an oscillograph suitable for most investigations disclosed the fact that *extremely* high-speed records ordinarily were not necessary. It was found that a recording speed up to 10 inches per microsecond was satisfactory for most purposes in practice. Results obtained by this new type oscillograph are shown in Figs. **14–16** and **14–17**.

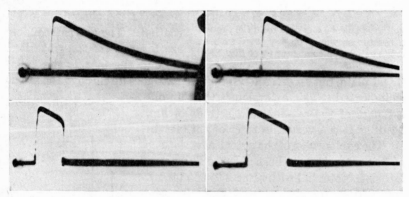

FIG. 14–17. Impulse oscillograph records of $1\frac{1}{2} \times 40$-microsecond impulse waves and rod gap flashovers as recorded with a high-voltage thermionic cathode-ray oscilloscope. (From Reference 2.)

139. Cathode-Ray Indicator Tube.—This is a form of a cathode-ray tube developed for use as a tuning indicator for radio receiving sets. By its use, the portion of the fluorescent screen which glows can be taken as an indication of the closeness with which the set is tuned to the carrier of the station to be received.[19, 20]

The conventional diagram of this indicator tube and its associated circuit are shown in Fig. **14–18**. The tube consists of a *long* cathode, a grid, a ray-control electrode (which includes the conventional plate), and a target. The *inside* of the target is coated with a fluorescent material. Note that this material is *not* coated on the end of the glass bulb as in conventional cathode-ray tubes. A light shield for the upper portion of the cathode also is provided.

Referring to Fig. **14–18**, it is evident that when the grid is at a low negative potential, a large current will flow to the plate (the ray-control electrode) and since this current must flow through the resistor R, the plate becomes *less positive* than the target. That is, a negative voltage will exist between the control electrode and the target. When the grid potential becomes *more* negative, *less* current flows to

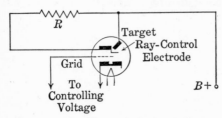

the control electrode, *less* drop occurs across the resistor R, and a *smaller* negative potential will exist between the ray-control electrode and the target.

FIG. 14–18. The cathode-ray indicator tube and its associated circuit. For operation as a tuning indicator the controlling voltage would be obtained from the drop in a resistor or would be a voltage such as exists across the condenser C_2 of Fig. 12–4.

To give a complete understanding of the action, Fig. 14–19 has been drawn. The shaded portions of the cathode represent the thermionic oxide coating. The two rows of dots are the ends of the grid wires. Around the grid is the cylindrical plate, but an extension from the plate goes up through the target as indicated. This extension is the thin off-set part of the ray-control electrode of Fig. 14–18. It is a very thin piece of flat metal.

The explanation of the potential variations of this extension has been given. These variations in potential with respect to the target, control the area of the target struck by electrons given off by the *upper* end of the cathode. Thus, when a *large* negative potential is placed on the grid of the lower triode portion, a large area of the target glows as in Fig. 14–20; that is, the **shadow angle** is small. When a *small* negative potential is placed on the grid, the ray-control electrode and the

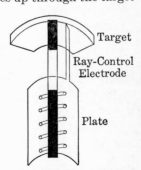

FIG. 14–19. Showing the essential features of a cathode-ray indicator tube. The light-shield is omitted.

target are at a high difference of potential and the shadow angle is large.

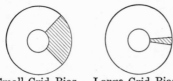

Small Grid Bias   Large Grid Bias

FIG. 14–20. Showing the effect of grid bias on the shadow angle of a cathode-ray indicator tube.

The negative voltages for controlling the "electric eye" as a sharpness of tuning indicator are obtained from the drop across a resistor such as R in the cathode circuit of a diode detector (Fig. 12–2, page 340). When the radio set is sharply tuned, the received carrier signal is the maximum value, and the direct voltage drop across R will be maximum. This will place a *large* negative voltage on the grid, which will cause the shadow angle to be *small,* indicating that the radio receiving set is tuned. Characteristic curves for an indicator tube are given in Fig. 14–21.

140. Thermionic Vacuum Tubes in Measurements.—The *previous* pages of this chapter have been devoted to a study of the theory and application of cathode-ray tubes, particularly to electrical measurements. The *following* pages will consider *conventional* vacuum tubes (and several miscellaneous types) as used for electrical measurements.

In most of the measuring circuits to be considered, the vacuum tubes are used merely as amplifiers and as rectifiers or detectors. The theoretical considerations involved in such usages have been fully treated in preceding chapters, and little further consideration need be given.

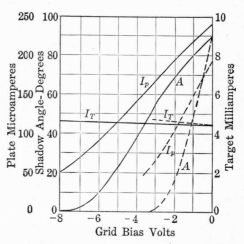

FIG. 14–21. Characteristics of a cathode-ray indicator tube. Curves I_T and I_p represent the target and plate currents. Curve A is for the shadow angle. Solid lines are for plate supply, $+B$, of 250 volts, and R (Fig. 14–18) of 1.0 megohm. Broken lines are for $+B$ of 100 volts and R of 0.5 megohm. (From Reference 20.)

The treatment of the subject of vacuum tubes in measurements will be further limited by the following facts. *First,* little which is new from an electronic standpoint is involved. *Second,* the circuits are many in number and specialized in nature. *Third,* excellent and complete discussions [11, 19] of the subject are available. And furthermore, an exhaustive bibliography of five hundred and ninety-six articles on the use of vacuum tubes in measurements was published [21] by Horton in 1935. Articles appearing since that date will be found listed [19] in the references given by Henney.

Thus, in the following pages the theoretical considerations will be limited to the basic uses of vacuum tubes for measuring the fundamental electrical quantities. The special applications are so numerous [19] that they cannot be treated.

Voltage Measurements.—Referring for a moment to the cathode-ray and indicator tubes, these are well suited for voltage measurements. The cathode-ray tube can be calibrated so that when an unknown voltage (either direct or alternating) is connected across one pair of deflecting plates, the value of this unknown voltage can be determined from the magnitude of the deflection obtained. The indicator tube can be used as a voltage measuring device [19] because the shadow angle is determined by the magnitude of an unknown voltage when it is impressed on the grid.

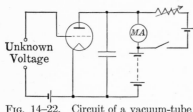

FIG. 14–22.   Circuit of a vacuum-tube voltmeter.

The conventional thermionic vacuum tube will operate as a voltage-measuring device in the simple circuit of Fig. 14–22. The tube is operated with a high grid bias so that the *average* value of the plate current as measured by the direct-current milliammeter will *change* when the alternating voltage to be measured is connected in the grid circuit. These relations are indicated in Fig. 14–23.

If the tube were biased to point A, then operation would be on the *straight* portion of the curve. Only amplification would result; the *average* value of the current would remain the same (assuming no distortion), and the direct-current milliammeter would not deflect. With the bias at point B, however, rectification will result and a direct component I_p' will be created as for any distorted wave (page 178). This will *increase* the current through the milliammeter. The circuit can be calibrated, with a 60-cycle voltage if desired, so that from the increases in plate current the voltages impressed on the grid circuit are known.

Operation as in Fig. 14–23 is known as **full-wave square-law action** because the *change* in plate current is closely proportional to the *square* of the effective value of the applied voltage.[11] If the grid bias is

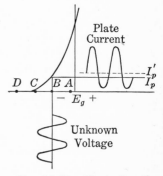

FIG. 14–23.   Illustrating the operation of the vacuum-tube voltmeter of Fig. 14–22. When the unknown voltage to be measured is connected, the plate current increases from I_p to I_p', and this increase is measured by the milliammeter.

shifted to point C, then the operation is termed **half-wave square-law action**. The negative half cycles are largely suppressed and the *change* in plate current is closely proportional to *effective* value of the positive half cycles.[11] When the grid bias is increased past cut-off to some point D, then the change in plate current is determined by the peaks of the positive half cycles, and the circuit of Fig. 14–22 tends to become a **peak voltmeter** (defined [22] as a **crest voltmeter** although the term *peak value* is listed as preferable to *crest value*).

In his excellent treatment of the subject of measurements,[11] Terman discusses in detail the characteristics, design, and calibration of vacuum-tube voltmeters. From his work a few statements regarding the characteristics of vacuum-tube voltmeters will be summarized.

When the circuits are calibrated on sinusoidal voltages, and when the voltages to be measured are sinusoidal, operation as in Fig. **14**–23 with the bias adjusted to any of the three points B, C, or D is satisfactory. If the voltages to be measured contain harmonics, however, the indication of the direct-current milliammeter will depend on the type of adjustment used With *full-wave square-law* action, obtained with the bias voltage adjusted to point B, the circuit (when calibrated with a sinusoidal wave) will measure the effective value of an unknown wave, and the result is independent of the phase of the harmonics. For *half-wave square-law* action with the bias at C, the result depends on the magnitudes and phases of the harmonics if the voltage being measured is not sinusoidal. This is also true for the peak reading voltmeter with the bias adjusted to point D. It is thus evident that vacuum-tube voltmeters must be correctly designed and operated for reliable results. The effect of **turnover,**[11] or reversal of the input leads, may be of importance.

When the switch in Fig. **14**–22 is closed so that the rheostat and battery are connected across the milliammeter, the current I_p, which flows through the milliammeter with no impressed unknown voltage, can be reduced to zero. Then, the only deflection of the milliammeter will be due to an unknown alternating voltage connected across the input circuit.

When the circuit is arranged as in Fig. **14**–22, the unknown voltage is connected directly to the grid of the tube, and the power taken from the circuit under test is negligible; that is, the input impedance of the vacuum-tube voltmeter approaches infinity. If desired, a resistor of very high value (for instance, several million ohms) can be connected across the input terminals of Fig. **14**–22. If this is done, at low frequencies the input impedance equals the resistance of the resistor. A condenser often is inserted in one of the input leads to prevent direct-voltage components in an unknown voltage from reaching the grid.

Crest Voltmeters.[22]—These are commonly called **peak voltmeters.** As was mentioned in the preceding paragraph, as the grid bias on the tube of Fig. **14**–22 is made more negative, the circuit approaches that of a peak or crest voltmeter. Thus, if the grid gradually is made more negative, and observations made of the direct grid voltage at which *increases* in plate current are *just noted*, this observed negative grid voltage will just equal the *peak value* of the positive half cycle of the unknown alternating voltage.

The widely used **slide-back peak voltmeter** (as it is commonly called) is shown in Fig. **14–24** and operates as follows: The bias voltage

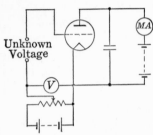

Fig. 14–24. Circuit of the "slide-back" peak voltmeter.

as measured by the voltmeter is adjusted until the milliammeter (or microammeter since a sensitive device is desirable) just indicates. The voltage measured approximately equals the peak value of the positive half cycle of the unknown alternating voltage connected across the input terminals. A slight error exists in measurements made with a crest voltmeter of this type due to the initial velocity of the electrons when they are emitted from the cathode. For precise results a correction must be made for this effect.[11]

Crest (or peak) voltmeter circuits utilizing grid-controlled, gas-filled triodes (Thyratrons) have been developed [15, 23] and used with excellent results.

The Inverted Vacuum-Tube.—The principle of operation of the conventional vacuum tube as an amplifier is that an alternating voltage impressed on the grid will be amplified in proportion to the amplification factor of the tube, and an increased voltage of substantially the same wave form will be available in the plate output circuit. It has been shown [24] that if the tube is *inverted*, with the input alternating voltage connected to the *plate*, and the output voltage taken from the *grid* circuit, then the tube will act as a *voltage-reducing device* instead of as a voltage amplifier. For such operation the *plate* is operated highly *negative* and draws no current. The grid is operated at a positive potential and draws considerable current.

When operated as just explained, the inverted vacuum tube sometimes is used to supply, from high-impedance circuits, a current, corresponding to the voltage across the circuit, for operating a current-driven oscillograph. The inverted tube is also used [11] in vacuum-tube voltmeters for measuring high voltages.

Current Measurements.—The vacuum-tube voltmeter can be used conveniently for determining the current flow in a circuit by measuring the voltage drop across a known resistor placed in that circuit. Of course an I^2R loss will occur in the resistor, and power must be supplied by the circuit under test.   The resistor may be of low value, however, and this loss often is not objectionable.   The resistance should not vary with frequency, or should be determined at the frequencies at which the current is to be measured.

Power Measurements.—Reliable measurements of voltage, current, and power are more difficult to make in the ordinary low-level audio or radio-frequency communication circuit than in the ordinary 60-cycle power circuit.   This was true especially before the development of copper-oxide rectifier instruments (page 195) and vacuum-tube methods.   Voltages and currents are now measured quite readily and reliably, but *power* in communication circuits is often difficult to measure.   Although the problem has received some attention (for a complete bibliography, see Reference 19), no device or circuit, having the reliability, simplicity, and ease of operation of the conventional 60-cycle power wattmeter, has been perfected for communication circuits.

As was mentioned (page 401), the cathode-ray tube can be used to measure power.   Methods using both the conventional and special vacuum tubes also have been studied.[19]   None of these has had wide adoption, however.   The problem of developing a *reliable* and *simple* method of measuring power in communication circuits is very interesting and one which soon should be solved.

At present the most widely used method of determining the power in communication circuits is to measure the current flowing with a thermocouple, or by vacuum-tube voltmeter methods, and to calculate the power by the relation I^2R.   In this expression I is the effective value of current and R is the effective resistance of the load.   This resistance is usually measured with an impedance bridge, and if it varies with current magnitude or frequency, these factors must be taken into account.

Phase Measurements.—If the voltage, current, and power are known, the phase angle between the current and voltage, in a circuit containing sinusoidal waves, can be readily measured.   When analyzing a complex wave as explained on page 275, the *phase relations* of *each* harmonic with respect to the fundamental may be desired, and this measurement is not so simple a problem.

The phase position of any frequency component of a complex wave can be determined by superimposing upon the complex wave, a sinusoidal wave having variable frequency and phase position.[11]   For instance, suppose that a complex wave is being analyzed, and the analyzer is measuring the *magnitude* of the *fifth* harmonic.   If the analyzer is adjusted to this frequency, and if a wave of the *same* frequency and of *variable* phase relation is impressed, minimum deflection will occur when the two waves are equal and 180° out of phase, because in this condition they exactly cancel. The amount that the phase of the *variable* wave had to be changed (with respect to some reference point such as the phase of the fundamental) to bring the two waves into this phase relation, is a measure of the phase of the fifth harmonic of the complex wave being analyzed. Thus, in turn, each component can be located with respect to the fundamental and its magnitude measured.

141. Special Tubes for Measurements.—Several special tubes have been developed—largely for measurement purposes—by the various manufacturers. These will be discussed briefly.

A **low grid-current tube** with the control grid held in a special quartz mounting and with an especially high vacuum has been developed [25] for measurements [26] of currents as low as 10^{-16} ampere. Operating voltages are held at *very low values*, below the voltage at which traces of residual gas would be ionized. The result is a vacuum tube with a grid-circuit resistance of as high as 10^{16} ohms. This is often referred to as an **electrometer tube**, because it sometimes has been used instead of an electrometer.

Special **low-noise tubes** also have been developed [27] for measurement purposes. What is meant by the "low-noise" feature is that in the design and operation of the tube, precautions have been taken to reduce the *random* fluctuations of the plate current, such fluctuations appearing as noise in vacuum-tube amplifiers. With such a tube used in a vacuum-tube voltmeter, voltages as low as 1.0 microvolt can be measured. [28]

The **internal-grid tube** has been used in oscillographic and other work. [28, 29] In the *conventional* vacuum tube the control grid *surrounds* the cathode, and the electrons flowing to the plate *must pass through* the grid. With such construction, large currents ordinarily flow to the plate only when the grid is at a positive potential and when the plate is highly positive. When operated in this way, the grid draws current and causes other undesired characteristics.

Fig. 14–25. Top view of two forms of internal-grid thermionic vacuum tubes. In each the grid is a metal sheet at the center. This is surrounded by the filament wires shown by dots, and then by the plate or anode.

In the internal-grid tube, the filament is placed *around* the grid (which is usually a sheet of metal) as in Fig. 14–25. When this grid is made negative, the electric field between it and the cathode (the wires of which are widely spaced) is not entirely confined to the region between these two electrodes but extends to the region beyond the filament; furthermore, electrons are emitted from all sides of the cathode wires. The result is that the potential of this internal grid can control the flow of electrons to the plate. With this tube, large currents to the plate result with *negative* grid voltages and *low* plate voltages. Furthermore, this plate current may be controlled as in any amplifier tube by grid-voltage variations. One disadvantage is that in the triode the amplification factor is usually less than unity. This is offset by the fact that it has a very *low* plate resistance, well adapting it to the operation of current-driven oscillographs. A *screen-grid tube* of this type would have a higher amplification factor.[28]

REFERENCES

1. Johnson, J. B. *The cathode ray oscillograph.* Journal of the Franklin Institute. Dec., 1931. Also, Bell System Technical Journal, Jan., 1932, Vol. 11, No. 1.
2. Kuehni, H. P., and Ramo, S. *A new high-speed cathode-ray oscillograph.* Electrical Engineering, June, 1937, Vol. 56, No. 6.
3. Johnson, J. B. *A low voltage cathode ray oscillograph.* Journal of the Optical Society of America and Review of Scientific Instruments, Sept., 1922. Also, Bell System Technical Journal, Nov., 1922, Vol. 1, No. 2.
4. R.C.A. Manufacturing Co. *Cathode Ray Tubes and Allied Types.* Pamphlet TS–2.
5. Maloff, I. G., and Epstein, D. W. *Theory of electron gun.* Proceedings of the Institute of Radio Engineers, Dec., 1934, Vol. 22, No. 12.
6. Zworykin, V. K. *On electron optics.* Journal of the Franklin Institute, May, 1933, Vol. 215.
7. von Ardenne, M. *A double-beam cathode-ray tube.* Electronics, Oct., 1936. Vol. 9, No. 10.
8. George, R. H., Heim, H. J., Mayer, H. F., and Roys, C. S. *A cathode ray oscillograph for observing two waves.* Electrical Engineering, Oct., 1935, Vol. 54, No. 10.
9. Rasmussen, F. J. *Frequency measurements with the cathode ray oscillograph.* Transactions American Institute of Electrical Engineers. Nov., 1926, Vol. 45.
10. Ryan, H. J. *A power diagram indicator for high tension circuits.* Transactions American Institute of Electrical Engineers, 1911, Vol. 30.
11. Terman, F. E. *Measurements in Radio Engineering.* McGraw-Hill Book Co.
12. Johnson, J. B. *A Braun tube hysteresigraph.* Bell System Technical Journal, April, 1929, Vol. 8, No. 2.
13. Willis, F. C., and Melhuish, L. E. *Load carrying capacity of amplifiers.* Bell System Technical Journal, Oct., 1926, Vol. 5, No. 4.
14. Henney, K. *Radio Engineering Handbook.* McGraw-Hill Book Co.

15. Pender, H., and McIlwain, K. *Electrical Engineers' Handbook.* Vol. 5, Electric Communication and Electronics. John Wiley & Sons.
16. Stinchfield, J. M. *Cathode ray tubes and their application.* Electrical Engineering, Dec., 1934, Vol. 53, No. 12.
17. Zworykin, V. K. *Improvements in cathode-ray tube design.* Electronics, Nov., 1931, Vol. 3, No. 5.
18. Metcalf, G. F. *A new cathode-ray oscillograph tube.* Electronics, May, 1932, Vol. 4, No. 5.
19. Henney, K. *Electron Tubes in Industry.* McGraw-Hill Book Co.
20. R.C.A. Manufacturing Co. *Receiving Tube Manual RC–13.*
21. Horton, J. W. *Use of vacuum tubes in measurements.* Electrical Engineering, Jan., 1935, Vol. 54, No. 1.
22. American Institute of Electrical Engineers. *Definitions of Electrical Terms.*
23. McMillan, F. O., and Barnett, H. G. *A radio inteference measuring instrument.* Electrical Engineering, Aug., 1935, Vol. 54, No. 8.
24. Terman, F. E. *The inverted vacuum tube, a voltage-reducing power amplifier.* Proc. I.R.E., April, 1928, Vol. 16, No. 4.
25. Metcalf, G. F., and Thompson, B. J. *A low grid current vacuum tube.* Physical Review, Nov., 1930.
26. DuBridge, L. A. *Amplification of small direct currents.* Physical Review, Feb., 1931.
27. Metcalf, G. F., and Dickinson, T. M. *New low-noise vacuum tube.* Physics, July, 1932.
28. McArthur, E. D. *Electronics and Electron Tubes.* John Wiley & Sons.
29. Eastman, A. V. *Fundamentals of Vacuum Tubes.* McGraw-Hill Book Co.

SUGGESTED ASSIGNMENTS

1. A quotation on page 388 states that the dimensions of an electron-gun structure are "less than the mean free path of electrons in the gas so that no appreciable ionization can build up." Explain why this is true.
2. Referring to the discussion on page 392, draw anodes A_1 and A_2 approximately to scale, and show how the electric field between these electrodes focuses the electron beam.
3. Calculate the velocity of the electrons shot from an electron gun of a typical cathode-ray oscillograph.
4. For given conditions of operation, calculate the deflection of the spot on the screen that a certain voltage will produce. Check experimentally with the cathode-ray tube.
5. Following the method used in drawing the curves of Figs. 14–12, 14–13, and 14–14, plot the trace of the cathode spot for equal voltages 45 degrees out of phase.
6. On page 408 it is stated that the *change* in plate current is closely proportional to the *effective* value of the positive half cycles. Prove this to be true.
7. Prove that for half-wave square-law action in vacuum-tube voltmeters the result depends on the magnitudes and phases of the unknown voltage.
8. Explain the "turnover" effect in vacuum-tube voltmeters.

INDEX

415